Air Quality Management and Land Use Planning

George Hagevik
Daniel R. Mandelker
Richard K. Brail

The Praeger Special Studies program—utilizing the most modern and efficient book production techniques and a selective worldwide distribution network—makes available to the academic, government, and business communities significant, timely research in U.S. and international economic, social, and political development.

Air Quality Management and Land Use Planning
Legal, Administrative, and Methodological Perspectives

PRAEGER SPECIAL STUDIES IN U.S. ECONOMIC, SOCIAL, AND POLITICAL ISSUES

Praeger Publishers   New York   Washington   London

HD
205
1974
,H33

Library of Congress Cataloging in Publication Data

Hagevik, George H
    Air quality management and land use planning.

    (Praeger special studies in U.S. economic, social, and political issues)
    Bibliography: p.
    1. Land—United States. 2. Land tenure—United States—Law. 3. Air quality management—United States.
I. Mandelker, Daniel R., joint author. II. Brail,
Richard K., joint author. III. Title.
HD205 1974.H33   333.7'0973   74-3142
ISBN 0-275-28857-9

PRAEGER PUBLISHERS
111 Fourth Avenue, New York, N.Y. 10003, U.S.A.
5, Cromwell Place, London SW7 2JL, England

Published in the United States of America in 1974
by Praeger Publishers, Inc.

A number of persons contributed to the preparation of this study. Dr. George Hagevik, Chief, Environmental Resources Division, Association of Bay Area Governments, served as director of the study and as editor of this book. In addition, he wrote Chapters 1, 4, 9, 10, and 11 and parts of Chapters 5 and 6. Dr. Daniel Mandelker, Professor of Law, Washington University, prepared Chapter 2 with Susan Rothschild (J.D., Columbia University, 1974) and contributed to Chapter 6. Dr. Richard Brail, Assistant Professor of Urban Planning and Policy Development, Livingston College, Rutgers University, prepared Chapters 8 and 9. Judy Bever (J.D., Columbia University, 1974) prepared Chapter 3. Ben Suckewer (J.D., Columbia University, 1974) contributed to Chapter 6, and Mark Yecies (J.D., Columbia University, 1974) prepared part of Chapter 5. Bill Gustafson (M.U.P., Rutgers University, 1973) and Kevin Guinaw (M.U.P., Rutgers University, 1974) assisted in various stages of the research project and report preparation.

The study was prepared under Contract No. 68-02-0278 awarded to Rutgers University by the Transportation and Land Use Planning Branch, Office of Air Quality Planning and Standards, U.S. Environmental Protection Agency. The conclusions expressed in this volume are those of the authors and not those of the Environmental Protection Agency.

v

AUTHORS' NOTE

Most of the research discussed in this book was carried out prior to the preparation of guidelines for air quality maintenance by the Environmental Protection Agency. The reader is therefore cautioned to read the Federal Register in order to keep up to date on EPA regulations.

Since this study was completed, "complex source" regulations have been re-titled "indirect source" regulations and were formally issued by EPA in early 1974 (Federal Register, February 14, 1974).

CONTENTS

LIST OF TABLES AND FIGURES

Air Quality Management and Land Use Planning

There is now widespread agreement in American society that many of our environmental problems are related to land use. Although we in the United States have long given lip service to the need for land use planning, it seems that only in the 1970s will the combined effects of the energy crisis and environmental pollution result in governmental plans and procedures that effectively limit and control the use of land.[1] The focus of this study is on how one type of environmental pollution—air pollution—relates to land use planning. If we were doing a comprehensive study, we should also be concerned about the relationship between land use and transportation and about how the control of air pollution relates to control strategies for other kinds of environmental pollution. However, the scope of this study is sufficiently broad that we found it impossible to give more than passing attention to these important topics.[2]

A central concern of this volume is the land use planning implications of the 1970 amendments to the Clean Air Act. The guidelines promulgated under the Act require that the respective states develop and enforce "implementation plans" that will ensure that national air quality standards are achieved and maintained. The regulations of the U.S. Environmental Protection Agency (EPA) provide generally that state plans must set forth a control strategy for the attainment and maintenance of the standards, a legally enforceable set of regulations, and a set of compliance schedules for the implementation of the state's control strategies.[3] Also included are a contingency plan for preventing the occurrence of air pollution levels that would cause significant harm to the health of the state's population, a set of source surveillance procedures to ensure that the construction or modification of stationary sources will not interfere with the attainment or maintenance of the national standards, provisions for an air quality surveillance network, and a description of resources needed to carry out the implementation plan.

With one exception, the states were required to have the specific legal authority available to them to implement their plans at the time of their submission to EPA. The one exception was the authority to carry out land use and transportation control measures if the plan included them. Where a state's control strategy included such measures, the plan was to set forth a timetable for obtaining the necessary legal authority. Where it was determined that a state's air pollution control statute did not provide all of the required legal authority, the state's attorney general was consulted for an opinion on whether the necessary authority is conferred by a general grant of powers in the air pollution control statute or provided in other statutes. Where a state plan indicated that one or more local agencies would be responsible for carrying out any portion of the implementation plan, a similar assessment was made of the legal authority available to such agencies.

Where existing air pollution levels exceeded the national standards, state plans were expected to provide for the degree of emission reduction necessary for attainment and maintenance of the national standards, including the degree of emission reduction necessary to offset the probable impact of projected growth of population, industrial activity, motor vehicle traffic, and other factors. As is discussed in Chapters 7 and 8, there is a great deal of uncertainty involved in projecting growth and predicting its impact on air quality. At the present time, growth projections extending more than three years into the future are generalized, and they are inevitably based on a variety of assumptions, many of which are tenuous. Even where growth policies have been adopted by state or local governments, such policies usually provide only general guidelines at best. Techniques do not exist for translating generalized projections of population growth and industrial growth into accurate predictions of future air quality. Accordingly, the states have had considerable difficulty developing control strategies adequate not only for the attainment but also for the maintenance of the national standards. Since EPA is little better equipped to predict future levels of air quality, the agency increasingly is looking towards land use planning as the mechanism both for predicting future levels of air quality and for ensuring that these levels will not violate the air quality standards.

In Chapter 2, the analysis of the Clean Air Act as it relates to land use controls yields the following conclusions:

1. The lack of clarity in the federal law on the issue of land use controls has resulted in the absence of a clear strategy for using land use controls at the state and local levels to achieve air quality objectives.

2. There is an important need for state coordination of land use planning since land use controls affecting air quality may be inconsistent if not counterproductive unless they are coordinated carefully with land use controls having other objectives.

2

3. State and local agencies already possess many of the important legal powers relating to land use control. The need is to work out an appropriate package of controls that in combination can achieve the objectives of air quality control.

4. In some cases, controls over land use will require the payment of compensation, for example, payment for the acquisition of buffer strips. But the Clean Air Act's reference to land use "controls" appears to preclude resort to compensatory techniques when needed.

5. Both the Senate and House versions of the Land Use Policy and Planning Assistance Act contain a provision requiring that state land use programs provide for a method for prohibiting the location of major sources of pollution where they would violate air quality standards. One can conclude that this provision makes land use controls the handmaiden of air pollution source controls. But the Clean Air Act reads as if land use controls are independently to establish land use patterns that will assist in achieving and maintaining air quality standards.

Chapter 3 is an attempt to determine the nature of practical problems of relating land use planning to air quality management at the state level. The development of air quality implementation plans is a state responsibility, and the development of state controls over land use must be considered a critical issue in implementing the Clean Air Act. Since Vermont and Maine have been leaders in state land use planning in the United States, operating procedures of the planning agencies of these states were examined. Experience with Maine and Vermont state land use control legislation suggests that coordination of state land use with state air pollution controls has not yet proceeded very far and that additional analysis of this coordination must be carried out before successful complementary programs can be developed at the state level. To this end, Chapter 9 examines recent experience in California with a program for facilitating such coordination.

Chapter 4 examines administrative review procedures for relating land use planning to air quality management that have utility either in the planning agency or in the air pollution control agency. The National Environmental Policy Act (NEPA) provides a potentially effective tool for relating air quality management to land use planning, but experience to date suggests that this potential has not been fully realized. Continuing revisions to the guidelines promulgated under the Act by the Council on Environmental Quality are making NEPA less of an ad hoc review mechanism and more of a tool-encouraging consideration of the secondary impacts of federal investments. The Office of Management and Budget's A-95 Circular, which requires a review by state and metropolitan "clearinghouses" of projects using federal funds, has resulted in the establishment of metropolitan planning agencies which can theoretically play a significant role in relating land use planning to air quality management. But since the primary function of A-95 is to avoid duplication of federal investments and not to promote comprehensive regional land use planning, the clearinghouses are at present, with very few exceptions, poorly equipped in terms of staff, financial resources, and political power to make an effective contribution to air quality management. Like the NEPA guidelines, the A-95 Circular has recently been strengthened.

The permit system used by many air pollution control agencies to control new sources of air pollution emissions has traditionally been based on the application of "state of the art" emission controls to individual sources ("point sources"). The aim has been to control industrial-process and space-heating emissions to the extent that proven technology is available. Increasingly, as air pollution control agencies have attempted to reduce emissions from existing sources as part of their control strategies to achieve the air quality standards, the permit system is being applied to all point sources in the agency's jurisdiction. The permit system also has considerable utility as a land use control device, but is not at present extensively applied for this purpose.

EPA's "complex source" regulations are an attempt to fill a regulation gap covering indirect sources of air pollution emissions. These are facilities that do not in themselves emit significant amounts of pollutants but that generate a considerable volume of traffic. The best examples are regional shopping centers and sports complexes. The respective states have developed the necessary regulations but at the time of this writing these regulations have not been tested in application.

Chapter 5 deals with the utility of buffer zones as an air pollution control technique, since one often sees general statements on their value but can find little in-depth analysis. We have found that buffer zones have a specific but limited role in reducing the impact of air pollution emissions. Creating green areas of this type appears to be a proper purpose for which public funds may be used and is permissible, to some extent, under state and local regulatory powers.

Chapter 6 concentrates on selected local controls and concludes that performance standards in zoning ordinances are an important local regulatory control that can supplement direct control of pollution sources. However, performance standards were developed more to control incompatible land uses than to control air pollution, and their usefulness as an air pollution control device has yet to be proved.

The potential application of procedures for spreading out or spacing sources of air pollution in order to reduce localized concentrations is also examined in Chapter 6, which uses the example of gasoline filling stations. It is concluded that the zoning ordinance is poorly suited for this purpose and that the air pollution regulations based on health and welfare considerations should be relied on. The effect of architectural controls that are insensitive to air pollution considerations receives attention, and it is concluded that there are small but significant benefits to be gained by revising building codes.

Chapter 7 is concerned with the methodology of estimating emissions from land use categories. After a review and development of land-use-based emission equations, the planning implications of moving from land use categories to land-use-based emissions are discussed. Given the current state of the art, the estimation of emissions from land use categories will give a rough approximation of what actually will be emitted into the air. However, the process will permit the evaluation of alternative land use plans in terms of air quality as well as the evaluation of the localized impact of a particular site development on air quality.

Chapter 8 focuses on the dispersion of pollutants by meteorological influences. After discussing the general structure of a commonly utilized dispersion model, the potential errors from dispersion modeling are reviewed and analyzed. In attempting to relate land use plans to air quality, it is important to understand that significant errors can enter the analysis. These errors can be dampened by a judicious use of simpler models and a careful handling of data.

Chapter 9 concentrates on recent developments in California, where specific procedures for relating land use planning to air quality management at the state and local levels have considerable implications for how we treat the issue in the rest of the country. Attention is directed to the technique of "emission allocation," a first attempt to make the land use planning process the basis for air quality management.

Chapter 10 reviews the recent history of the development of "nondegradation" as a policy issue in air quality management. Since at the time of this writing EPA had not promulgated final regulations on nondegradation, our treatment is tentative. However, the major issues in a policy of nondegradation are summarized.

Chapter 11 offers recommendations for both the land use planner and the air pollution control official and raises a number of questions that must be dealt with before we can effectively relate land use control and planning to air quality management.

NOTES

1. For a discussion of recent trends in land use controls see F. Bosselman and D. Callies, The Quiet Revolution in Land Use Controls (1971), and William Riley, The Use of Land: A Citizen's Policy Guide to Urban Growth (1973).

2. A broader treatment of this is found in G. Hagevik, The Relationship of Land Use and Transportation Planning to Air Quality Management (1972).

3. 37 Fed. Reg. 10842 (1972). A "control strategy" is a combination of measures designed to achieve the aggregate reduction of emissions necessary for the purposes of attainment and maintenance of a national standard. EPA's regulations set forth procedures—that is, proportional or diffusion modeling—to be employed by the states in demonstrating that their control strategies will be adequate for these purposes. Evaluation of the control strategies generally included assessment of the accuracy of the data relied upon by a state in demonstrating the adequacy of control strategies, the validity of any assumptions made by the state, and the accuracy of the calculations employed in the modeling exercises. In addition, a determination was made as to whether the control strategy would be sufficiently comprehensive.

2

THE POTENTIAL USE OF LAND USE CONTROLS UNDER THE CLEAN AIR ACT OF 1970

Growing public awareness of and concern with air pollution dangers have led to increasingly comprehensive state and federal legislation directed at the air quality problem.[1] While legislative attention to air pollution has largely been confined to the direct regulation of pollution sources, studies of air quality control have long recognized that land use planning and control is necessary to achieve and maintain clean air.[2] Since 1970 the federal Clean Air Act has authorized both land use and transportation controls as part of the state plans for implementing federal air quality standards.[3]

This chapter initiates a review of the role that land use controls can play in achieving the air quality levels mandated by the federal statute and considers the extent to which land use controls have been and are likely to be used for this purpose. First we discuss the regulatory system introduced by the 1970 federal legislation, directing special attention to the role of land use controls prescribed in that act. We then analyze ways in which land use controls at the state and local levels might be used as an air pollution control strategy, discussing implementation of the federal land use controls provision by the Environmental Protection Agency. The present role of land use controls in a federal air pollution strategy is contrasted with other enacted and pending federal statutes that require national land use policy implementation at state and local levels. Finally, we suggest a role for land use controls in regulating air pollution.

THE LAND USE CONTROLS PROVISION

The 1970 Clean Air Act Amendments[4] provide a combined federal and state attack on the problem of air pollution. Both authority

7

to set pollution standards and enforcement responsibility had been delegated to the states under earlier federal legislation,[5] but difficulties of administration and enforcement led to extensive amendments in 1970 which broadened the scope of the law and the regulatory authority of the federal government. As a first step in the pollution abatement procedure contemplated by the 1970 amendments, the Environmental Protection Agency (EPA), the national agency presently administering the federal air pollution law,[6] established primary and secondary national ambient air quality standards for various air pollutants.[7] These standards establish air pollutant levels that must not be exceeded for longer than a specified period of time.[8] The statute authorizes two sets of complementary standards. Primary standards are to reflect "an adequate margin of safety . . . requisite to protect the public health." Secondary standards are more strict and are designed to "protect the public welfare from any known or anticipated adverse effects associated with the presence of such air pollutants in the ambient air."[9] The states are required to prepare plans for the implementation of national primary and secondary air quality standards. These implementation plans must in turn be approved, or disapproved and modified as required, by EPA.[10] The statute requires that air pollution be attacked within each state on a regional basis, so state plans must direct each local air quality region to implement and enforce national primary and secondary standards.[11] State plans must provide for the achievement of national primary standards as soon as practicable, in any event within three years after EPA approval of such plans, while national secondary standards must be achieved within a reasonable time.[12]

In addition to national ambient air quality standards, the Act provides for emission standards for designated pollutants emitted by new sources.[13] While national ambient air quality standards set limits on the allowable average pollutant concentration in the atmosphere, new source performance standards limit the amount of pollutant that any individual new source (such as a power plant or new factory) may emit. Ambient air quality is monitored by stations spaced throughout a region, while new source standards are monitored at the site of each new source. Each national ambient air quality standard thus measures the cumulative effect of a pollutant emitted from all sources. Pollutants emitted by both stationary sources, such as factories, and by mobile sources, such as automobiles, will contribute to a violation of ambient air standards. New source standards, on the other hand, apply only to new stationary sources.

This review of the standard-setting and implementation provisions of the Clean Air Act of 1970[14] provides in outline form the statutory context within which the land use controls provisions of the statute must be analyzed. The 1970 amendments authorize land use controls

8

at several points. First, as enacted, the statute contains an explicit reference to land use.[15] It requires state implementation plans to include:

> emission limitations, schedules, and timetables for compliance with such limitations, and such other measures as may be necessary to insure attainment and maintenance of such primary or secondary standard, including, but not limited to, land use and transportation controls.[16]

This statutory provision contains a mandate to utilize, without further specification, any form of land use control that "may be necessary" to achieve and maintain air quality standards.

The provision in the Clean Air Act for regulation of stationary pollution sources can also be construed as a land use control measure. The Act calls for supervision of new statutory sources of pollution as one of the techniques for achieving ambient air quality standards. State implementation plans must include:

> [a] procedure . . . for review, prior to construction or modification, of the location of new sources . . . [of air pollution which] shall provide for adequate authority to prevent the construction or modification of any new source to which a [federal] standard of performance [for pollutant emissions] will apply at any location which the state determines will prevent the attainment or maintenance . . . of a national ambient air quality primary or secondary standard.[17]

To the extent that this provision authorizes state review of the location of stationary pollution sources,[18] it sanctions land use regulation.

Thus the Clean Air Amendments include land use control measures at several points. The statute contains a specific mandate to the states to use land use control measures "where necessary" to achieve and maintain air quality standards and also requires states to grant some statewide, regional, or local agency authority to prevent construction or modification of any new source that would interfere with attainment or maintenance of air quality standards.

The legislative history of the Act reveals that Congress approved land use controls as a general method for achieving air quality standards. The scope of potential regulation grew as the bill developed in Congress. The House version made no provision for land use controls.[19] The Senate added a provision allowing control over the location of stationary pollution sources, but it was merely permissive and designed only to prevent <u>interference</u> with the attainment and maintenance of air quality standards.[20] As discussed above,[21] the final version of the Act directed states to review the location of new sources. In addition, the statute as enacted contained a specific provision that went beyond preventing interference and authorized land use control measures "where necessary" to implement and maintain national standards. This progression suggests a much wider application of land use control provisions than was originally intended. Although this interpretation is not supported by any explicit legislative history, it has been adopted by Congressional spokesmen who were close to the drafting of the Act,[22] and by EPA itself in its administration of the statute.[23]

While Congress apparently has approved land use controls, there is little in the hearings on the 1970 amendments to the Clean Air Act,[24] in the debate recorded in the Congressional Record,[25] or in later Congressional hearings on the implementation of the amendments[26] to indicate how EPA and the states are to administer them. Additional language in the Senate Committee Report does disclose that "land use policies must be developed to prevent location of facilities which are not compatible with implementation of national standards."[27] This language, however, appears to reflect the earlier and narrower "interference" version of the land use controls provision.

Other statements in Congressional debate were rhetorical or inconclusive. Senator Spong, a member of the conference committee that reported the final bill, stated that "implementation plans to meet the primary national air quality standards must include provision for land use and transportation controls."[28] Senator Muskie, Chairman of the Senate Subcommittee on Air and Water Pollution, which was responsible for the Senate version of the Clean Air Act, believed that "implicit in the concept of [state] implementation plans" is the requirement that "urban areas do something about . . . the modification and change of housing patterns, employment patterns and transportation patterns generally."[29] The legislative history thus gives scant guidance to the states in selecting specific land use control measures to implement their air quality programs.

LAND USE CONTROLS IN STATE IMPLEMENTATION PLANS[30]

The inconclusive legislative history coupled with the cursory treatment of land use in the language of the Act left to EPA the major task of interpreting the land use control provisions. Since the statute places major emphasis on direct emission restrictions, we must determine whether land use controls are intended only as a supplement to direct regulation when such regulation is insufficient, or whether they are intended as a major weapon that can and should be used in place of a more direct emission control strategy. Analysis of this question depends on further elaboration of Congressional intention in adopting the land use controls provision contained in Section 110 of the Act. But, as discussed above,[31] the legislative history reveals little more than a general endorsement of land use measures, so we are left to speculate on this point. Given the types of land use control powers presently exercised by state and local governments, it is possible to isolate three issues that must be resolved before we can define a possible land use control strategy within the Clean Air Act.

Direct Controls versus Indirect Land Use Controls

Does the federal statute limit land use measures to direct controls, such as relocation or bans on construction of possible pollution sources? Or may indirect controls, such as regulation of density, be included as well? Direct restrictions are clearly mandated by the Act at two points. First, the statute explicitly provides for regulating construction of stationary pollution sources as part of state air pollution abatement programs.[32] Secondly, it could be argued that the land use controls authorized for state implementation plans "as may be necessary"[33] should be likewise applied only to new pollution sources.

There is little difference between the types of land use controls authorized by these two sections. Controls over location of and emissions from new sources are limited to the individual polluter. Thus the San Francisco Bay Area Pollution Control District has experimented with a direct ban on the construction of new filling stations, a source of hydrocarbon pollution.[34] Under the "as necessary" clause, states could utilize more conventional land use measures, such as zoning. For example, a filling station construction ban or its equivalent could be legislated through a revision of the local zoning ordinance.[35] Preference for one approach over the other may depend on the relative effectiveness of the two measures. That a construction ban imposed by the pollution control district can be made applicable throughout the region may be enough argument for preferring this approach over the more localized zoning ordinance approach. Even the gasoline station example, however, reveals that any of the direct land use controls over potential polluters may restrict economic opportunities within air quality control regions where the air pollution program, to achieve and maintain air quality, requires restriction on the entry of new sources. In these instances, local policy makers may resist the application of direct land use controls.[36]

Changes made in the original language of the land use controls provision of the Clean Air Act indicate that more extensive controls over land uses were contemplated.[37] These controls are indirect; they are not used to restrict emissions or the location of pollution sources but are applied throughout the community to all land uses with the more general objective of improving air quality. Many indirect land use controls of this nature may have limited immediate effect, but may restore the air quality over a longer period of time. For example, ordinances requiring setbacks from streets and highways, minimum distances between residential and other dwellings, and the dedication and maintenance of open-space areas in new residential developments allegedly have an aggregate impact on air pollution by providing open areas which can absorb atmospheric pollutants.[38] The immediate effect of any such controls in these situations may be quite small, but over a longer period and on a larger scale many types of land use control will improve air quality.

Residential zoning offers an example. Since the dispersal of air pollutants is to some degree dependent on residential densities throughout a metropolitan region, a local zoning ordinance whose density requirements reflect dispersal patterns clearly would help achieve and maintain air quality. Similarly, air quality can be bettered by zoning restrictions on the location of nonpolluting uses that contribute indirectly to air pollution problems. Typical examples include major sports complexes, which generate additional automobile traffic and thus cause an increase in motor vehicle emissions.[39] EPA has extended its authority over preconstruction review of new stationary sources to include new developments that add to air pollution problems by generating additional motor vehicle traffic.[40]

Comprehensive and Regional Planning

Indirect land use controls must be exercised with a regional context in mind. First, the entire approach of the Clean Air Act is regional: states are subdivided into Air Quality Control Regions, and state implementation plans must provide control strategies on a region-by-region basis.[41] Secondly, since indirect land use controls have limited immediate impact, they are effective only if practiced on a large scale. Only through planning that encompasses entire metropolitan regions can attention be given to a comprehensive land use control program that would significantly improve the air.

Experience with comprehensive plans that consider air quality for metropolitan regions is still quite limited, and there is presently no consensus regarding the kind of metropolitan development pattern best suited to optimizing air quality.[42] Moreover, the links between comprehensive planning and land use controls are generally quite weak in most jurisdictions. There are few states in which local zoning regulations must be based on a comprehensive plan.[43] Given this situation, there is some question about the extent to which air quality planning can be translated directly into a land use control strategy. But at the same time, air quality standards are uniformly applicable throughout air quality regions; therefore some form of comprehensive regional planning clearly is needed.

Governmental Entities

Comprehensive planning for land use control raises a third question: Which state, regional, and local governments are to be delegated authority to administer those land use control provisions which are adopted as part of state air quality implementation plans? To be effective, any land use plan to reduce air pollution must have authority vested at a level higher than the local municipality. Any control over major land use developments that are likely to generate pollutants or to have a major effect on land use and transportation patterns will have to be exercised at the regional level if not at the state level. Although local governments may take a parochial view of their land use control responsibility, local zoning agencies may simply not have the expertise or the necessary information to make judgments about land use measures related to regionwide programs.

The problem is complicated further because air pollution control agencies ordinarily do not have the authority to adopt and enforce land use measures,[44] although it is possible for that power to be delegated to them.[45] Where land use controls are to be exercised by an air pollution control agency, however, an accommodation will have to be developed between that agency and local governments exercising zoning authority. It is also possible to provide for supervening statewide control of land use, such as that required by federal legislation dealing with management of land uses in coastal zones.[46] Prototypes of this kind of state management have already been adopted in several jurisdictions.[47] Matters are further complicated because some air quality control regions contain portions of more than one state. These issues are difficult to resolve, and because they did not receive attention in the adoption of the Clean Air Act, the statute itself does not assist in resolving them.[48]

Thus at least three problems are raised by the land use controls provision of the Clean Air Act. First, a choice must be made among competing alternatives—to apply land use controls directly to sources of pollution, to apply land use controls indirectly to regulate indirect sources, or to use a combination of direct and indirect measures. Next, given the regional focus of strategies for air quality control, any effective use of land use regulations in the context of air pollution control will have to be based on planning policies that consider regional growth and development patterns. As we have noted, regional planning that takes air pollution factors into account is still in an early and developing state. The importance of regional planning as the basis for land use regulation raises two questions: Which governmental level will exercise the authority, and how will these powers be apportioned between the air quality control board and conventional zoning agencies?

THE DUTY UNDER THE ACT TO IMPOSE LAND USE CONTROLS

Primary Standards

The federal Clean Air Act requires that primary ambient air quality standards be met "as expeditiously as practicable," but not later than three years from the date of approval of a state's implementation plan.[49] For most states this date is 1975. Secondary air quality standards must be met within a "reasonable time."[50] Because land use controls may be part of a state's implementation plan and because the state plan must provide air pollution control measures that will achieve required air quality levels within the statutory periods, it could be argued that states may adopt only land use control measures that meet the statutory timetable. Most indirect land use and planning controls require a long period of time before their effect on the pollution source base is noticeable. On the other hand, direct controls over the location of emissions sources can usually be imposed more quickly and may lead to more dramatic and immediate reductions in air pollution. Thus, in meeting primary standards, the statute arguably may not require the exercise of other than short-range and thus direct land use controls, such as those affecting the location of pollution sources. This reasoning finds support in the statutory language that requires primary standards to be met as "expeditiously as practicable,"[51] and at most by the three-year deadline. It may be that the federal Clean Air Act will have to be interpreted to limit land use controls to those relevant to the short timespan the statute allows for compliance with the primary standards mandate.

States may attempt to alleviate the burden of these time constraints in the implementation of national primary standards by requesting an extension of the three-year time limit. Under the federal statute, the Administrator of EPA may grant a two-year extension to meet primary standards, but only if the state has "considered and applied as part of its plan reasonably available alternative means of

14

attaining such primary standards"—that is, means other than emission controls.[52] Presumably, the reference to "alternative means" includes land use controls. But, as indicated earlier, strict control over pollution sources to achieve air quality standards may inhibit growth in all or a part of a particular air quality region.[53] Therefore, state governments are likely to be under intense pressure to avoid such controls. The question, then, is whether a state can refuse to consider land use controls as a "reasonably available" strategy on the ground that they would have adverse socioeconomic effects.

There is very little in the legislation that can help to answer this question. Except for a reference in the provision authorizing preconstruction review of new sources, economic balancing language is conspicuously absent from the Act.[54] However, the statutory language requiring air quality standards to be met only as expeditiously as "practicable"[55] may imply some limitation on the exercise of land use controls that inhibit economic growth. The difficulty with any interpretation of this statutory language is that social and economic issues in the enforcement of the Clean Air Act received very little explicit consideration in the legislative development of the Act. The Senate Report on the 1970 amendments did discuss the technical feasibility claim as an excuse for delay in attaining air quality standards and concluded: "The health of people is more important than the question of whether the early achievement of ambient air quality standards is technically feasible."[56] Yet here, as elsewhere, the limited Congressional consideration of social and economic issues appears more directed towards the economic costs of compliance with ambient air quality standards than towards the economic and social dislocations that would result from the exercise of land use controls. This omission is not surprising, since the scope of the provision for land use controls broadened greatly during consideration of the 1970 amendments, and Congressional attention focused largely on the role of emission limitations. As a result, it is not clear to what extent EPA and the states are entitled to consider socioeconomic consequences in developing land use controls as part of air quality implementation plans. The limited discussion of social and economic factors in the legislative history, however, implies that states can take advantage of the Section 110 extension provisions to utilize long-range land use controls, but that states may not use the prospect of adverse socioeconomic impact to claim that land use controls are not "reasonably available."[57]

Secondary Standards

We now may consider the extent to which the Act requires land use controls to achieve secondary air quality standards. Secondary

15

standards are not developed merely to serve as an extra margin of safety to protect the public health. They are designed to "protect the public welfare from any known or anticipated adverse effects associated with the presence of such air pollutants in the ambient air."[58] The 1970 law as finally passed contained no specific deadline for the attainment of secondary standards but only indicated that such standards must be attained within a "reasonable time."[59]

Since secondary standards are more stringent than primary standards, they require a greater total reduction in emissions and correspondingly tougher controls, which have greater socioeconomic impact. If a state were to rely at all on land use controls to attain secondary standards, such controls would have to cover a wider range than those adopted to attain primary standards. A state might have to consider the adoption of land use controls strictly regulating indirect as well as direct sources of pollution. Such regulation of secondary standards would be easier than regulating primary standards, since secondary standards need only be achieved within a reasonable time rather than within three years. Thus a state would have the freedom to exercise land use controls that are long range in scope and to contemplate more fundamental changes in urban development patterns.

The "reasonable time" requirement also suggests that socioeconomic factors, whether or not they can be considered in programs for attaining primary standards, might be more relevant in a program to achieve secondary standards. Nevertheless, even if states may balance socioeconomic costs against environmental gains in achieving and maintaining secondary standards, the extra benefit to be gained in meeting secondary standards seems clear. This benefit suggests that the need to meet these standards may at some point overcome substantial socioeconomic considerations. For example, if it could be shown that direct control of emissions had been applied to the fullest extent possible, and yet secondary standards had not been achieved in an air quality control region, land use controls might be treated as necessary despite adverse socioeconomic effects.

Maintenance of Air Quality

As discussed above,[60] the time limits set for achieving primary standards restrict state implementation plans to direct short-range land use measures. However, the Clean Air Act also requires state implementation plans to contain measures mandating the maintenance of air quality levels once they are achieved.[61] For this task, indirect land use controls may be useful. For example, if it could be shown that in meeting primary standards an air quality control region had directly reduced pollutant emissions to the fullest extent possible, it might be necessary to adopt land use controls in order to meet the "maintenance" mandate of the federal statute by maintaining the air quality levels thus achieved. This interpretation would create roles for both short-term and long-term land use control measures in the implementation of primary standards.

As with primary standards, there is a statutory duty to "maintain" secondary standards once they are achieved. Indirect controls would be particularly well adapted to this task. Since secondary standards are more stringent than primary standards, it may turn out that secondary standards can be maintained only through a comprehensive program of such indirect long-range land use controls. In addition, states would have the time necessary to set up and implement such indirect long-range controls carefully because of the longer time allowed for achieving secondary standards.

A related issue concerns regions where air quality already meets or exceeds the level required by EPA and the Clean Air Act. The recent case of Sierra Club v. Ruckelshaus[62] held that in such regions state implementation plans must provide means to ensure that the existing air quality will not deteriorate significantly. Both direct and indirect land use controls are appropriate tools to ensure such nondegradation.

This review of the duty to impose land use controls reveals that unclear statutory language is but one barrier to construing the nature of the land use controls mandated by the Clean Air Act. The short time period specified for achieving primary standards suggests that only direct short-range land use controls such as those regulating the location of polluters may be feasible means for achieving those standards. Long-range controls based on comprehensive planning may be more relevant to the attainment of secondary standards, which do not have such an urgent compliance schedule, or to the maintenance of both primary and secondary standards once they have been attained. Thus far we have not explicitly discussed the problems posed by the choice of governmental agency to implement whatever land use controls are adopted. Clearly, however, the more we rely on long-range controls based on wide-scale comprehensive planning, the more we will have to rely on governmental agencies whose jurisdiction is statewide or regional and which can respond to the demands of regionwide planning. Broad jurisdiction is especially important if the socioeconomic impact of land use controls must be considered as part of any strategy adopted.

EPA IMPLEMENTATION

To understand the role EPA has assigned to land use controls, we must examine the regulations issued by EPA under the Clean Air

Act.[63] Analysis of these regulations will also contribute to an understanding of how land use controls might fit into a state air quality control strategy. It should be noted that major changes in the content of EPA regulations for state implementation plans were made between the original publication of these regulations and their final adoption. These changes, which many critics of EPA claim have weakened the implementation of the Clean Air Act, have had an indirect but important impact on the exercise of land use controls in air quality programs.[64]

The regulations include certain basic land use guidelines, such as a general requirement that state plans contain "other measures necessary for attainment and maintenance of national standards"[65] and a provision requiring that, in regions where air quality does not meet national standards, the control strategy must provide for the "degree of emission reduction necessary to offset emission increases . . . reasonably expected . . . to result from projected growth of population, industrial activity, motor vehicle traffic, or other factors."[66]

In an important sense the EPA regulations expanded state authority to utilize land use strategies in their implementation plans. While there is no explicit statutory basis for the concept, the regulations introduce what is referred to as a "control strategy" for the abatement of air pollution. A "control strategy" is defined as

> a combination of measures designated to achieve the aggregate reduction of emissions necessary for attainment and maintenance of a national standard, including but not limited to, measures such as . . . any land use or transportation control measures not specifically delineated herein.[67]

In short, the "control strategy" is the sum total of the measures the state adopts to achieve the required air quality standards.[68] This strategy, it may be noted, includes measures not explicitly authorized by the statute as appropriate for inclusion in a state implementation plan. For example, a control strategy may include "federal or state emission charges or taxes or other economic incentives or disincentives not specifically authorized by the Act."[69] Thus the regulations ensure that indirect, longer range land use control measures may be included in state implementation plans even though they are not explicitly permitted under the Act.

Recognition of Socioeconomic Factors

As stated in a preamble thereto,[70] the final regulations of August 14, 1971, changed many of the earlier proposed regulations which had been issued on April 7. The most controversial change, and the one most likely to affect the exercise of land use controls to achieve air quality standards, was the inclusion of several provisions allowing socioeconomic factors to influence policy decisions in the preparation of state plans. These regulations stated in part:

> Nothing in this part shall be construed in any manner . . . (b) To encourage a State to adopt any particular control strategy without taking into consideration the cost-effectiveness of such control strategy in relation to that of alternative control strategies. . . . (d) To encourage a State to prepare, adopt, or submit a plan without taking into consideration the social and economic impact of the control strategy set forth in such plan, including, but not limited to, impact on availability of fuels, energy, transportation, and employment.[71]

In developing their plans, states are also "encouraged to identify alternative control strategies, as well as the costs and benefits of each such alternative, for attainment and maintenance of the national standards."[72] Do these provisions mean only that states need give some attention to socioeconomic effects when developing the land use control element of their implementation plans? Or do they mean that if socioeconomic disruption can or may occur through the exercise of land use controls the states can be excused from including these controls in their implementation plans?

The most pressing problem posed by these questions is the extent to which meeting air quality standards in any region will require the exclusion from that region of industry that may stimulate economic growth. Where socioeconomic considerations must be weighed in developing an implementation plan, construction of new but heavily polluting industry may be permitted on the ground that the region's growth otherwise might be curtailed. In this event, meeting primary standards within the statutory three-year period will have to be achieved by increased reliance on the use of source controls on emissions. This strategy has less effect on economic growth, but it places a greater share of the cost of abatement on existing as compared with new industries within an air quality control region.

Extension of Deadlines

Assuming that immediate and direct land use controls prohibiting the location of new pollution sources would create socioeconomic disruption, EPA may feel obligated to provide two-year extensions in meeting the deadlines for primary standards to states that request them. As the basis for such an extension, EPA regulations require only a showing that the "necessary technology or alternatives" will not be available within the three-year period.[73] The state must also make a "clear identification of any alternative means of attainment of such primary standard which were considered and rejected."[74] Presumably, rejection of land use controls because of adverse socioeconomic effects would qualify under this language.

Study of the May 31, 1972, EPA regulations approving and disapproving various portions of state plans indicates that this policy may have been followed. Few state plans contained land use controls, and those that did provided only for minor measures.[75] Yet EPA granted numerous extensions of the attainment date for various pollutants without requiring a showing that land use controls were not reasonably available or would not aid in the attainment of air quality levels by the three-year limit.[76] Where EPA disallowed requests for extensions, the agency found that the plan in question indicated the standard would be attained within the three-year limit. No state was asked whether it could achieve primary standards before the deadline by instituting land use controls.[77] In this connection, it is interesting to observe that while some states did indicate that they would attain primary standards within the time limit, when EPA had to specify an attainment date for those plans which had failed to do so or which had specified unreasonable dates, the agency never set a date less than three years away.

Similarly, EPA avoided even mentioning land use controls when dealing with state plans to implement secondary standards. Its regulations state that a "reasonable time" to attain secondary standards is three years only if the necessary "degree of emission reduction" can be achieved through "the application of reasonably available control technology."[78] If the necessary reduction cannot be achieved through available control technology, a "reasonable time shall depend on . . . the social, economic, and technological problems involved in carrying out [an adequate] control strategy."[79] EPA routinely granted requests for 18-month extensions authorized by the Act for delaying submission of a secondary standards plan. The agency approved dates as far away as July 1978 with no mention of the possibility that land use controls might shorten the time required to attain secondary standards.[80]

In general, EPA made no comment about the widespread failure of state plans even to consider the exercise of land use controls. One minor land use measure was required by EPA's implementation plan guidelines—a projection of growth and how this projection would affect the attainment and maintenance of air quality standards.[81] However, such measures were not included in many state plans. EPA excused even this failure on the ground that the expertise necessary to make such projections was lacking.[82] When EPA's approval of state implementation plans was remanded by a federal court of appeals because inadequate attention had been given to <u>maintenance</u> of air quality standards,[83] EPA amended its implementation plan regulations to require state identification of those areas where projected growth could jeopardize maintenance of air quality standards.[84] These new requirements and statutory provisions are consistent with the earlier observation that indirect land use controls based in long-range comprehensive planning are more properly exercised in carrying out the duty to maintain air quality once national standards have been attained. EPA's actions also suggest that, at least with respect to long-range planning for air quality control, socioeconomic factors may have to be set aside if the maintenance of standards requires constraints on growth and population.

Weakening the Act

Many critics of EPA's administration of the Clean Air Act have objected even more fundamentally to EPA's unilateral introduction of socioeconomic factors into air pollution control strategies, arguing that such regulations weaken the Act.[85] A full airing of the controversy over the introduction of socioeconomic considerations in the preparation of state implementation plans can be found in the Oversight Hearings held by the Senate Subcommittee on Air and Water Pollution on the Implementation of the Clean Air Amendments of 1970. Senator Eagleton, who chaired most of the hearings and who had been active in the drafting of the Clean Air Act Amendments of 1970, maintained that Congress never intended to have socioeconomic factors included in state implementation plans.[86] He and other witnesses charged that EPA had been pressured by the White House Office of Management and Budget (OMB) into withdrawing its own final guidelines and substituting the set which became the August 14 regulations, with the significant addition of the socioeconomic provisions. These witnesses asserted that OMB's purpose was to give industry an economic excuse to delay full compliance with air quality standards—an excuse the Senate-House conference committee intended to delete from the Act by striking out all references to socioeconomic considerations in the section in the final bill on state implementation plans. EPA's answer at the hearings was that while economic factors could not be weighed in setting primary standards, once they were set EPA was free to encourage states to develop a control strategy that would reflect the economically least disruptive way of achieving those standards.[87]

This review of EPA's implementation of the land use controls provision suggests that the agency has just begun to see the many difficult problems involved in an interpretation of this section of the law. Strangely enough, EPA's attention to socioeconomic needs as a factor in developing land use as well as other elements of the air pollution control strategy contrasts with the usual failure to explicitly consider these needs in the more traditional land use regulation setting.[88] Nevertheless, since traditional air pollution controls operate directly on industries and other employers essential to the economic growth of a region, EPA will be forced to consider this issue more explicitly than it has so far. Its decision to permit balancing of social and economic costs against achievement of air quality standards may have been justified by ambiguities in the legislative history of the Clean Air Act. But whether EPA's interpretation of this history is correct or not is less important than the fact that any control strategy, whether direct or indirect, will have an impact on regional growth and development. Therefore, we should look next at that provision of federal law which, apart from the land use control provision, requires direct controls over stationary source location. The implementation of stationary source controls, more than any others, is likely to produce socioeconomic impacts on growth and development.

CONTROLS OVER STATIONARY POLLUTION SOURCES

As we have seen, at least for primary standards, direct controls over land use are more likely to fit the scheme of the Clean Air Act because of their immediate impact. Local governments are only beginning to consider the relationships between such long-range indirect controls and air pollution; EPA itself has refrained from insisting on indirect controls and has yet to define its own policy. Thus in the near future much attention will focus on the direct land use controls clearly authorized by the Act—preconstruction review of new sources of pollution.

Under this section of the Clean Air Act, the Administrator must publish a list of categories of stationary sources that "contribute significantly to air pollution which causes or contributes to the endangerment of public health or welfare."[89] After listing a category, the Administrator must propose and ultimately publish federal standards of performance for that category of sources.[90] A standard of performance is defined under Section 111(a)(1) as a

standard for emissions of air pollutants which reflects
the degree of emission limitation achievable through the
application of the best system of emission reduction
which (taking into account the cost of achieving such

reduction) the Administrator determines has been adequately demonstrated.[91]

The land use provision relating to these new sources appears in Section 110, which deals with state implementation plans. Section 110(a)(2)(D) requires a "procedure . . . for review (prior to construction or modification) of the location of new sources to which a standard of performance [under Section 111] will apply." This procedure must "provide for adequate authority to prevent the construction or modification of any [such] new source . . . at any location which . . . will prevent the attainment or maintenance . . . of a national ambient air quality primary or secondary standard."[92]

Federal Preemption

The authors of the Act believed that the new source provision granted the states great power to control major sources of pollution; the Senate Report lists nineteen categories of sources that could be regulated under this section.[93] Congress asserted federal control over these sources because it feared that major industries would exert "economic blackmail" on the states by threatening to leave any state that tried to impose strict emission controls in an effort to meet air quality standards. By imposing uniform emission controls on major new sources at the federal level, Congress felt that these industries would lose that economic weapon. But by authorizing direct federal governance of sources that previously had been subject only to state pollution control, the Clean Air Act raises the question whether regulation of stationary sources is now to be based solely on considerations of health and welfare or on land use factors as well.

We can resolve this question by comparing the original Senate version of Section 111 with the section as finally enacted. The original Senate bill did authorize a land use measure at the federal level, requiring a mandatory EPA certification procedure for new sources to determine whether each new source complied with Section 111 performance standards. It ordered the federal agency to review the proposed location of each new source to ensure that its construction would not cause a violation of air quality standards.[94]

Did the imposition in the Senate bill of federal performance standards and a federal preconstruction review process mean that the federal government had fully preempted regulation of future major stationary sources of pollution? If so, Congress would have utilized its commerce power to override the police power under which states traditionally regulate industries that contribute to air pollution. It is worth noting that the Senate provision dealing with federal

23

preconstruction review was expressly concerned only with preventing interference with <u>national</u> air quality standards.[95] Thus we are left with the following problem: Under the Senate bill, could a state have imposed upon a Section 111 new source a land use measure not required by the federal government in an attempt to enforce ambient air quality standards more stringent than federal standards? More important, could a state have achieved national air quality standards by imposing land use measures on proposed new sources covered by Section 111 that already met federal new source performance standards?[96] Or could affected industries have claimed that the federal government had fully preempted the area of new source regulation, so that if a new source complied with federal guidelines under Section 111 the state could attain its air quality standards only by restricting those older sources left to its control?

In the Senate hearings on air and water pollution, Senator Muskie questioned Dr. John Middleton, former EPA Deputy Assistant Administrator for Air Programs, as to whether the states would still be able to exclude these sources for health reasons if they so desired. Middleton replied that if the proposed source would have a detrimental impact on health, construction could be prohibited whether or not it met federal performance standards and that the state would always have the power to exclude a new source under an applicable land use plan.[97] This response does not clarify the problem. If a proposed source did pose a health threat, it automatically would not meet federal performance standards, since a proposed source can pass the required preconstruction review only if it does not prevent attainment or maintenance of national standards, which are designed to protect the public health and welfare. Furthermore, if states could not justify the imposition of land use measures on new sources because of federal preemption in regulating new sources to protect the public health, attempts to assert land use controls by means of state powers would raise serious legal problems.

In comparing the Senate bill with the law finally enacted, it seems clear that Congress did not intend the federal government to preempt state control over the location of new stationary pollution sources. First, the original Senate bill allowed the EPA Administrator to achieve the "greatest degree of emission control" possible through the use of the "latest available control technology, processes, operating methods, or other alternatives" (emphasis added),[98] thus apparently allowing land use control measures. Presumably, then, under the original bill the Administrator could both set emission standards for new sources and, if necessary, limit or prohibit the entrance of certain industries in a given region. But the final statutory provision only authorizes the Administrator to set emission standards for new sources, thus eliminating federal control over new source location. Consistent with Congressional intent, regulations issued by EPA to implement Section 111 performance standards do not permit discretion at the federal level to impose land use controls on new sources but only prescribe emission standards and monitoring and testing procedures.[99]

Preconstruction Review

In addition to limiting the federal role to setting emission standards, the bill as finally enacted shifted the preconstruction review process entirely to the states.[100] Section 110 requires state implementation plans to provide for mandatory preconstruction review of the location of new stationary pollution sources or their modification, with authority to prevent construction or modification "at any location which . . . will prevent the attainment or maintenance . . . of a national ambient air quality . . . standard."[101] As this process at the state level is intended to protect air quality standards and not just to ensure that federal new source performance standards are recognized at the construction planning stage, land use considerations presumably can form a part of the required review. Thus the states could use this review process to implement land use decisions about the location of stationary pollution sources so long as those decisions were related to the state's pollution control strategy.[102]

One difficulty with this interpretation is that location controls over stationary sources are only one of several options open to a state seeking to achieve or maintain required air quality levels. An industry faced with a ban on new construction because it would violate air quality standards might thus argue that the state should adopt alternative methods for achieving or maintaining air quality so that the construction ban could be lifted. For example, more stringent air pollution measures could be imposed in other parts of the air quality regions, either through direct performance controls on emissions or through limits on the construction or modification of stationary sources elsewhere.

EPA's Interpretation

EPA regulations designed to implement the Section 110 requirement that states have a preconstruction process may provide the states with an answer to this kind of objection. Procedures for state review are required by regulation to include "means of disapproving such construction or modification if it will result in a violation of applicable portions of the control strategy or will interfere with attainment or maintenance of a national standard."[103] The importance of this directive lies in the reference to the state's control strategy.

As we have indicated, control strategies consist of all the measures that the state has adopted to implement its air quality plan, including land use controls. Although land use controls are authorized as a means by which the state can achieve national air quality standards, there is no requirement that any particular land use control be justified by the need to meet a national standard. Therefore, it would appear that state preconstruction review, including land use controls, may be imposed on new stationary sources even where national air quality standards are not threatened, provided this review is intended to implement some other aspect of the control strategy. For example, if the land use controls contemplated by an implementation plan required a limitation on new industry in a region to provide a margin of safety in maintaining air quality standards once achieved, preconstruction review of new sources could be utilized to carry out this maintenance objective whether or not the construction of any particular new source would lead to a violation of a national standard. Thus if a state control strategy dictates that no construction or modification may take place at certain locations whether or not the proposed construction would violate federal ambient air quality standards, the state must acquire the authority to insist that its control strategy be honored. The state can thus avoid the difficult problem of defending its ban on the ground that a particular construction or modification would lead to a violation of an air quality standard.

EPA regulations concerning the scope of this preconstruction review procedure are nevertheless contradictory. Section 51.11(a) (4) implies that preconstruction review is limited to achieving national standards. It requires states to have the legal authority to "prevent construction, modification, or operation of any stationary source at any location where emissions from such source will prevent the attainment or maintenance of a national standard." Two other regulations, however, imply a broader scope. Section 51.18(a) describes such a provision in the state plan as

> legally enforceable procedures that will be used to implement the authority described in Section 51.11(a)(4), which procedures shall be adequate to enable the State to determine whether construction or modification of stationary sources will result in violations of applicable portions of the control strategy or will interfere with attainment or maintenance of a national standard. [Emphasis added.]

Section 51.18(c) states that "such procedures shall also include means of disapproving such construction or modification if it will result in violation of applicable portions of the control strategy or will interfere with attainment or maintenance of a national standard" (emphasis added).[104] These sections differ in that the first restricts the required authority to the power to prevent construction or modification at a particular location if air quality standards are threatened, while the latter two do not mention location but are only concerned with interference with the national standards or the applicable control strategy.[105]

The Need for Local Authority

EPA has been fairly consistent in disapproving some state new source review procedures because they failed to provide adequate authority as required by the latter two regulations.[106] We might infer from these disapprovals that EPA requires each state to acquire the authority to implement any portion of its control strategy, including land use controls, and that state review of new source locations is not limited to instances in which national standards would be violated. However, the power to prevent construction that would interfere with relevant parts of the control strategy is not necessarily a land use power. If the portion of a state implementation plan applicable to industry consists entirely of emission limits and design requirements, the power to prevent construction vanishes once these requirements are met, since land use controls are not part of the control strategy. If national air quality standards are directly threatened, the regulations empower states to prevent construction whether or not their control strategies specifically authorize land use restrictions. However, it is not clear how this power is to be exercised. Perhaps it believes that the states will make calculations for each proposed source or modification to determine whether the projected emissions from that source will violate air quality standards for that region, but this expectation is not spelled out in any of the regulations. Furthermore, projected emission levels are tentative at best; it is significant that EPA regulations defer performance tests on stationary sources until after construction is completed.[107]

Another EPA omission reduces the possibility that state preconstruction review procedure provides land use control authority. EPA nowhere requires that even partial responsibility for preconstruction review be given to the state or local bodies traditionally responsible for land use decisions, nor does it require such bodies to delegate part of their land use powers to the responsible air pollution control agency. State and local air pollution agencies usually are not authorized to exercise land use control powers and their strategies are limited to requiring technological improvements.[108] Consequently, preconstruction review procedures used by these agencies are limited to assuring that these technical requirements are met before permission to construct or modify is granted. EPA regulations have recognized that implementing air quality standards may require authority beyond that traditionally found in air pollution control agencies; they have stated that responsibility for implementing a part of the plan can be delegated to another state or local agency provided it has the necessary legal authority to implement that part.[109] However, EPA regulations approving or disapproving state plans make no comment on whether the preconstruction review procedure has been vested in an agency capable of exercising land use powers.[110]

The regulations promulgated by the EPA Administrator in accordance with his statutory duty to propose federal regulations for inadequate state plans do not shed much additional light on the required scope of the preconstruction review procedure.[111] The new source review provisions which the Administrator proposed for those states whose control of new stationary sources was found inadequate give him authority to grant or deny permission for construction or modification. However, the regulations do not indicate what part land use considerations will play in the Administrator's determination. The applicant must demonstrate to the Administrator's satisfaction that the proposed source "will operate without causing a violation of any applicable local, State, or Federal regulation which is part of the applicable [implementation] plan" and "will not prevent or interfere with attainment or maintenance of any national standard."[112] There is no indication of what the Administrator would consider an adequate showing.

Complex Sources

Thus the preconstruction review procedure required by the Clean Air Act and outlined by EPA regulations is not necessarily a land use measure. Yet according to the preamble to the May 31 regulations approving or disapproving state plans, EPA is relying upon it exclusively —at least for the moment—to maintain air quality standards in those states whose plans envision just meeting the standards.[113] To implement this policy, EPA has now substantially extended its control over stationary sources by including so-called "complex" sources within its preconstruction review procedures.[114] Requirements for state implementation plans now include commands to:

> prevent construction, modification, or operation of a facility, building, structure, or combination thereof, which directly or indirectly results or may result in emissions of any air pollutant at any location which will prevent the attainment or maintenance of a national standard. [Emphasis added.][115]

While no definition of a complex source is given, it is the intent of the regulations to reach "major highways and airports, large regional shopping centers, major municipal sports complexes or stadiums"[116] and similar uses. These uses contribute indirectly to air pollution by generating large amounts of motor vehicle traffic emitting vehicle-related pollutants. EPA has therefore asserted jurisdiction over decisions about their location in order that the decisions take adequate account of the impact of such uses on potential increases in air pollution levels.

Several problems are presented by EPA's entry into complex source regulation, most of which arise because the agency for the first time has asserted jurisdiction over land use activities that do not in themselves aggravate air pollution problems. These uses have not previously been subject to regulation by air pollution control agencies; decisions over their location and design formerly have been left entirely to traditional land use agencies. Moreover, the uses specified for review as complex sources are significant generators of related land use activities and have received very close attention in most land use programs. Asserting jurisdiction over complex sources in the air quality program thus will conflict directly with the exercise of land use controls over these sources by traditional agencies. The problem is further complicated because the strategic character of these sources as land use generators has led to related federal legislation which requires land use controls over these very same uses at the state level.[117] Since the state agencies that have been selected to implement federally required land use restrictions are not air pollution control agencies, additional problems of coordination will develop.

In the earlier discussion of the potential role of land use controls in air quality programs, we noted the importance of comprehensive planning in the utilization of land use measures. Assertion of control over strategic complex sources by EPA and state air pollution control agencies will provide the badly needed regional perspective on decisions about the location of these sources. Yet the air pollution agencies do not have the necessary expertise to provide the planning framework within which decisions about complex source locations must be made. This problem is only partly alleviated by a provision in EPA's complex source regulations that permits the delegation of authority over complex source review to a local agency other than the air pollution control agency.[118] The difficulty is that responsibility for planning and land use control in metropolitan areas is severely fragmented, and no agencies at the regional level have the substantive authority to exercise definitive land use control powers.

On balance, these considerations suggest that EPA might have been better advised to leave control over complex sources to the traditional land use authorities. It could then have exercised its powers under the Clean Air Act to require an additional clearance from air pollution control agencies on the air quality effects of decisions about complex sources. But this approach would force major changes in the legal structure of air pollution and land use controls at the state level, a problem complicated by the enactment of federal legislation requiring the assumption of land use control powers by state land use agencies. In addition, the Clean Air Act's single-minded concentration on air pollution abatement and the rigid deadlines built into the Act foreclose the development of interrelated strategies that can consider the objectives of both land use and air pollution legislation. These problems are discussed in more detail in the text that follows.[119]

Ambient Air Quality Standards and
Federal Performance Standards

A final complexity in the control of stationary sources arises because the Clean Air Act does not require national ambient air quality standards for every pollutant emitted by a source subject to federal performance standards.[120] Therefore, where federal performance standards have been set for particular pollutants for which no national ambient air quality standards have been prescribed it is unclear what authority a state has over a stationary source of such pollutants in its preconstruction review process. Since the purpose of state preconstruction review, according to the regulations, is to protect ambient air quality standards or a control strategy designed to implement those standards, a state logically has no statutory authority under the Clean Air Act to review a proposed source that would emit a pollutant for which no air quality standard has been set.

This gap in the controls may have been remedied, however. The statute, as well as EPA regulations establishing performance standards for stationary sources, defines a stationary source as "any building, structure, facility, or installation which emits or may emit any air pollutant."[121] In addition, EPA guidelines for implementation plans do not limit the preconstruction review process to stationary sources covered by Section 111 but anticipate that the construction or modification of "any stationary source" may be reviewed.[122]

When no air quality standard has been set, however, and when the new stationary source can show that it will comply with emission performance standards, the legal basis for the state's control over the new stationary source must be carefully examined. In the absence of health reasons for disapproving the location of the new source, the state (or local agency) will have to rely on other constitutionally acceptable reasons for disapproving the construction of the new source. These may be lacking if the new stationary source does not otherwise violate applicable state or local regulations and meets federal performance standards. For example, if no applicable federal air quality standard has been adopted, it may be difficult to preclude construction of a new stationary source in a substantially developed heavy industry zone as long as the new source meets performance standards. On the other hand, the state or local agency might be able to demonstrate, even in the absence of an air quality standard, that the quality of the air will not meet the required levels in the immediate area where the proposed new source is to be built. In that event, there would be an adequate health reason for disapproving the new construction even though national ambient air quality standards have not been established. The availability of air quality standards for most pollutants should assist states in finding such a justification, even though not all of these standards have been officially adopted by EPA.[123]

IMPACT OF RELATED FEDERAL LAND USE CONTROL AND ENVIRONMENTAL LEGISLATION

A consideration of the role of land use controls in the achievement and maintenance of air quality levels also requires some examination of related federal legislation, enacted and pending, that will have a bearing on the air quality problem. One such law, enacted by Congress in 1969 as the National Environmental Policy Act [NEPA],[124] requires environmental impact statements to be filed by federal agencies responsible for "major Federal actions significantly affecting the quality of the human environment."[125] While the environmental impacts listed in the federal law do not explicitly include air quality, the effect of federal and federally funded facilities such as highways on air pollution levels has definitely been a factor that agencies have been forced to consider in the environmental review process.[126]

There are at least two difficulties, however, in relating the requirement for an environmental impact statement to a larger air pollution control strategy. While NEPA sets forth a procedure under which environmental effects are to be considered, it does not provide a substantive standard against which they are to be evaluated.[127] Therefore, since air pollution is only one of several environmental effects considered in the impact statement, there is no formal way to relate the environmental assessment carried out under the impact statement process to enforcement of state air pollution control strategies.

Another problem posed by the environmental impact statement process is its limited coverage. Since the federal statute applies only to federal or federally funded projects, the impact statement requirement does not reach private developments affecting air quality, especially industrial and other employment facilities that do not receive federal subsidies. Indeed, the environmental impact statement process has benefited air pollution programs primarily through its effect on the siting and location of federally funded highways.[128] Highway agencies have had to consider the effects of air pollution created by motor vehicle traffic. Presumably these considerations affect the planning of the highway network and thus indirectly affect the impact that network will have on urban development and growth patterns.[129] It should be noted that at least one state environmental quality law has now been interpreted to extend the impact statement requirement to some private as well as public and publicly funded development.[130] Where this extension occurs, the environmental impact statement process will be more relevant to air pollution considerations since all major private development will at least be forced to make a published report of environmental effects. Nevertheless, state environmental quality acts, like their federal counterparts, are usually without substantive guiding criteria that can provide a rule for assessing impact statements once they are filed.[131]

Another piece of federal legislation that could have a more direct effect on the exercise of land use restrictions as a part of state air pollution control strategies is the federal Coastal Zone Management Act of 1972.[132] Although its coverage is limited to the 30 coastal and Great Lakes states, it provides a prototype state land use control power which would be required of all states if similar but more general national legislation were passed.[133] For coastal zones within the coastal states, the federal legislation requires a state land use control program that can, when necessary, supersede local governmental authority. Briefly, the federal law requires state control of "land and water uses within the coastal zone," which shall include as alternatives: directly exercised state land use controls; establishment of state criteria for local implementation; state administrative review of "all development plans, projects, or land and water use regulations," or a combination of these measures.[134]

As discussed above,[135] land use controls for abatement of air pollution may be direct or indirect, long range or short range. State land use restrictions under the federal Coastal Zone Act can be exercised similarly, either to prohibit the location of potential new pollution sources or, in a more general way, to control land uses so that air pollution impacts can be minimized. Indirect and long-range land use controls to achieve clean air likewise must be based on comprehensive long-range planning. On this point, although the federal Coastal Zone Act does not mandate formal adoption of a coastal zone plan,[136] it does require all the major elements of a planning inventory in coastal zone areas. State land use powers exercised as part of a coastal zone program will be comprehensive since they will be exercised pursuant to land use and development strategies based on statewide policies and criteria.

In addition to serving as a prototype, the Coastal Zone Act may provide state air pollution control agencies with part of the authority they need to carry out state implementation plans under the Clean Air Act. The Coastal Zone Act provides that nothing in that Act

> shall in any way affect any requirement (1) established by . . . the Clean Air Act . . . (2) . . . or by any state or local government pursuant to such [Act]. Such require-ments shall be incorporated in any program developed pursuant to [the Coastal Zone Act] . . . and shall be the . . . air pollution control requirements applicable to such program.[137]

This section is ambiguous, especially since the term "requirement" is not defined. But the provision is subject to the interpretation that actions taken by state or local air pollution control agencies to regulate stationary sources bind state agencies exercising land use control powers in the coastal zone. Under such an interpretation the ability of state air quality control agencies to preempt the exercise of land use controls by other state agencies will be substantial. Indeed, statutes like the Coastal Zone and Clear Air Acts, when read together, appear to confer substantial preemptive authority on air quality agencies over the actions of local governments. State coastal zone agencies will have substantial preemptive powers over local land use agencies when coastal areas are affected, but these state agencies will in turn be subject to air pollution control requirements established pursuant to the federal Clean Air Act. Indirectly, then, state air quality require-ments can be read to preempt local land use powers whenever they are exercised so as to affect coastal zone areas.[138]

PRACTICALITIES OF EXERCISING LAND USE CONTROLS IN AIR POLLUTION PROGRAMS

As noted above, Congress and the states are committed to achiev-ing and maintaining national air quality standards, and it is clear that land use controls have some role to play in meeting this objective. The question is whether we can discover a role for land use controls in air pollution programs that is consistent with the Clean Air Act and yet capable of being implemented, considering both the limitations and requirements imposed by the Act and the practicalities of adopting and enforcing such controls at state and local levels. The statutory framework of the Clean Air Act presents problems of interpretation that make elaborating a land use control strategy more than a routinely difficult task. Problems arise from the legislation both because of the absolute air pollution control objectives it imposes and because it fails to prescribe administrative tradeoffs among various authorized control techniques or to provide a method for considering these tradeoffs on a state-by-state basis.

The Clean Air Act is directed towards the reduction of air pollution to appropriate levels and makes this goal its single and paramount objective. A program based on attainment of a single environmental objective is ill suited to the exercise of land use powers, which ordinarily are directed to a multiplicity of developmental and environmental goals. Indeed, the accommodation of competing and even conflicting growth and development objectives is one of the earmarks both of land use control programs and of the comprehensive planning process which in theory they are intended to implement. Strict implementation of a singleminded approach to air pollution to the exclusion of possible land use and development criteria thus would be inconsistent with the statutory framework under which land use controls are usually exercised.[139]

Other difficulties arise because federal clean air legislation authorizes a series of pollution control strategies without specifying how these strategies are to be combined into an integrated and effective air quality control program. It is conceivable that stringent application of direct restriction of emissions at the source would obviate any need to adopt land use controls in some areas. Important problems of cost allocation in air pollution programs are involved in this mix of strategies. For example, to the extent that existing industries are required to bear the cost of complying with technological standards, the compliance burden will be shifted almost entirely to these industries in order that additional industries which may contribute to air pollution can enter the area. Banning new stationary pollution sources to allow relaxation of standards applicable to existing industries will shift the burden of compliance to potential new entrants to the extent that location elsewhere imposes extra costs. The general public will also suffer from such a ban to the extent that it restricts economic growth. This allocation problem must receive more explicit consideration in air pollution control legislation before a realistic and acceptable role can be found for land use control powers in achieving clean air.

These problems are compounded by the comparatively short compliance schedules required by the Clean Air Act. Primary standards are to be achieved within three years, and secondary standards within a reasonable time; yet experience with land use controls everywhere suggests that a much longer period of time is needed to accomplish the goals for which land use control programs are designed.[140]

Reversal of long-term development trends through planning and land use restrictions takes time, and we still know very little about the ways in which urban environments can be regulated so as to minimize the effects of development patterns on air pollution levels.[141] At the same time, short-term direct regulation of stationary pollution sources duplicates legal authority in the Clean Air Act itself, permitting the states (and their local government units) to carry out preconstruction review of stationary source locations. Gaps in the Clean Air Act's authority over stationary source locations, however, may leave room for the exercise of some land use powers over these sources as well.

Other problems are intergovernmental as well as conceptual. Historically, land use authority in this country has been delegated to local governments with full autonomy to pass and administer regulations. Air quality control has been delegated to the states subject to federal criteria, and while the states may in turn delegate powers of administration to regional and local agencies, the basis for the exercise of pollution control is regional and not local. Any mechanism for reconciling the possibly divergent objectives of air pollution and traditional land use regulation will have to take these varying governmental structures into account.

To date, no such statutory or administrative mechanism exists, and ambiguities in policy have been reinforced by the practically concurrent adoption of potentially conflicting and inconsistent federal legislation. Congress cannot simultaneously require environmental impact assessments of major federal and federally funded projects without guiding substantive criteria, centralization of broad land use controls at the state level to accomplish such limited environmental objectives as regulation of coastal zones, and the adoption of federal and state programs to achieve specified air quality goals within absolute time limits.

Apart from its requirements for state regulation of complex sources, EPA thus far has not insisted that states begin to develop an adequate land use control program in their efforts to attain clean air. EPA's failure to require or even encourage the states to seriously consider comprehensive land use regulation is no incentive to state development of land use programs needed to achieve air quality standards. State initiative in adopting land use controls in the absence of a clear federal directive is all the more unlikely as these controls may place severe restrictions on residential and industrial growth and thus stimulate controversy. But Congress, and the agencies established to implement its environmental programs, cannot avoid the land use problem forever. Even deletion of the land use provision from the Clean Air Act would not foreclose consideration of the land use issue. State land use regulations are now required under related federal legislation, and land use control strategies unavoidably affect the achievement of air quality objectives whether or not they are explicitly required under the federal air pollution control statute.

CONCLUSION

Perhaps the central problem raised by this discussion is how to reconcile inevitable conflicts between the narrow goals of air pollution legislation and the more broadly defined objectives of land use control programs. Spelling out the desired relationship between land use restrictions and direct emission and performance controls in the development of an air quality implementation plan may even be impossible within the confines of federal legislation concerned principally with guidelines and policies. But the issue must be faced at some point in the federal or state administrative hierarchy. If statewide land use control programs are more widely adopted as a result of the Coastal Zone Management Act and any subsequent related federal legislation, the resolution of competing objectives in land use and air pollution control strategies may perhaps be more properly resolved within the comprehensive legal framework provided by these programs. In this event, the development and implementation of land use regulations would be left to state and local land use agencies, while the air pollution agency would be vested with the responsibility for determining overall air quality objectives to which these land use programs must conform.[142] If this occurred, Congress would first have to reconsider the absolute nature of its air pollution control objectives. Areas of potential conflict would still exist, as in the case of preconstruction review of stationary sources, although this problem could be handled by delegation of authority to land use agencies. Nevertheless, assuming that regional and statewide land use control programs are more widely adopted and implemented, the comprehensive framework of the land use regulation process is a better legal and policymaking setting in which to resolve the many problems created by the interaction of air pollution and land use control strategies.

NOTES

1. See, for example, Trumbull, "Federal Control of Stationary Source Air Pollution," 2 Ecology L. Q. 283 (1972).
2. See A. Voorhees and Associates, "A Guide For Reducing Air Pollution Through Urban Planning" (1971) (NTIS No. PB 207 510); Kurtzweg, "Urban Planning and Air Pollution Control: A Review of Selected Recent Research," 39 J. Am. Inst. Planners 82 (1973), hereinafter cited as Kurtzweg. A recent study of land use controls and

the Clean Air Act by the Bay Area Pollution Control District stated:

> Historically, land use regulation as an air pollution control technique might be considered to be the logical culmination of pollution control effort. Technological source control as applied almost exclusively in the past has inherent limitations for reasons of economics and technological feasibility. . . . Clearly, the density and geographical distribution of sources, as well as the individual sources themselves, must be subject to control if the Federally mandated air quality standards are to be achieved, and once achieved, maintained.

See also R. Thullier, "A Regional Air Pollution Modeling System for Practical Application of Land Use Planning Studies" 1 (May 17, 1973).

3. 42 U.S.C. Secs. 1857c-5(a)(2)(B) (1970).

4. Id. Secs. 1857-58a, amending the Air Quality Act of 1967, 42 U.S.C. Secs. 1857-571 (Supp. V, 1970). The Air Quality Act of 1967 itself consisted of amendments to the Clean Air Act of 1963, Pub. L. No. 88-206, 77 Stat. 392 (1963) (formerly codified at 42 U.S.C. Secs. 1857-571 (1964)). Thus, the present version of the 1963 Act, as amended by the 1967 Act and the 1970 Amendments, is still properly referred to as the Clean Air Act.

5. Under the Air Quality Act of 1967, the federal government could take initiative only in interstate cases and had virtually no role in setting air quality standards. The Clean Air Act of 1963, Pub. L. No. 88-206, Sec. 5 (f), 77 Stat. 392 (1963). See Trumbull, supra note 1, at 296.

6. The Secretary of HEW was previously charged with the administration of federal air and water pollution control legislation. This responsibility was then shifted to the Secretary of the Interior, and finally to the Administrator of EPA. See Reorg. Plan No. 2 of 1966, 3 C.F.R., 1966-1970 Comp., p. 1021 (eff. May 10, 1966); Reorg. Plan No. 3 of 1970, Sec. 2 (a)(1), 3 C.F.R. 1966-1970 Comp., p. 1072.

7. See 42 U.S.C. Sec. 857c-4(a)(1)(A) (1970). Primary and secondary ambient air standards have been promulgated for sulfur oxides, particulate matter, carbon monoxide, photochemical oxidants, hydrocarbons, and nitrogen dioxide. 40 C.F.R. Sec. 50.4.11 (1972).

8. The standards are based on criteria developed by EPA for each pollutant that "reflect the latest scientific knowledge useful in indicating the kind and extent of all identifiable effects on public health or welfare which may be expected from the presence of such pollutant in the ambient air, in varying quantities." 42 U.S.C. Sec 1857c-3(a)(2) (1970).

9. Id. Secs. 1857c-4(b)(1), (2).

10. Id. Secs. 1857c-5(a)(2), (b), (c).

11. Id. Sec. 1857c-5(a)(1). State plans must also provide for intergovernmental cooperation where required, for example, where an air quality control region is divided among two or more states. Id. Sec. 1857c-5(a)(2)(E).

12. Id. Sec. 1857c-5(a)(2)(A).

13. Id. Sec. 1857c-6. To date, standards for five such sources have been set: fossil-fuel-fired steam generators, incinerators, Portland cement plants, and nitric and sulfuric acid plants. 36 Fed. Reg. 24, 876 (Dec. 23, 1971). This year EPA set standards for asphalt concrete plants, petroleum refineries, storage vessels for petroleum liquids, secondary lead smelters, secondary brass and bronze ingot production plants, iron and steel plants, and sewage treatment plants. 38 Fed. Reg. 15406 (1973). EPA had announced that stationary source standards for 15 other basic industries would be set. 3 Env. Rptr. 884 (1972).

14. 42 U.S.C. Sec. 1857c-5(a)(2)(b) (1970). While not explicitly discussed in this article, transportation controls authorized for inclusion in state implementation plans also have a bearing on land use and other related measures in the abatement of air pollution. For example, EPA regulations list "measures to reduce motor vehicle traffic" and "expansion or promotion of the use of mass transportation facilities" as transportation controls. 40 C.F.R. Sec. 51.1(n)(7), (8) (1972).

15. In addition, the statute requires EPA to establish national emission standards for hazardous air pollutants and for all nonstationary sources, 42 U.S.C. Secs. 1857c-7(b)(1), 1857f-1(a)(1) (1970). For further analysis of the 1970 legislative changes see Note, "Clean Air Act Amendments of 1970: A Congressional Cosmetic," 61 Geo. L.J. 153 (1972).

16. 42 U.S.C. Sec. 1857c-5(a)(2)(B) (1970).

17. Id. Sec. 1857c-5(a)(4).

18. It is not clear from the statute whether or not states may delegate authority to control stationary sources to local governments. But cf. 40 C.F.R. Sec 51.11(f), authorizing delegation to local governments of power to carry out state implementation plans. See note 48, infra.

19. H. Rep. No. 91-1146, 91st Cong., 2d Sess. (1971).

20. The purpose of the original text authorizing land use controls is echoed in the Senate Committee Report on the bill, which paraphrases the original statutory language:

> In addition to direct emission controls, other potential parts of an implementation plan include land use and air and surface transportation controls. These should insure that any existing or future stationary source of air pollution will be located, designed, constructed, equipped

and operated, . . . so as not to interfere with the implementation, maintenance, and enforcement of any applicable air quality standard or goal.

S. Rep. No. 91-1196, 91st Cong., 2d Sess. 12 (1970), hereinafter cited
as S. Rep. The statutory language as it appeared in the Senate version
of the bill is reprinted in id. at 87. For a similar statement of Senate
intent see also id. at 2.

21. See text accompanying notes 17-18 supra.

22. Letter to the authors from Leon G. Billings, Senior Staff
Member, Subcomm. on Air and Water Pollution of the Senate Comm.
on Public Works, Jan. 5, 1973, on file with the authors.

23. See text accompanying notes 63-69 infra.

24. Joint Hearings on Air Pollution 1970 Before the Subcomm.
on Air and Water Pollution of the Senate Comm. on Public Works,
91st Cong., 2d Sess. (1970), hereinafter cited as Senate Hearings.

25. 116 Cong. Rec. 42381 et seq. (1972).

26. Hearings on Implementation of the Clean Air Act Amendments of 1970 Before the Subcomm. on Air and Water Pollution of the
Senate Comm. on Public Works, 92d Cong., 2d Sess. (1972), hereinafter cited as Oversight Hearings.

27. S. Rep., supra note 20, at 2.

28. 116 Cong. Rec. 42303 (1972).

29. Id. at 42387.

30. See generally E.J. Croke, K.G. Croke, A.S. Kennedy, and
L. J. Hoover, The Relationship Between Land Use and Environmental
Protection (Argonne Nat'l Laboratory, 1972).

31. See text accompanying notes 19-28 supra.

32. 42 U.S.C. Sec. 1857c-6(c)(1) (1970) directs the Administrator
upon approving a state's plan to delegate to the state his authority for
"implementing and enforcing standards of performance for new sources
located in such State." 42 U.S.C. Sec. 1857c-5(a)(4) (1970) provides
for preconstruction review of all such new sources and confers the
authority to prevent construction if any national air standard is threatened.

33. The Act provides that the Administrator of EPA must approve any state implementation plan that contains eight listed items,
the second of which mandates that the implementation plan must include:

emission limitations, schedules, and timetables for compliance with such limitations, and such other measures
as may be necessary to insure attainment and maintenance
of such primary or secondary standard, including, but not
limited to, land use and transportation controls.

Id. Sec. 1857c-5(a)(2)(B).

34. The Bay Area Air Pollution Control District (BAAPCD) denied authority to construct 18 gasoline stations throughout the Bay Area in late October 1972. Under section 1309 of the BAAPCD Permit Regulations, the Air Pollution Control Officer must deny permits for facilities that emit air pollutants in areas where air quality standards are exceeded. The air in most of the district exceeded the air quality standard. Of the 1500 tons of smog-producing organic gases emitted per day in the Bay Area in 1971, about 75 tons per day came from filling stations. BAAPCD, Air Currents No. 11, at 1 (Nov. 1972). The ban was lifted after ten weeks. Marin County Independent Journal, Jan. 4, 1973, at 1. However, construction will only be permitted if stations install devices designed to cut emissions at the gas pump by 90 percent. Telephone interview with David Self, Counsel for BAAPCD, Mar. 15, 1973.

35. See Buck v. Kilgore, 298 A.2d 107 (Maine, 1972). In this case the municipality enacted an ordinance requiring filling stations to be located at a stated distance from places of public assembly. The effect of the ordinance was to ban all filling stations from the community. The court held the ordinance unconstitutional on the ground that the spacing requirement was not justified by reasons of health.

36. See discussion accompanying notes 70-74 infra.

37. See note 44 infra.

38. See, for example, Ill. Ann. Stat. ch. 24, Sec. 11-14-1 (1962), authorizing street setbacks in part to obtain "pure air."

39. See In re: Sports Complex in Hackensack Meadowlands, 62 N.J. 248, 300 A.2d 337 (1973). The court refused to disapprove the site of a new sports complex in the meadowlands though it had been alleged that motor vehicle traffic generated by the complex would cause air pollution in violation of federal standards.

40. See text accompanying notes 114-16 infra.

41. 42 U.S.C. Sec. 1857c-5(a)(1) (1970) provides in pertinent part: "Each State shall . . . adopt and submit to the Administrator . . . a plan which provides for implementation, maintenance, and enforcement of such primary standard in each air quality control region (or portion thereof) within the State."

42. See Kurtzweg, supra note 2. Rutgers University has completed a study evaluating the effects of a comprehensive county general plan on air pollution levels. G. Hagevik, "The Relationship between Land Use and Air Pollution in Middlesex County, New Jersey," Rutgers University Dep't of Planning and Policy Development (1973).

43. See D. Mandelker, The Zoning Dilemma 57-63 (1971).

44. It is interesting that the Clean Air Act does not require states to possess powers of condemnation by eminent domain when they are needed to implement air pollution control programs. Such powers could be helpful, to take one example, in instances in which

the state needs to acquire pollutive industrial plants that must be shut down in order to help reduce air pollution levels. Condemnation authority is required by recent federal legislation calling for the exercise of state powers in coastal zones. 16 U.S.C.A. Sec. 1455(d)(2) (Supp. 1973).

45. Land use control powers have been delegated to the air quality control agency in Philadelphia, Pennsylvania. See Keeney, "Enforcement of Philadelphia's 1969 Air Management Code: The First Three Years," 18 Vill. L. Rev. 173 (1972).

46. Coastal Zone Management Act of 1972, 16 U.S.C.A. Sec. 1451 et seq. (Supp. 1973). See especially id. Sec. 1455 (d) (Supp. 1973). See also text accompanying notes 133-39 infra.

47. See F. Bosselman and D. Callies, The Quiet Revolution in Land Use Control (Council on Environmental Quality, 1971).

48. While the question of delegation of authority to implement a state air quality plan is not covered by the Act, EPA regulations allow delegation of authority to carry out a portion of a plan to a state agency other than the state air pollution control board. 40 C.F.R. Sec. 51.11(e). Further, 40 C.F.R. Sec. 51.11(f) provides that the state may authorize a local agency to carry out a plan or portion thereof. EPA appears to assume that once a state implementation plan is approved, the state itself has authority to carry the plan out normally through its air pollution control agency.

49. 42 U.S.C. Sec. 1857c-5(a)(2)(A) (1970). For the EPA regulations promulgating these standards see 40 C.F.R. Sec. 50.1 et seq.

50. 42 U.S.C. Sec. 1857c-5(a)(2)(A) (1970).

51. Id.

52. Id. Sec. 1857c-5(e)(1)(B). Cf. the order of the court in Natural Resources Defense Council v. EPA, 475 F. 2d 968, 4 ERC 1945 (D. C. Cir. 1973). Section 1857c-5(e) also provides, however, that such extensions are allowable only if technology required to attain primary standards is not available in time to meet the statutory deadline.

53. For example, concerning The Los Angeles Basin, see Calif. Inst. of Technology Environmental Quality Laboratory, Smog: A Report to the People (1972).

54. The exception is quoted in text accompanying note 91 infra.

55. 42 U.S.C. Sec. 1857c-5(a)(2)(A) (1970).

56. S. Rep., supra note 20, at 2. For example, the Senate Report also called for rigorous controls on "existing sources in order to provide a margin for future growth" in regions where air quality levels are below standard. Id. at 13. When the socioeconomic issue surfaced during subsequent Oversight Hearings on the enforcement of the Clean Air Act, a Congressional intent to permit consideration of such impacts again was hotly denied:

Senator Eagleton: . . . In respect to economic feasibility,
it is clear again beyond any shadow of a doubt that Congress intended that this not be a factor insofar as the
primary standards were concerned relating to public
health. Economic feasibility was included in the House
bill, it was hotly debated in conference and it was deleted.
Oversight Hearings, supra note 26, at 18, 19. See also id. at 308,
312. These statements were also made in the context of a discussion
about emission limitations.

57. This argument, of course, is not universally valid. Recent
experience with transportation control plans under Sec. 1857c-5 indicates that EPA will not require extreme economic dislocation or social
disruption for the sake of attaining clean air on schedule. See Los
Angeles transportation control plan, 38 Fed. Reg. 17683 (1973) (preamble).

58. 42 U.S.C. Sec. 1857c-4(b)(2) (1970). The Act declares that
the term "public welfare" includes:
effects on soils, water, crops, vegetation, man-made materials, animals, wildlife, weather visibility, and climate,
damage to and deterioration of property, and hazards to
transportation, as well as effects on economic values and
on personal comfort and well-being.
Id. Sec. 1857h(h).

59. Id. Sec. 1857c-5(a)(2)(A).

60. See text accompanying note 50 supra.

61. See Natural Resources Defense Council v. EPA, 475 F. 2d
968, 4 ERC 1945 (D.C. Cir. 1973), in which the court found that EPA
may not have properly reviewed state plan provisions for maintaining
air quality and ordered a new EPA review of those provisions.

62. 344 F. Supp. 253, 4 ERC 1205 (D.D.C. 1972), aff'd mem.,—
F. 2d—. 4 ERC 1815 (D.C. Cir. Nov. 1, 1972), aff'd by equally divided
court sub non. Fri v. Sierra Club,—U.S.—, 5 ERC 1417 (June 11, 1973).
See Note, "The Clean Air Act and the Concept of Non-degradation:
Sierra Club v. Ruckelshaus," 2 Ecology L.Q. 801 (1972). See also
EPA's proposed regulations on nondegradation in 38 Fed. Reg. 18986
(1973).

63. EPA first published regulations on April 30, 1971, setting
the "National Primary and Secondary Ambient Air Quality Standards."
36 Fed. Reg. 8186 (1971). These regulations were reissued in 36 Fed.
Reg. 22384 (1971), and are presently codified in 40 C.F.R. Sec. 50.1
et seq. (1972). On August 14, 1971, EPA issued regulations setting
forth requirements for the preparation, adoption, and submittal of
implementation plans. 36 Fed. Reg. 15486 (1971). These regulations
were reissued in 36 Fed. Reg. 22398 (1971), and are presently codified
in 40 C.F.R. Sec. 51.1 et seq. (1972). Minor changes were made in

the regulations as finally issued in the Code of Federal Regulations to correct errors in the regulations as they appeared in the Federal Register.

The Clean Air Act required that within nine months after the standards were published (that is, by January 30, 1972), each state submit implementation plans designed to attain and maintain the national standards in each air quality control region under its jurisdiction. 42 U.S.C. Sec. 1857c-5(a)(1) (1970). On May 31, 1972, EPA issued further regulations, on the "Approval and Promulgation of Implementation Plans," which approved or disapproved specific provisions in each state plan. 37 Fed. Reg. 10842 (1972). Then, on June 14, 1972, the Administrator proposed changes or additions to various state plans as he is required to do under Section 110 of the law, and these changes or additions were open to public debate. 37 Fed. Reg. 11826 (1972).

64. See text accompanying notes 85-87 infra.

65. 40 C.F.R. Sec. 51.11(a)(1) (1972).

66. Id. Sec. 51.12(a).

67. Id. Sec. 51.1(n).

68. Although the term "control strategy" as used in practice refers to any particular technique for reducing emissions (a vehicle ban or an emission charge, for example) rather than to the panoply of techniques included in a state plan, the definition which the regulation provides may be used to augment state land use authority under the Act. See text accompanying notes 102-10 infra.

69. 40 C.F.R. Sec. 51.1(n)(2) (1972).

70. 36 Fed. Reg. 6680 (1971). In regard to land use, perhaps most obvious was the deletion of the requirement for a state permit system to review construction, modification, or operation of stationary sources; general authority for preconstruction review was still required. 40 C.F.R. Secs. 51.11(4), 51.18 (1972). One of the reasons given privately for dropping the permit requirement was EPA's fear that an environmental impact statement might be required for each permit. The requirement that any necessary land use control authority be in effect immediately upon submission of the plan was also deleted. Instead, the state was required to submit a timetable for obtaining the requisite legal authority if its plan contained land use or transportation control measures. Id. Sec. 51.11(b).

71. 40 C.F.R. Sec. 51.2 (1972). See also preamble to Appendix B, authorizing states to consider the "social and economic impact" of emission limitations.

72. Id. Sec. 51.10(a).

73. Id. Sec. 51.30(c)(2).

74. Id. Sec. 51.30(d)(3).

75. Project on Clean Air, Natural Resources Defense Council, Analysis of Twenty-four Proposed State Implementation Plans for the Control of Air Pollution, to Determine Their Compliance with the Clean Air Amendments of 1970 (Apr. 18, 1972). California listed a number of proposed land use regulations in its implementation plan; controls also were listed as under consideration for the metropolitan areas of Portland, Oregon; Baltimore, Maryland; and Washington, D.C.

76. See 37 Fed. Reg. 10842, 10846, Sec. 52.03 (1972), and the relevant portions of approvals and disapprovals of state plans. Note, however, that if EPA disapproves a state implementation plan, it must itself publish regulations that substitute for those disapproved and that meet the requirements of the Clean Air Act. City of Riverside v. Ruckelshaus,—F. Supp.—, 4 ERC 1728 (C.D. Calif. 1972) (transportation controls).

77. EPA also had permitted the states to defer submission of their transportation control plans beyond the statutory deadline, on the ground that it was still studying the effectiveness of transportation control measure. 37 Fed. Reg. 10842 (1972).

78. 40 C.F.R. Sec. 51.13(b)(1) (1972).

79. Id. Sec. 51.13(b)(2).

80. 37 Fed. Reg. 10847 et seq. (1972).

81. 40 C.F.R. 51.12(a) (1972).

82. 37 Fed. Reg. 10843 (1972).

83. Natural Resources Defense Council v. EPA, 475 F.2d 968, 4 ERC 1945 (D.C. Cir. 1973).

84. 38 Fed. Reg. 15836 (1973). See also the discussion of complex source regulations in text accompanying notes 114-16, infra. Later changes in what EPA requires of the states are also made possible by provisions in the Act to the effect that, as part of their plans, states must retain the power to revise their plans (1) "to take account of revisions of [a] . . . national . . . standard or the availability of improved or more expeditious methods of achieving such . . . standard or" (2) "whenever the Administrator finds . . . that the plan is substantially inadequate to achieve . . . [a] national . . . standard". This authority could presumably be exercised to require the state to include land use controls in plans that had not previously included them. Also see discussion in Chapter 4.

85. Cases have been brought which challenge EPA's interpretation of this aspect of the statute. Petitioners' Brief at 43-46, Natural Resources Defense Council v. EPA, Civil No. 72-1458 (10th Cir. 1973). See Oversight Hearings, supra note 26, at 3-47.

86. For example, Oversight Hearings, supra note 26, at 19. Eagleton also claimed that Congress did not intend socioeconomic considerations to enter into the implementation of air quality controls

at all. See the discussion of legislative history accompanying notes 54-57 supra.

87. Administrator Ruckelshaus testified:

We are not permitted to take cost into account in setting that [primary] standard. What we are saying in these guidelines is that in order for the states to meet the standard . . . they ought to take into account the socioeconomic costs of achieving it.

Oversight Hearings, supra note 26, at 276. See also Buckeye Power Co. v. EPA,—F.2d—, ERC 1611 (6th Cir. 1973), in which the court, though with little analysis, accepted EPA's interpretation concerning the role of socioeconomic factors in imposing emission limitations on air polluters. But cf. NRDC v. EPA, Civil No. 72-1219, 72-1224 (1st Cir., May 2, 1973).

88. Interest in local planning programs with growth limitation as the objective has been increasing, however. See, for examples, McGivern, "Putting a Speed Limit on Growth," 38 Planning 263 (1972) (Petaluma, Calif.).

89. 42 U.S.C. Sec. 1857c-6(b)(1)(A) (1970).

90. Id. Sec. 1857c-6(b)(1)(B).

91. Id. Sec. 1857c-6(a)(1).

92. Id. Sec. 1857c-5(a)(4).

93. S. Rep., supra note 20, at 16.

94. Id. at 17.

95. Regulations were to be published with provisions for "preconstruction review of . . . locations," and "methods to insure that any . . . new source . . . not prevent implementation of national ambient air standards," S. 4358, 91st Cong., 2d Sess. Sec. 113(e)(1)(A) (1970).

96. A positive answer to this question is suggested by Allway Taxi v. City of New York, 340 F. Supp. 1120 (S.D.N.Y. 1972). A city ordinance required all pre-1970 taxis to have emission control devices complying with federal standards and later models to be equipped with such devices as might be specified by the city. This requirement was held not preempted by the provision of the federal Clean Air Act prohibiting the states and their subdivisions from creating standards for exhaust emission control devices for new motor vehicles and motor vehicle engines. Citing Chrysler Corp. v. Tofany, 429 F. 2d 499 (2d Cir. 1969), the court noted that the preemptive effect of national legislation should be narrowly construed when local regulations serve the federal purpose. See also Strong, "The Impact of Preemption on Environmental Regulation," 1972 Land Use Controls Ann. 15; Comment, "The Constitutionality of Local Anti-Pollution Ordinances," 1 Fordham J. Urban L. 208 (1972).

97. Senate Hearings, supra note 24, at 1495-96.

98. S. 4358, supra note 95, Sec. 113(b)(2).

99. Section 60.6 of the regulations does allow the owner or operator of the proposed new source or modification voluntarily to request "technical advice" on his project from the EPA Administrator. Although this request must identify the location of the affected facility, it does not appear from reading the regulations that the Administrator need consider the location of the source when giving technical advice. While the technical advice which the Administrator is to give is not limited in the regulations to determining compliance with federal performance standards, there is no way to interpret the term to include advice on land use questions, such as the appropriate location for a new statutory source. These regulations are codified in 40 C.F.R. Sec. 60.1 et seq. (1972).

100. 42 U.S.C. Secs. 1857c-5(a)(2)(D), 1857c-5(a)(4) (1970).

101. Id. Sec. 1857c-5(a)(4).

102. This process presumably could also be used to enforce stricter air pollution standards than those required under the federal law. See 40 C.F.R. Sec. 51.2(f) (1972).

103. Id. Sec. 51.18(a).

104. Id. Secs. 51.11(a)(4), 51.18(a), 51.18(c).

105. Note also that Section 51.11(a)(4) of the regulations requires the authority to prevent the operation of an existing source if its "location . . . will prevent the attainment and maintenance of a national standard." This requirement must be read taking the definition of a control strategy to include the "closing or relocation of industrial facilities." Sec. 51.1(n)(3). Read together, these provisions would require the state to have the authority to close down existing stationary sources, but only in cases where a violation of national standards is threatened.

106. When the preconstruction review process was inadequate to achieve compliance both with national standards and the control strategy, this fact was usually mentioned. E.g., 37 Fed. Reg. 10876, Sec. 52.1329 (1972) (Missouri).

107. 40 C.F.R. Sec. 60.8 (1972).

108. See note 44 supra.

109. 40 C.F.R. Sec. 51.11(b) (1972).

110. See 37 Fed. Reg. 10842 (1972).

111. For example, 37 Fed. Reg. 11827 (1972) (Sec 52.426 applying to Delaware).

112. Id.

113. 37 Fed. Reg. 10842, 10843 (1972). Interview with Robert Baum, Assistant General Counsel, EPA, August 9, 1972.

114. See 38 Fed. Reg. 6279 (1973) (preamble to proposed complex source regulations). EPA was responding to a court order that required EPA to review state implementation plans to assure that adequate strategies had been adopted to maintain air quality standards once they had been achieved. See text accompanying note 84 supra.

115. 40 C. F. R. Sec. 51.18(a), as added by 38 Fed. Reg. 15834, 15836 (1973).

116. 38 Fed. Reg. 15834, 15837, 29893 (1973).

117. For example, the Federal Coastal Zone Management Act of 1972, discussed in text accompanying note 133 infra.

118. 40 C. F. R. Sec. 51.18(e), as added by 38 Fed. Reg. 15834, 15836 (1973).

119. See Part VI infra.

120. This conclusion is supported by Section 111(d)(1) of the Act, which provides that the states will be required to submit a plan establishing

emission standards for any existing source for any air pollutant (i) for which air quality criteria [and therefore air quality standards] have not been issued . . . but (ii) to which a [federal] standard of performance . . . would apply if such existing source were a new source.

Thus the Act itself recognizes the possibility that federal performance standards will be set for some sources, even though no air quality standards are set for the pollutants they emit.

121. 42 U.S. C. Sec. 1857c-6(a)(3) (1970); 40 C. F. R. Sec. 60.2(d) (1972).

122. 40 C. F. R. Sec. 51.11(a)(4) (1972).

123. For a favorable view of supplementary local authority to regulate emission sources, which limits the preemptive effect of the Clean Air Act, see Allway Taxi v. City of New York, 340 F. Supp. 1120 (S. D. N. Y. 1972).

124. Codified at 42 U.S. C. Sec. 4321 et seq. (1970).

125. Id. Sec. 4332(2)(c).

126. See, for example, United States Department of Transportation, Office of the Secretary, Procedures for Considering Environmental Impacts, 36 Fed. Reg. 23679, 23682, Attachment 1, Sec. 4(a)(6) (1971). The phrase "significantly affecting" the environment is defined to include "(a) any action which . . . (b) has a significantly detrimental impact on air or water quality."

127. Most courts have held that the National Environmental Policy Act does not provide a substantive standard under which they may, if they wish, set aside an agency decision to proceed with a project on the ground that its environmental impact will be adverse. But cf. Environmental Defense Fund v. Corps of Engineers, 470 F. 2d 289 (8th Cir. 1972); Note, "Substantive Review Under the National Environmental Policy Act: EDF v. Corps of Engineers," 3 Ecology L. Q. 173 (1973).

128. See "Symposium: The Impact of the Highway on the Urban Environment," 20 Catholic U. L. Rev. 1 (1970); Note, "Litigating the Freeway Revolt: Keith v. Volpe," 2 Ecology L. Q. 761 (1972).

47

129. Even more comprehensive consideration of air pollution effects is required by recent Federal Highway Administration regulations which promulgate "air quality guidelines for use in planning and construction of proposed highway improvements." 23 C.F.R. Part 770, added by 38 Fed. Reg. 23970 (1973). See also the Highway Administration's guidelines for highway Action Plans, 23 C.F.R. Sec. 795 (1973).

130. Friends of Mammoth v. Mono County, 8 Cal. 3d 247, 104 Cal. Rptr., 502 P.2d 1049, 4 ERC 1705, modifying 8 Cal. 3d 1, 500 P.2d 1360, 104 Cal. Rptr. 16, 4 ERC 1593 (1972). See Note, "Aftermammoth: Friends of Mammoth and the California Environmental Quality Act," 3 Ecology L.Q. (1973). The statutory analysis used by the court was based largely on NEPA guidelines and therefore would readily allow a finding that private projects requiring federal agency permits fall within NEPA's purview.

131. See, for example, the New Mexico statute, which is set forth in City of Roswell v. New Mexico Water Quality Control Comm'n, —N.M. 561, 505 P.2d 1237 (1972).

132. 16 U.S.C.A. Sec. 1451 et seq. (Supp. 1973).

133. Legislation now pending before Congress would require the enactment for all states, as a condition to federal planning assistance, of a state land use control program similar to the coastal zone management program discussed in the text. See Land Use Policy and Planning Assistance Act of 1973, S. 924, 93d Cong., 1st Sess. (1973). See Comment, "Recent California Planning Statutes and Mountain Area Subdivisions: The Need for Regional Land Use Control," 3 Ecology L.Q. 107, at 141 (1973).

Though it does not directly affect air pollution, another federal Act that can serve as a prototype for relating land use management and pollution control is the federal Water Pollution Control Act Amendments of 1972. Those amendments have been called a land use act within the Water Act; see 3 Env. Rptr.-Curr. Dev. 1488 (1973). The areawide waste treatment management which Section 208 of the amended Act mandates can be used to solve land use problems caused by industrial concentration or other factors having an impact on water quality. Indirect effects on air pollution will undoubtedly accrue from the no-effluent limitation which the Act imposes in the mid-1980s. Current discharges might then be solidified or burned only to become either solid wastes or air pollution.

134. 16 U.S.C.A. Sec. 306(e) (Supp. 1973).

135. See text accompanying notes 32-40 supra.

136. 16 U.S.C.A. Sec 1454(b) (Supp. 1973).

137. Id. Sec. 1456(b).

138. Pending federal legislation would require state and federal control over the location of power plants. Since power plants make

significant contributions to air pollution, the enactment and exercise of review powers under legislation of this kind could have a substantial impact on state air pollution control programs. For general discussion see Special Committee on Electric Power and the Environment, Association of the Bar of the City of New York, Electricity and the Environment: The Reform of Legal Institutions (1972).

139. These tensions are particularly evident when seen in light of the role of socioeconomic considerations in the development of air pollution implementation plans. See text accompanying notes 70-74 supra.

140. See generally D.E. Boyce, N.D. Day and C. McDonald, Metropolitan Plan Making (1970).

141. See discussion of complex sources accompanying notes 114-20 supra and in Chapter 4.

142. Some such accommodation appears to have been contemplated by the federal coastal zone legislation, but the legislative solution is imperfect. See text at note 138 supra.

3

THE VERMONT AND MAINE COMPREHENSIVE LAND USE STATUTES: AN ANALYSIS

The fragmentation of land use controls at the local governmental level in the United States is a major barrier to the introduction of land use planning considerations into the process of air quality management, since air quality implementation plans are adopted and administered largely at the state level. A coordinate system of state-level land use control should therefore receive serious consideration as part of a state's air pollution control strategy. This chapter examines two such statewide land use control systems, in Vermont and Maine, with attention to the role that these systems can play in the achievement and maintenance of air quality standards.[1]

The most prominent difficulty in such statewide land use control statutes is the tension between the sentiment for local control, anchored in the traditional delegation of state zoning power to local bodies, and the need for management of environmental problems that are typically regional or statewide in scope.

This tension, in combination with the technical problems of making very specific land use decisions at the state level, has resulted in the sometimes uneasy compromises exemplified by the structure of the Vermont and Maine statutes. The compromises have led to a great deal of innovative legislative and administrative solutions to the problems of land use control, but they have also left unsolved many serious issues. These issues include the legislative and administrative integration of authority over environmental issues fragmented by piecemeal legislation, the coordination of planning and regulatory functions, and the coordination of overlapping jurisdictions of state regulatory agencies and the concurrent jurisdictions of state, regional, and local planning agencies.

Many less general questions—such as how to acquire control of development, how to establish environmental standards for land use decisions, and how to develop effective enforcement sanctions—arise whatever the environmental values involved. Others arise specifically in connection with incorporating air quality considerations into land use regulation and planning, such as how to integrate the expertise of air quality specialists into the legal structure of the land use control process.

The structure of the Vermont law and the manner in which these problems have been met in administering it are discussed in this chapter. It should be kept in mind that although both the Maine and Vermont statutes establish air quality effects as one of the relevant criteria in controlling land use, neither state has a significant air pollution problem and consequently very little actually has been done to incorporate air quality considerations into the planning process. The functional equivalent of performance standards, however, seems to have been developed on an ad hoc basis in the permit review process whenever air pollution issues have arisen.

The following should be seen as a study in administrative practice as well as legal structure, since, at least in Vermont, the broadness of the statutory language and the paucity of specific statutory criteria for planning and permit decisions have given the responsible agencies a great deal of latitude to carry out the law on a flexible, case-by-case basis. It should also be kept in mind that the permanent land use plan called for by the statute had not been completed in Vermont at the time of this study, and that the Interim Plan and the permanent Capability and Development Plan had been in effect for too short a period to noticeably affect the permit review process. It is therefore too early to reach any firm conclusions about the effectiveness, in terms of air quality control or any other criterion, of the existing legal and administrative structure for planned control of development in these states. Still, a review of experience to date yields useful insights.

STRUCTURE OF THE STATUTES

Vermont's Act 250

Vermont's Land Use and Development Law, popularly known as Act 250, arose from a crisis of public and legislative concern over the accelerated pace of uncontrolled development in Vermont. Although the statute[2] is quite comprehensive in implementing its purpose of guiding development in order to preserve Vermont's environment, the particular contemporary concerns at the time of its enactment undoubtedly determined its ultimate strengths and weaknesses. One major concern was the effect on lakes and streams of increased numbers of septic tanks in a state where soil conditions rarely permit such a system of waste disposal;[3] this concern is reflected in the ample provisions in Act 250 for meeting water quality standards[4] and in the burden of proof that has been placed on the applicant to prove that they have been met.[5] Another issue affecting the shape of the Act was a desire for as much local control as possible, short of frustrating the comprehensive purposes of the legislation; this led to the establishment of District Commissions, which review applications in the first instance.[6]

It seems likely that the same sense of urgency that resulted in Act 250 also accounts for its primary structural weakness, which lies in the unspecified form of coordination between the two roles of the board established to administer the Act—comprehensive planning for development, and review of permit applications. The Act is, in effect, two acts—one providing for land use planning and one for land use regulation—and the only link between the two roles on the face of the statute lies in the provision[7] that the District Commission must find that the application is "in conformance" with a duly adopted plan. As will be seen in the following discussion, this language means many things to many people.

Act 250 establishes an Environmental Board consisting of nine members appointed by the governor; all members have terms of four years except the chairman, who serves only two years.[8] There is no statutory provision for expert or professional members, although the Board may appoint executive and administrative personnel as necessary.[9] The Act also establishes seven District Commissions in existing administrative districts. These Commissions have two members appointed for two years. Again, there is no requirement of expertise or representativeness. The Board may apply for and receive grants,[10] require information, facilities, and personnel of other state agencies,[11] and adopt rules to carry out the Act.[12] Both the Board and the District Commissions may subpoena witnesses and require the production of evidence.

One of the basic functions of the Environmental Board is to "adopt" three land use plans—an Interim Capability Plan, which has been developed and adopted and has already expired under the statute,[13] a permanent Capability and Development Plan,[14] which has passed the legislature, and a Land Use Plan.[15] The statute makes few prescriptions on how the Board is to arrive at these plans, except that it must hold public hearings in appropriate regions[16] and in each district.[17] The plans must also be submitted to regional and municipal planning commissions for comment, and the Board must respond to all recommendations so made.[18] Most importantly, the Board must submit all plans to the governor for approval, although his failure to act within 30 days shall be deemed approval, and furthermore must submit the two final plans to both houses of the legislature for approval by joint resolution.[19] The original mechanism for legislative approval of the plans, which was somewhat unclear, has been changed in the recent amendments to Act 250.[20] The Capability and Development Plan enacted by some of these amendments was passed by an act of the legislature rather than as a resolution, and the permanent Land Use Plan will also be an act.

Act 250 allows for petitions by state agencies, municipalities, or property owners for changes in the boundaries designated by the plans. The significance of these rather elaborate provisions for amendments will be considered further in a later section.

The nature of the plans is broadly sketched in the statute. The Interim Plan is to describe present uses and "define in broad categories" the capability for use and development.[21] The section describing the permanent Capability and Development Plan[22] provides that it must be consistent with the Interim Plan, but otherwise only lists several purposes it is to serve rather than prescribing any form it is to take.

The Land Use Plan, on the other hand, is to determine, again in "broad categories" based on the Capability Plan, the proper use of the land in the state. This plan is to consist of maps and statements of present and prospective land uses and is to be "further implemented at the local level by authorized land use controls."[23] The language leaves many questions unanswered, and the last section, especially, raises several rather fundamental issues concerning the legal status of the plans once they are adopted. Although the 1973 amendments to the section governing the permanent Land Use Plan did not clarify the nature of the land use designations, it did resolve the issue of whether the policies of the Act 250 plan would govern land use decisions not strictly within the jurisdiction of the Act 250 permit review process. The new provisions[24] strictly limit the authority of the Plan; for instance, it can only apply to uses involving more than ten acres. The amendments also added a requirement that the plan take into consideration regional and local plans and that it incorporate nonregulatory approaches to implementation of the Capability Plan, such as state acquisition of conservation easements and adjustment of taxing practices.

The Environmental Board also functions in a quasi-judicial manner in appeals from permit decisions of the District Commissions, which are taken de novo.[25] In such a case the Board is to follow the same procedure as the District Commissions.[26] This decision can in turn be appealed to the state Supreme Court, but the Board's findings of fact are conclusive and the issues are limited to those raised before the Board.[27] The 1973 amendments also allow for removal of the appeal from the Environmental Board to a county court.[28]

The permit review process, which is the primary function of the District Commissions, is the heart of the regulatory mechanisms of Act 250. With certain exceptions—such as existing developments, electric power companies, and farming and logging operations below 2500 feet—the Act requires permits of anyone commencing any development or construction or selling any interest in a subdivision.[29]

Anyone proposing to undertake such activities must file an application with the District Commission if they involve a tract of land larger than ten acres, a subdivision of more than ten lots, housing of more than ten units, land above the elevation of 2500 feet, or more than one acre in a municipality that has not adopted permanent zoning and subdivision regulations.[30] The applicant must file a plan of his proposed project and must permit the Commission or its agents to make any necessary on-site examinations or tests.[31] Statutory parties to be notified are the municipality, municipal and regional planning commissions, and adjacent municipalities and commissions where relevant.[32] The Commission must also notify the Board and any state agencies directly affected.[33] Any of these statutory parties or an adjoining property owner may request a hearing, or the Commission itself may order a hearing.[34] The date must be set within 25 days of receipt of the application (or notice of appeal), with timely notice, including publication, to all parties.[35] Parties are those receiving notice, adjoining property owners requesting a hearing, and others designated by rule of the Board.[36] If there is no hearing, which is not essential, a permit must be granted or denied within 60 days, and if not it is deemed approved.[37] In addition, the 1973 amendments permit the Board to classify applications according to complexity and to provide for simplified procedures where appropriate.[38]

In issuing a permit, the District Commission must find that the project meets ten different criteria[39] which are cast in very broad terms but form the substantive standards by which Act 250 regulates development (see Appendix A). Criteria 1 to 4 refer to burdens on the environment and are almost wholly concerned with water quality. Like criteria 5, 6, and 7, which concern burdens on municipal services, criteria 1 to 4 require a finding that the project does not create an "unreasonable" or "undue" effect. Criterion 8 is the broadest of all, an omnibus clause requiring the commission to find that the project will not have an "undue adverse effect" on scenic beauty, aesthetics, historic sites, or rare and irreplaceable natural areas. Criterion 9 requires conformance with duly adopted land use or capability plans, and 10 requires conformance with regional and municipal plans. These notably terse clauses are the sole statutory basis on which to rest the authority of the plans once promulgated, and they apparently give equal authority to regional and municipal plans.

The applicant has the burden of proof with respect to criteria 1 through 4 and 9 and 10, but his adversaries must demonstrate the undue adverse effect with respect to 5 through 8.[40] As noted before, appeals are de novo to the Environmental Board.

The recent amendments to the permit criteria are extensive, adding considerably to the specificity of some while leaving others untouched.[41] Since this expansion constitutes the permanent Capability and Development Plan, it will be discussed in greater detail below. In brief, however, criterion 1 has been enlarged to give more detailed standards under which permits that affect water supplies, quality, and shorelines may be granted. Specific conditions for granting permits affecting endangered species and natural habitats have been included under criterion 8, which had been particularly criticized for a lack of discernible standards. Criterion 9 has mushroomed from one paragraph to eleven, since it now embodies the permit review standards of the Capability and Development Plan.

A permit is granted for a specified period, which is to be determined by the Board and based on a reasonable projection of the time the land will remain suitable for that use; it can be revoked for violations of any of its conditions or any other rules of the Board. The District Commission may attach to a permit such conditions as are within the scope of the police power and appropriate to meeting these criteria, as well as impose conditions and requirements appropriate under certain sections of another statute covering municipal and regional plans.[42] The Board may rule that a permit from a relevant state or municipal agency can serve in lieu of evidence by the applicant on that issue.

No permit may be denied unless detrimental to general health and welfare, and specific reasons for each denial must be given. No permit can be denied solely on the basis of criteria 5, 6, or 7, which refer to burdens on municipal services.[43]

In addition to the power to grant, deny, or revoke permits for development, a fine of $500 for each day of violation, or imprisonment for up to two years, may be imposed for infraction of the provisions of the Act or rules promulgated thereunder.[44] The Board may also institute actions, injunctions, or any other proceeding to prevent or correct any such infraction. Recent legislation[45] has given the Secretary of the Agency of Environmental Conservation the power to institute proceedings on behalf of the Environmental Board, inter alia, to enforce the provisions of Act 250 and the Water and Air Pollution Acts. The Secretary may also bring action in the name of the agency in a court of competent jurisdiction to obtain a temporary or permanent injunction to restrain the continuation or repetition of a violation.[46] Another alternative available to the Secretary is to obtain an "assurance of discontinuance" to be filed with the Attorney General and the court of competent jurisdiction in lieu of the former remedies.[47] The Attorney General can request a hearing if he objects to the terms of the assurance, and a violation of the assurance constitutes prima facie evidence of a violation of the statute. Short of these measures the Secretary can issue a notice of violation and, apparently, cease and desist orders. The statute provides a civil penalty of $100 to $10,000 for violations of orders issued under the subsection.[48]

On the face of the statute, Vermont's Act 250 is straightforward and its two-level hierarchy and division of function seem fairly simple. But the administrative facts belie this apparent simplicity of operation, since the Act represents the confluence of many land use controls and regulatory programs affecting the use of land. Many of these programs and controls were already in existence when Act 250 was passed, others were created by legislation passed around the same time, and others represent concerns unique to Act 250. Although an administrative reorganization act was passed in the same session of the legislature[49] that created the Agency of Environmental Conservation, of which the Environmental Board is part, a developer still must obtain as many as 26 permits from various divisions before commencing work. The effort to coordinate these programs and to channel their expertise into the decisions of the District Commissions in order to provide a rational and uniform basis for permit review appears to have required a good deal of the time and ingenuity of the Act's administrators at all levels during its initial years. The steps taken have just begun to be recognized legislatively, and the further complexities that will be introduced by the permanent plans—for example, the problems of concurrent authority with regional and municipal plans and their integration into the permit review process—are just beginning to be explored. Later sections of this chapter will discuss the present administrative structure under Act 250 and some of the problems posed by the duty to develop, adopt, and administer the plans.

Maine's Two Land Use Laws

The Site Location of Development Law[50] must be considered in conjunction with the Maine Land Use Regulation Commission Law. Together the two acts confer roughly the same powers as the Vermont statute and incorporate many of the same mechanisms. There are differences, however, that may prove extremely significant when all three are in full operation. For example, the Maine laws reserve all decision making to the state-level agency, with no regional or district commissions, and the Site Location Law does not require a plan. The Site Location of Development Law is more spare in its statutory structure than the Vermont law and is administered by a single agency, the Water and Air Environmental Improvement Commission. The Commission membership is specified under other statutory provisions and includes representative members from industry, municipalities, the public, conservation interests, and, notably, two members knowledgeable in matters relating to air pollution.[51] Any commercial or industrial development that requires a license from the Environmental Improvement Commission under other statutes, or that would occupy a land area in excess of twenty acres, excavate or drill for natural resources, or occupy a structure in excess of 60,000 square feet[52] that could "substantially affect" local environment shall "notify" the Commission of the nature and location of the development before commencing construction or operation.[53] The Commission must either approve the location or schedule a hearing within 14 days.

There are four criteria for approval of a proposal. It must have (1) financial and technical ability to meet state standards for air and water pollution, solid waste disposal, and maintenance of water supplies; (2) adequate provision for parking and traffic movement; (3) no adverse effect on the natural environment; (4) a location on suitable soil types. These standards are not only fewer in number but even less specific in their language than those found in the Vermont legislation. The burden is upon the developer to demonstrate that all of the criteria are met, and he is obliged to suspend operations pending the hearings. The Maine law makes somewhat specific provisions for action by the Commission in the event that development is begun without notification. These include public hearings, injunctions, and orders to restore the area affected,[54] and are to be enforced by the Attorney General.[55] There are no criminal penalties, as in Act 250, and the Attorney General is empowered only to bring "an appropriate civil action to secure compliance". One section[56] provides for judicial review by the Supreme Judicial Court; this and another section[57] are so far the only ones that have received a judicial construction.[58]

Generally, the Site Location of Development Law is directed at major commercial and industrial undertakings, wherever they are in the state. Other types of development covered by Vermont Act 250, such as subdivisions and smaller commercial enterprises, are covered in Maine by the Land Use Regulation Commission, but only if they occur in unorganized portions of the state. The law regulating developments in these areas[59] is an extremely detailed, well-articulated statute which provides for planning at the state level and gives the state-level agency the authority to designate four types of districts, each representing a particular level of permissible development.[60] The statute lists five quite specific purposes that the land use "standards" developed for these four types of districts are to serve; these include the best use of resources, reduction of pollution, traffic planning, setting performance standards to minimize adverse impacts on adjacent uses, and relating land uses to the natural resources base. These statutory standards, although general, are also considerably more definite than those of the Vermont law, which merely state the broad policies to be reflected in the land use plans. The status of the Maine land use guidance districts and standards as authority for local plans as municipalities become organized is very clear, and the Land Use Commission is to retain jurisdiction of the district until the local body adopts plans and regulations that are no less protective.[61]

The Commission adopted interim districts and land use guidance standards in 1973 and final districts and standards after public hearings. These provisions differ from those in Act 250 in several respects. Notice of hearings on the plans must be given to affected property owners as well as to relevant state and federal agencies, all of whom may be heard and may file statements. The districts and standards are to be adopted by the Commission, with no need for approval by the governor or legislature, although a Comprehensive Land Use Guidance Plan must be adopted and approved by July 1, 1973, to guide the development of districts and standards.[62] Procedures for changes in the boundaries and standards are similar to those provided for in the Vermont law, including a showing that conditions have changed, that the area is needed for a different use, and, in the Maine statute, that the area is not usable for the use in which it is classified. Individual variances may also be obtained in Maine, and there is specific provision for periodic review of boundaries and standards.

The mechanism for control of land use in the Maine statute is roughly similar to that of Vermont, as both depend upon the required approval of development proposals. However, the Maine statute[63] requires permits for any construction on existing developments, any construction or sale of an interest in a subdivision, or any construction or operation of any development, apparently regardless of size. If the proposal also requires approval under the Site Location Law, it is not exempt from review under this statute, but the hearing may be waived. Approval by this Commission is prima facie evidence that the development meets the requirements of the Site Location Law, unless the Environmental Improvement Commission has already set general requirements which are more protective of the environment. The Land Use Commission is to hold hearings on the application and to approve or disapprove it, giving reasons in the latter case.[64] The criteria of decision are given in virtually the same language as those for approval of permits under the Site Location Law, with the additional requirement of conformance with the duly adopted interim or permanent land use guidance standards. The Commission may also impose conditions, as in Vermont. The burden of demonstrating satisfaction of all criteria lies upon the applicant. Changes in use or construction from those authorized by the Commission are considered violations and can lead to revocation or suspension of the permit. In addition, recordings of plats and subdivision conveyances must evidence the Commission's approval, and are void if in violation of that provision.

The Land Use Regulation Commission has what should prove to be an interesting addition to the powers available to the Vermont Board—the power to regulate and prohibit expansion and undue perpetuation of nonconforming uses.[65] It also has a sizable arsenal of enforcement tools in addition to the voiding of plat recordings and conveyances. Use or occupancy of land without a certificate of compliance is made unlawful, and the standards, rules, regulations, and orders of the Commission are given the force of law.[66] Any real estate or personal property in violation of the standards is a nuisance, and the Commission can institute action for injunction or abatement. Other incentives for accomplishing the purposes of the Act include acquisition of conservation easements and the filing of district plans and standards with tax assessor offices as an incentive to adjust assessment practices.[67]

Unlike the Vermont statute, which makes only one general reference on its face to air quality considerations,[68] both of the Maine land use statutes make the meeting of state air pollution standards an express condition of approval. As will be seen below, Vermont has filled this gap administratively in the process of permit review. However, under the Maine Land Use Regulation Law it is statutorily required that the land use guidance standards, which would be analogous to regulations developed under Vermont's Land Use Plan, reduce air pollution as well as other environmental "intrusions."[69] The requirements for the Vermont plan incorporate air pollution considerations only by reference to additional permissible goals under another law. Another noteworthy difference with respect to air quality considerations lies in the fact that precisely the same body that regulates land use in Maine under the Site Location Law also regulates air quality under another statute.

In sum, the Maine statutes taken together are similar to Vermont's Act 250 in administrative structure, except for the lack of regional-level review bodies, and in the use of permits as a tool of control. The most significant differences would seem to lie in the more comprehensive jurisdiction of the Maine Land Use Regulation Statute and in the clear power under the Maine statutes to designate land use districts in unorganized areas under fairly well elaborated statutory standards. Since the Vermont statute leaves the legal authority of its plans very unclear, some questions arise about their ultimate effectiveness as tools for planned control of land use and development. This possibility will be explored below, and the Maine approach considered as an alternative. Unfortunately, since both statutes are still in the early stages of implementation and since no plans have been adopted under the Maine Land Use Regulation Statute and very few applications have been processed,[70] it is as yet impossible to assess the relative practical value of the two laws.

ADMINISTRATIVE STRUCTURE

Under Vermont's Act 250

Although the imposition of the Act 250 permit system upon existing regulatory programs created many duplications and left many unanswered questions about what role the standards and regulations of existing programs were to play in the decisions of the District Commissions, some potential difficulties were avoided by the simultaneous administrative reorganization of the state government. The same legislative session that passed Act 250 created the Agency of

Environmental Conservation,[71] which incorporated the Environmental Board as well as various state agencies that had traditionally been concerned with conservation. All the powers of those departments were vested in the Secretary of Environmental Conservation, except for those of the Environmental Board and the Fish and Game and Water Resources Boards.[72]

The Act also created a Division of Protection, which functions as the enforcement arm of the Agency,[73] and delegated to the Division those activities previously under the Department of Health which concern water and air pollution, waste disposal, and the granting of permits for buildings and land. The Division of Protection is to perform other duties prescribed by the Secretary, including the enforcement of the rules and regulations of any agency or board within the Agency of Environmental Conservation. This deceptively simple administrative creation of the legislature appears to have been the focus of efforts to create an integrated and uniform approach to land use decisions under Act 250.

Once an application has been filed with the regional environmental coordinator (acting as staff for the District Commission) and notice served on the statutory parties, copies of the application are routed both to the Environmental Board and the "environmental advisor" (a state forester). The latter makes on-site inspections, advising the applicant in the application process[74] as well as reporting to the District Commission. The Environmental Board forwards a copy to the Act 250 Review Committee, a body created to provide the technical expertise of the relevant conservation agencies to the District Commissions. The Review Committee originally consisted of representatives from all state agencies having a continuing interest in land use control. It has recently been expanded by the governor to involve all state agencies, including Taxes and Education, although it will now only review applications of some importance.[75]

The actual process of obtaining state agency opinions on an application's conformance with the criteria of Act 250 is handled by the Land Use Administrator within the Division of Protection. The Division formulates a position paper incorporating agency opinions for consideration by the Review Committee and forwards the result to the District Commission before the date of the hearings. The recommendations of state regulatory agencies, like the ultimate decisions of the District Commissions, ordinarily consist of a set of proposed conditions rather than a flat approval or denial.

Additional opinions and information may be provided at the hearing by regional or local planning commissions, although the regional plans are usually too general to offer realistic bases for decision[76] and local plans, although more specific, often do not exist.[77] Apparently it is also the case that municipalities and their representatives are frequently unfamiliar with Act 250 and its functioning, as well as with the land use controls that antedated Act 250, so that local participation in the hearings is less complete than was envisioned by the legislature.[78]

The tendency to grant conditional permits rather than to deny approval entirely indicates that Act 250 is viewed, at least at the state agency level, as a tool for obtaining control of development in order to ensure compliance with state environmental standards. Presumably because the state plans have not yet been in operation for very long, the permit review process is not regarded as a vehicle for the implementation of planning.

Since the Protection Division also administers the permit review process under other land use related programs—such as public buildings permits (which includes virtually every building except barns), subdivisions, sewage disposal, mobile homes, and air pollution and solid waste control—it can and does function as a clearinghouse for the multiplicity of permits that new projects require. Although the lines of authority for this "clearinghouse" function have not been formally established, either administratively or legislatively,[79] the permit-processing activities of the Protection Division and the technical assessment through the Act 250 Review Committee clearly serve not only as a source of expertise and coordination of policy but also as a point at which many, if not all, of the statutory and regulatory standards applicable to a development are administratively coordinated.

Nonetheless, the multiplicity and duplication of permits required for development[80] are a continuing concern to those administering Act 250, and there is a general desire for some form of permit consolidation. Several suggestions have been made concerning the form such a consolidation might take. According to the Director of Protection, a possible mode of alleviating the current lack of a unified set of standards for review of a project would be legislation that allowed state agencies to grant permits only to projects conforming with local and regional plans. In this case, on the theory that the permanent state plans were in some sense binding upon local planning, the review tasks of the Division of Protection would be vastly simplified by being able to refer to a single set of overall standards, whatever the specific permit for which application is made. As will be seen below, this possibility is a remote one.

Another possibility lies in the statutory power of the Environmental Board to rule that the permits of other environmental control programs may serve as prima facie evidence of compliance with the criteria of Act 250 on the point in question. Permit consolidation under this statutory power and the regulations of concerned agencies has, in fact, been the route taken. The Environmental Board has already moved in the direction of consolidation by establishing joint sessions with the Water Resources Board in order to coordinate policy and develop a single set of standards, eventually making it possible to accept a waste discharge permit from the Water Resources Board as prima facie evidence of compliance with the Act.[81] In a similar development, changes in the Air Pollution Control Regulations, effective June 5, 1972, allow permit consolidation for those seeking an Act 250 permit and an application for "additional air contaminant information." The applicant can submit solely to the Act 250 District Commission as long as the information he supplies meets the requirements of the air pollution statute and regulations; the Division of Protection reviews the application and informs the District Commission on what terms to issue the permit. In Vermont the Act 250 permit review process has become the primary mechanism for review of new contaminant sources.[82]

The most recent draft of the regulations of the Environmental Board allows for a master permit application which simultaneously fulfills the application requirements of Act 250, the public building regulations, subdivision regulations, mobile home park regulations, and tent and trailer regulations. The Board takes fulfillment of the specifications of the other permits as prima facie evidence of fulfillment of Act 250 requirements on the relevant point.[83]

The number of permit applications under all of the land use programs administered by the Division of Protection is increasing at a great pace. Of course, it is difficult to tell whether this is due to the pace of development or to better identification of projects that must meet the various standards. Whatever the reason, applications in the Technical Review Section of the Division, which administers subdivision and building permits as well as sewage disposal, rose from 450 in 1971 to 866 in 1972. Permit applications under the Air Pollution Section rose from 24 to 262.[84] Cases reviewed under Act 250 by the Division rose from 365 to 540 in 1972, and to an estimated 1,400 in 1973.[85]

Clearly, the need for some reduction in the number of required permits and in the morass of duplicate and overlapping jurisdictions and multiplicity of regulatory standards is an important issue which has been uncovered by the effort to administer Act 250. According to the administrators of the Act, much of the hostility to permit review under Act 250 has arisen from a lack of familiarity with pre-existing land use laws and the consequent conviction that the permit confusion was a product of Act 250. Despite the apparent confusion, however, Act 250 has served well in obtaining control of development, so that compliance with state standards under other statutes affecting land use has reached a much higher level than before.[86]

The theory that Act 250 was designed to discourage development across the board, and hence that the burdens of the permit process are immaterial, does not appear to be shared by the personnel of the Environmental Conservation Agency. Aside from their specific desire to see the permit system streamlined, there seems to be a general concern that the entire permit system, especially under Act 250, should function as an educational process which will result in developments that are technically, aesthetically, and ecologically satisfactory, rather than as a mechanism to prohibit development.

Experience to date suggests that although development has been brought close to a halt in some areas, this is relatively uncommon.[87]

A study of the early period of the Act's administration came to the conclusion that the Act had had no appreciable impact on the rate of development and that most of the apparent slowing effect was attributable to the general state of the economy.[88]

This compliance-oriented attitude is also reflected in the statistics on the permits processed by the District Commissions, which relatively seldom result in outright denials. In the first year of the Act's administration, 326 applications were processed, but only 11 were rejected in their entirety.[89] In the second year only 27 of 866 were rejected. In the third year only 33 of the 1,145 applications acted upon were denied.[90]

Although the Division of Protection is empowered to enforce the rules and regulations of the boards it serves, it has undertaken no criminal prosecutions and relatively few civil actions under Act 250, preferring to use the threat of such sanctions to obtain compliance.[91] Only one case of criminal action has arisen for gross violation of the terms of a permit.[92] To some extent the lack of criminal prosecutions arises from the difficulties the Division of Protection faces in terms of personnel and funds for follow-up procedures.[93] There is also some difficulty in gaining the attention of the state's Attorneys, who are also understaffed and underfinanced and hence inclined to leave environmental cases low on the list of priorities.[94]

This is not to say that the conditioned permits suggested by the Act 250 Review Committee and relied upon by the District Commissions are without the support of legal and administrative enforcement techniques, but these techniques are aimed at inducing compliance rather than punishing noncompliance. The assurance of discontinuance provided for by statute has proved to be a useful tool for inducing compliance with the three major environmental laws; it enables the Division of Protection to "lean" on the violator to obtain the equivalent of a compliance or abatement schedule. It also has the advantage that the "assurance" is filed in court and can be rapidly acted upon, since violation of the terms of the assurance is prima facie evidence of violation of the statute. The Division of Protection also finds that simple notices of violation are frequently sufficient to induce compliance, and it is seldom necessary to reach the point of issuing a cease and desist order.[95] One reason for the infrequent use of such orders is the feeling that they must be justifiable in court on the basis that the violation is causing "irreparable damage."

The Environmental Board has also made little use of its statutory power to obtain injunctions. This has been due in part to the relative unavailability of the services of the Attorney General's office, as mentioned above, but more important, it results from certain aspects of the process of obtaining injunctions. The measured speed at which the courts move often means that projects challenged by the Environmental Board are largely completed by the time the case comes before the courts, and traditional judicial reluctance to disturb the status quo without a showing of "irreparable harm" in effect shifts the burden of proof from the developer to the Environmental Board. Lacking the funds and personnel to develop evidence for such a showing, the Board has instead relied on the administrative remedies discussed above.[96] This kind of situation has also frustrated attempts to prevent environmental degradation in Maine.

Despite the lack of effective remedies for preventing unacceptable development and the relatively heavy reliance on postviolation administrative sanctions, the administrators of Act 250 feel that the prehearing stages of the permit review process have considerable impact on development proposals even before the hearing stage is reached. The fashioning of sophisticated and environmentally sound plans, especially among smaller developers who lack the resources for such planning themselves, has been an unexpected but gratifying side effect of the administration of Act 250, even before the enactment of substantive planning guidelines.[97]

The compliance-oriented approach is carried through to the hearing stage. Those who administer the permit application process appreciate the informal nature of the initial hearing procedure. Although the hearings frequently involve interested parties and expert witnesses from state agencies, they seldom involved the presence of counsel in the early period of Act 250's administration.[98] This practice is changing, however, as developers rely more heavily on counsel, and the Environmental Board is more frequently cast into an adversary role at District Commission hearings. At such times the Board will ask to be represented at the hearings by the Land Use Administrator or by counsel to the Agency of Environmental Conservation.[99]

After receiving the recommendations of the Act 250 Review Committee and holding the hearing, which is done more or less automatically although not required by law, the District Commission will issue findings of fact and law and will ordinarily grant the permit with conditions attached. According to one observer,[100] the Environmental Board has moved slowly in developing substantive guidelines for the imposition of conditions on the permits, and so far the District Commissions have relied on Model Subdivision Regulations, the regulations of the Water Resource Board, and Environmental Board guidelines on power line emplacement.[101]

Since permanent plans have only recently been enacted and the Environmental Board is still in the process of developing rules for implementing the plans, the District Commissions have been quite free to develop their own standards and to impose conditions according to their own judgment of the needs of the situation. In fact, in one of the few cases appealed to the Environmental Board, the decision of the District Commission was reversed on the grounds that it established conditions that were more restrictive than the standards of the appropriate state regulatory agency. This situation may change after the permanent land use plan is adopted.

In fact, the Board's conception of its role with respect to District Commission decisions is already changing, possibly as a function of the adoption of the Interim and Permanent Capability and Development Plans, but clearly as a function of gaining administrative control of the permit review process and integrating it with other state permit review programs. At this point the Board feels that it is in the forefront of environmental protection in Vermont and that it can and does impose more restrictive conditions on Act 250 permits than would be required by the relevant regulatory agency, if there is no other way to justify a finding of "no undue adverse effect" under the Section 6086 permit criteria.[102] An interesting effect of this change in the Board's attitude towards its regulatory role has been an administrative reinterpretation by other land-use-concerned agencies of their own regulations[103] to conform to the standards of Section 6086 of Act 250.

On the other hand, the initial review by the state-level agencies tends to place some constraints on the Commissions' rulings. It became clear early in the history of the District Commissions that they, as well as the Division of Protection, were performing a clearinghouse function, using the recommendations of the Act 250 Review Committee to guide the developer into conformance with the multiplicity of existing state standards.[104] The reliance on these recommendations also allows the Commissions to achieve a certain degree of uniformity in the decisions of the various districts. The Review Committee was instituted partly for this reason, since some of the early district-level decisions were felt to be both technically and substantively inadequate.[105] Thus, although the District Commissions were created specifically for local participation in the process of making land use decisions, the administration and development of substantive and technical standards has been centralized to a considerable degree. This can be partly explained by the lack of municipal and regional planning in many areas and by the generality of the planning where it does exist as well as by the reluctance of local officials to participate in the hearings.

The anomaly of the District Commissions' functioning as clearinghouses for state agencies may be resolved by the adoption of the permanent land use plans and maps and by the Environmental Board rules implementing them. Possibly the plans will give the Commissions guidelines on state land use policy tailored to their areas, thus allowing them more opportunity for substantive consideration of a project's value in the light of local conditions and eliminating the need for a series of ad hoc decisions on state policy for every project. However, since there is some question whether the permanent plans will reach this level of specificity, it is possible that the plans will not provide such a means of achieving consistency with statewide goals without sacrificing local participation in the review process.

Act 250 and Air Pollution Control

The District Commissions have been quite free in imposing conditions the few times they have been called upon to consider applications for projects that might lead to an air pollution problem. In one recent case, the consideration of a proposal to build a temporary asphalt plant, the District Commission required a source test before the plant commenced operation.[106] In another very early decision, the District Commission imposed ten different conditions upon the Spruce Tissue Mills Plant in Bennington County, a large project which was sponsored by the Bennington County Industrial Corporation. Most of these conditions were detailed requirements for compliance with state water pollution standards, but they included a requirement of compliance with current air pollution regulations and a further prohibition against using any fuel other than No. 2 fuel oil. These conditions were appealed by the corporation and were rewritten by the Environmental Board on the grounds that the fuel requirements, as well as several of the water pollution requirements, were more restrictive than the existing regulations of the Department of Health and the Department of Water Resources. At that time state officials considered it questionable whether the Commission had the legal authority to make a substantive decision that was more stringent than existing regulations and believed that the District Commission was only empowered to assure that the proposed fuel system would meet the standards of the 1968 Air Pollution Control Act.[107] As noted above, this attitude has changed considerably.

Conversely, the state-level authorities felt that the conditions imposed in the asphalt case were not adequate. The Air Pollution Control Division claimed that the proposed emission control devices were not sufficient to meet state regulations, that adequate devices did exist, and that the source test after construction would be an inadequate measure. Rather than going through the appeals process, the Division of Protection obtained from the company a "Stipulation to Operate" in which the company was required to obtain a particular form of emission control device, to present evidence of its purchase and delivery by a certain date, to perform a source test, the results to be submitted to the Air Pollution Control Officer, and to comply with the performance standards of the state.[108]

The jurisdictional overlap characteristic of the land use control programs in Vermont is evident in this exchange, since the letter was actually sent by another section of the Division of Protection, although the application was pending under the Act 250 permit process. In general, the administrative integration of air pollution control and land use control in Vermont is mediated by the Division of Protection. In addition to consolidating permit review under Air Pollution Regulations,[109] the Division can send applications to the Air Pollution Control Section for consideration through the Act 250 Review Committee mechanism. In this case, the Air Pollution Control Section functions as consultant to the Act 250 Review Committee and the District Commissions in responding to the permit application directly, or it may be asked by the District Commission to function as its staff with respect to air pollution control issues in a particular application.[110]

Aside from these administrative measures, however, the two statutes create two overlapping jurisdictions over new construction that might emit air pollutants. The Air Pollution Control statute is not limited to developments of a certain size, and at the moment the regulations require "applications for information" concerning construction of additional air contaminant sources only for certain listed industries and installations required to meet federal performance standards under the Federal Clean Air Act.[111] These industries must give notice to the Air Pollution Control Officer before undertaking the construction of new or additional contaminant sources and may be required, as a condition precedent to construction, to submit plans and specifications. The Air Pollution Control Officer may issue an order approving or prohibiting the construction if it is in violation of applicable regulations or if it will interfere with the state's air pollution control strategy or with the maintenance of a national air quality standard.[112] Approval may also be given upon specific conditions.

The Air Pollution Control Division has the additional power of requiring written reports on point sources. In the case of new point sources emitting more than 100 tons of all pollutants per acre, the report must include information on their impact on ambient air quality standards. Otherwise, the statute and regulations rely upon classification of sources and emission control requirements at the stack as the enforceable tools of air pollution control.[113]

Now that the full power of the Board of Health has been transferred to the Environmental Conservation Agency[114] and guidelines are being developed for review of new contaminant sources, the Air Pollution Control Agency would seem to have very broad powers over land use decisions affecting air quality. It is difficult to say, however, what the potential impact of these powers is, since they were exercised to a negligible degree when the air quality control program was administered by the Board of Health and since the ambient air pollution levels in Vermont would not ordinarily require reliance on land use controls.

In 1972 it was felt that existing air pollution regulations, coupled with the power granted under the Air Pollution Law of preconstruction review of major sources, were sufficient to Vermont's needs.[115] The regulatory structure of Act 250, however, has made the Act an attractive alternative route for control of new installations, since, under the criteria of Section 6086, it gives somewhat more control over purely visible pollution and because of the sheer efficiency of the Act's integrated administrative structure. The State Air Pollution

Control Officer estimates that 90 percent or more of new contaminant sources have been "captured" and reviewed in the past year through the Act 250 mechanism rather than through the regulatory structure of the Air Pollution Control Act.[116] The Director of the Agency of Environmental Conservation and the Air Pollution Control Officer still retain their powers under the Air Pollution Control Act and can exercise them over construction proposals that escape the jurisdiction of Act 250, but they have been able to rely to a great extent on the Act 250 review process, with a considerable saving in administrative personnel and energy. Channeling the expertise of the Air Pollution Section into District Commissions has not proved unduly difficult, requiring at most some educational efforts at hearings. Conceivably the jurisdictional overlap between the two statutes and the administrative solutions to the problem could result in some confusion and legal challenges by regulated industries and developers, but at the moment the system seems to be working smoothly.

Although it has not previously been necessary in Vermont to include air quality considerations in the planning process as well as in the regulatory process, recent developments in the courts and the regulations of the Federal Environmental Protection Agency may require Vermont to take a new look at this aspect of state-level planning.

As noted in the last chapter, two recent court decisions[117] have resulted in the Environmental Protection Agency's requiring of some states that their implementation plans include land use or transportation control elements or both. These implementation plans must now prevent "significant degradation" of air quality districts that already meet or surpass federal air quality standards. The Environmental Protection Agency has proposed four alternative regulatory mechanisms[118] for meeting the rather unclear standards of no "significant degradation" set by the courts. One proposal would involve the relevant state agency's designating various areas of the state as falling within one of two air quality "zones."

The implications of such a regulation for state land use planning are potentially immense, and the relevant Vermont agencies have responded accordingly. The Air Pollution Control Section and the Legal Services Division of the Agency of Environmental Conservation, with the aid of the Land Use Administrator, are cooperating in developing "complex source regulations."[119] This regulatory approach will obviously involve Vermont in land use planning for air quality control, and satisfying the new regulations will presumably be a factor in permit review under Act 250. At the moment, however, such planning considerations are not being integrated into the overall state planning for the permanent land use plan.

Maine's Administrative Structure

Some of the administrative difficulties in Vermont appear to have been avoided by the Maine laws, only to be replaced by others.

Since the Site Location Law is administered by the same state agency administering the air pollution law and numerous other aspects of the environmental and land use control efforts of the state, the Maine legislation has established a unity of authority and a streamlining of administrative efforts. On the other hand, the legislatively established structure and the more restricted criteria for permit review present some difficulties by limiting the options available to the Environmental Improvement Commission, especially in imposing conditions. However, as the Site Location Law is not currently regarded as zoning or land use controls legislation, the more rigid statutory structure and criteria may not be felt to hamper flexibility. The Site Location Law is seen rather as granting regulatory power, applied alike to all parcels of land, while planning and zoning powers are conferred under the Land Use Regulation Law.

Since the Site Location Law only provides for a fourteen-day period between receipt of the application and a decision on the permit, several devices have been adopted to decrease the burden on the Environmental Improvement Commission that would result from attempting to hold hearings immediately in all cases. A recent legislative amendment was obtained allowing the Commission to delegate its hearing powers, and the Commission has been allowed to count the fourteen-day period as running from the date of receipt of the completed application rather than from the date of notification. Since the application the developer must submit is lengthy and detailed, it obviates the need for hearings in many cases, especially in combination with review reports from other state and local planning and regulatory agencies. The burden of obtaining these review reports also lies upon the developer so that the actual function of the Commission is largely limited to a quasi-judicial role with little use of investigatory powers.[120]

The pressure of time also influences the Commission to grant conditional permits without a hearing rather than to deny them.[121] These conditions must be justifiable under the statute on the basis of a clear danger to public health and safety and are ordinarily limited to such historic police power concerns as air and water pollution. Some of the conditions are standard requirements for obtaining necessary permits, and specific conditions are usually imposed upon the recommendation of relevant state agencies,[122] who may thus enforce environmental criteria which ordinarily are only advisory. Thus, the Commission routinely requires that subsurface sewage disposal conform with the recommendations of the Soil and Water Conservation Commission. The Commission's own guidelines for reducing environmental impact have the status of formal regulations. The Commission has also been cautious about denying permits for substantive reasons,[123] and this practice parallels that of the Vermont District Commissions.

The statute is somewhat unclear about whether the developer must comply with state environmental standards in order to obtain a permit or merely demonstrate that he is capable of so doing. These standards are therefore enforced either by making compliance a condition of approval or by treating the application as an undertaking to meet the standards, so that the developer would have to comply with the standards in order to meet the terms of his permit.

Actual enforcement usually takes the form of court action under the Site Location Law. This is regarded as a satisfactory technique, although it is hampered by the need to show that the state has standing to sue and especially by the traditional requirement of a showing of irreparable harm to the environment. One commissioner[124] feels that the balance struck in injunctions issued after the damage is done favors a developer. Injunctions would be a more effective tool if violations of the terms of the permit or a failure to notify the Commission under the statute were a sufficient basis for issuing a temporary or permanent injunction in a court of general jurisdiction. As the practice stands, the developer can continue until the state makes a showing of special damage. By that time, the courts are reluctant to reverse the process or to disturb what has already been accomplished, and the compromises they reach are generally less protective of the environment than they would have been if the injunction had been issued at an earlier time.[125]

The Commission believes state-level administration to be a great advantage, since it allows the application of an integrated set of standards and removes the review process from local pressures favoring development. On the other hand, the statutory provision for members representative of various interest groups in the state tends to dilute this advantage, since these members are apt to feel that they have a constituency whose interests must be considered even when in conflict with the purposes of the Site Location Law.

There have not been a great many applications processed under the Law, which might be accounted for by the fact that the Site Location Law primarily affects large industrial developments of more than 20 acres or 60,000 square feet of floor space[126] and that Maine has been affected by general economic conditions reducing major economic development. It could also be that since the Vermont and Maine land use regulation laws do not provide a link between the Commission and the recording of plats and conveyances, the Commission is dependent on self-reporting by developers and on the alertness of other state agencies and citizens, and that this is not an adequate tool for identifying new development. However, the work of the Commission in its first year was felt to be highly effective, and one observer concluded that the small number of applications processed could probably be attributed to the Commission's initial reluctance to exercise its jurisdiction freely, especially in urban areas.[127]

The Maine Land Use Regulation Law is still in its infancy, and relatively little development is going on in the unorganized areas of Maine to which it applies. According to the Director of the Land Use

Regulation Commission,[128] only one application that could properly be called a development under the statute has been processed, and the remainder of the applications are for building permits or subdivisions. At this time the Commission's efforts are primarily devoted to developing interim standards and districts by 1973, as mandated by the law. No specific consideration is being given to air quality management, which will probably be dealt with by reference to the regions and standards developed by the Bureau of Air Quality Control of the Department of Environmental Protection. The Site Location Law also relies on the expertise of this agency in formulating its decisions, so in this area there is a functional as well as theoretical correlation of the standards applied under both of Maine's land use laws.

Otherwise, correlation of the two laws relies upon the identity of their permit criteria and upon the provision of the Land Use Regulation Law that allows approval by the Land Use Commission to serve as prima facie evidence of compliance with the Site Location Law. This is an attempt to eliminate duplication of applications rather than to coordinate planning and land use control.[129]

Since the Site Location Law, like the Vermont law, was passed in a period of response to a perceived environmental crisis, there was initially some feeling that it might not prove to be an enduring solution to the problems of land use control.[130] However, the existence of the Land Use Regulation Law and its plans and the difficulty of confining pollutants within jurisdictional lines may ultimately exert considerable pressure to bring the broad powers of the Site Location Law into line with a comprehensive state plan. One commissioner[131] believes that the need to centralize planning and expertise in the field of environmental control, which has already led to the creation of environmental superagencies even in such relatively unpolluted states as Maine and Vermont, will ultimately bring the Land Use Commission into the orbit of the Environmental Protection Department. Comprehensive land use planning and control for all areas of the state will then be administered by that agency. This opinion is echoed in part by the Land Use Regulation Commission.[132]

THE ROLE OF PLANNING IN
LAND USE CONTROL

Statewide Land Use Control?

The real test of Vermont's Act 250 as a tool for rational land use control will come when the permanent Capability and Development Plan and the Land Use Plan are adopted and put into use. These plans are the crux of the many important issues involved in the attempt to control land use at the state level. The most immediate question necessarily concerns the extent to which the plans can or should be regarded as statewide land use control, both under the statute as well as in the broader context of political realities and the traditional allocations of power over land use decisions. A corollary problem arises concerning the role of the state, regional, and municipal plans as well as the plans and standards of other state-level agencies that regulate land use. The most intriguing issue from the standpoint of the control of environmental quality is undoubtedly the question of the legal effect of these plans on permit decisions.

There is wide agreement that Act 250 was regarded by those who enacted it as conferring zoning powers on the Environmental Board, or at least conferring authority to designate land use districts and standards, which would roughly approximate zoning powers. The Executive Director of the Environmental Board believes that this was the case, as do members of the State Planning Office working on the permanent plans.[133] However, some of those responsible for developing the plans now believe that such specific land use decisions are not practical either in terms of the ability of a state-level agency to make such precise decisions or in terms of the possibility of having such specifications approved by the legislature.[134]

The statute itself provides some support for the notion that virtual zoning powers were intended, since one section[135] envisions actual land use maps.[136] (However, the last sentence of that section clearly distinguishes "zoning" at the local level from whatever it is that the land use maps are expected to accomplish.) Most notably, another section[137] provides for rather elaborate procedures for obtaining changes in the boundaries of the land use plans, implying that the districts and standards established by the Environmental Board are to have more than advisory effect. Under this section, any state or local agency, or property owner or lessee, may petition for a change in the boundaries[138] or in designated capabilities.[139] After forwarding a copy to the regional or municipal planning bodies and the District Commissions, the Board is to hold hearings, and the petitioner must meet a rather severe burden of proving that the area is needed for a use other than that for which it is classified, that it is usable for the proposed use, that conditions have changed since the original classification, and that the proposed classification is reasonable.[140] The unsuccessful petitioner may appeal the decision to the Supreme Court, as in permit applications. These requirements assume that more definite classifications will be developed under the plans and that they will have more authority over the use of lands so classified than would appear to have been intended from the broad language of the statute.[141] Perhaps one can only conclude that the legislators were not entirely clear about the nature and possible scope of the act they were passing.

Presumably the intention of the legislature may become significant at some later date if the provisions of Act 250 are challenged in the courts. In the meantime, the interpretation of those responsible for the development of the plans and administration of Act 250's regulatory scheme is the more relevant, and the personnel of the State Planning Office, the Environmental Board, and the Division of Protection are virtually unanimous in their conclusion that the permanent plans will not be equivalent to statewide zoning. In some cases it is felt that they will have no binding effect at all. According to the former Executive Director of the Environmental Board, the Interim Land Capability Plan adopted in March 1972 would have no legal force at all and the final plans would have to be so innocuous in order to pass the legislature that they would offer little guidance to the District Commissions in actually passing upon permit applications.[142] The Chairman of the Act 250 Review Committee regarded the plans as having little practical effect on the recommendations of that body, which relies upon much more specific plans developed by the planning body attached to the Agency of Environmental Conservation.[143]

The Land Use Administrator for the Division of Protection also noted that although the Interim Plan had not been in effect long enough to judge its effect on the permit review process, a permanent plan that was no more specific might well result in a greater number of appeals.[144] This has apparently been the case with District Commission decisions based upon the extremely broad statutory criterion concerning rare and irreplaceable areas,[145] most notably with the Ryder Pond case.[146] The Land Use Administrator felt it quite possible that the Interim Plan was too general to provide an adequate basis for permit decisions by the District Commissions. There seems to be some agreement that the policy statements of the projected plans as well as those in the Interim Plan will not be sufficiently tight to permit denials of permits on the basis of some kinds of considerations— densities of development, for example.[147] However, it is intended to make the policies sufficiently definite to serve as a basis for drawing up rules to guide the District Commissions in judging applications, and current formulations of the Plan hope to provide sufficiently refined policy statements to be legally enforceable, giving some general substantive standards which can be refined by subsequent regulations.[148]

The Interim Plan

According to the State Planning Office, the Interim Land Capability Plan of 1972 was a prototype of the form to be taken by the permanent plans as well as a substantive model under the statute.[149] The Interim Plan consisted of an inventory of the present capabilities and limitations for development of the state's land and waters. The inventory was divided into three sections: "Generalized Land Use," "Physical Limitations for Development," and "Unique or Fragile Areas." Each section was accompanied by a map that showed the distribution of the item inventoried throughout the state. More detailed maps for each county were also made available.

The Interim Plan diluted its own authority in an introductory statement on its use, claiming that it was intended only as a "guide" to the District Commissions and the Environmental Board and that its maps and inventories were to be used only as "supplementary information." It further restricted the Plan's usefulness as authority for District Commission permit decisions:

> Because of the broad statewide scale of this plan and possible resulting imprecision in mapping, conformance with the Plan and Inventory will be determined by the District Environmental Commissions and the Environmental Board only after authentification and verification of the land capability categories depicted on the maps at the site of the proposed development project.[150]

Following this discussion of its own reliability and authoritativeness, the Plan listed eleven policies, which were virtually the only recommendations it contained. These governing ideals were in some cases merely expanded versions of the criteria already embodied in the statute in Section 6086. In general, the listed policies were little more than exhortations for renewed efforts to solve major environmental problems such as recycling, strip development, absorption of the population explosion, and the conflict between the need for development and the burden such development places on the environment.

The Permanent Plans

Although the development of the permanent plans has undergone and continues to undergo many changes, the permanent Land Use Plan will remain on roughly the same level of specificity as the Interim Plan and the permanent Capability and Development Plan adopted in the last session of the legislature.[151] There are several reasons why land use classifications and development standards will be no more specific in the final plan. The most basic reason is the statutory requirement that the Land Use Plan be based on the Capability and Development Plan and that it consist of "a map and statements of present and prospective uses which determine in broad categories the proper use of the lands in the state."[152] Although the Environmental Board hopes that the final plan will provide a system of land use classification that will reflect state environmental policies and planning objectives and allow for substantive constraints on uses as well as the application of state standards regulating the quality of the uses (which is now possible under the Capability and Development Plan),[153] it seems likely that this hope will not be fully realized.

There are practical reasons limiting the effectiveness of the classifications developed under the permanent Land Use Plan aside from the political realities symbolized by the recent amendments which limited the authority of the Land Use Plan to developments falling within the jurisdiction of Act 250 review and made its classifications subordinate, in most cases, to the provisions of regional and local plans.[154] A practical obstacle in the development of the final plan arises from the lack of complete or sufficiently small-scale survey maps of the state of Vermont. Such a lack presents legal as well as planning difficulties, since the classifications drawn must provide a sufficiently definite and rational basis for state limitations on the use of land as well as provide a sound basis for decisions implementing planning policies.[155]

The task of specifying the standards and policies outlined in the plans will be left to the rule-making authority of the Environmental Board, which will develop rules to guide the District Commissions in passing upon development permits. The existence of the plans and the fact that they will have been adopted by the legislature should enable the District Commissions to make a larger number of substantive decisions on development rather than merely applying the standards borrowed from a medley of state agencies. As noted above, this process is already occurring to some extent, possibly as a result of the adoption of the Interim Plan in 1972. However, the extent to which the permit review system will ultimately reflect the state plans and the extent to which the state plans will affect decision making in other state agencies and local bodies, and thus the actual patterns of land use in Vermont, depends on many factors. At least as important as the actual content of the permanent plans will be the measures taken to make them an authoritative rather than an advisory influence on all land use decisions in Vermont.

The permanent Capability and Development Plan adopted by the Vermont legislature in its 1973 session warrants examination not only because of the substantive environmental policies it embodies but also because of its unusual role as a statutory realization of planning objectives. Thus we must consider not only the merits of those objectives but also the possible difficulties of implementation that may arise from the statutory form in which they are presented.

As law, the Capability and Development Plan consists of a substantial expansion and elaboration of the criteria of Section 6086, which function as standards of decision in District Commission review of permit applications (see Appendix A). The new provisions cover such specific areas as water pollution, the impact of growth, and permissible development on prime agricultural land. The provisions are cast in the form of fairly broad conditions which must be met by applicants before the Commissions can make a finding of no undue effect on the state's environment in that specific area. The actual planning goals and principles of the Plan are contained in the "legislative findings" of the act, and the District Commissions are specifically prohibited from using those findings as criteria of decision in permit review.[156]

As statutory standards for the granting of permits, these provisions are perhaps unusual only in the type and scope of criteria that must be met. However, as a planning document they present some problems that can be exemplified by considering their role as embodiments of policy.

The expanded criteria of Section 6086(a)(1) are interesting primarily because they include many environmental considerations affecting the preservation of Vermont's water supply and natural streams and shorelines. They may raise some questions about the validity of the exercise of the police power to regulate the aesthetic and ecological quality of the state's environment. This question is more squarely posed, however, by the expanded provisions of Section 6086(a)(8). The vagueness of the original section had already been attacked in the Ryder Pond case,[157] and this problem was not solved by the addition of a specific provision that a permit can be denied if a showing is made that the proposed development will affect natural habitats or endangered species. The new provision is a noteworthy extension of the traditional conception of the police power. Although there is some support in the Vermont cases for such an exercise of power, it is expected that developers will attempt to challenge it. The section has already been invoked to prevent a residential and recreational development that would destroy a winter deeryard, but the legal outcome is still unclear.[158]

Section 6086(a)(9) is, of course, the heart of the Capability and Development Plan as a statute and presents some of its major anomalies as a plan. The fact that the policies represented by the substantive criteria of this section are to be applied in an ad hoc manner to each permit raises the basic question whether such a mechanism will coherently implement those policies. When one considers the nature of some of the criteria, such as settlement patterns and the use of prime agricultural soil, the problem becomes quite acute. Conceivably the adoption of the permanent Land Use Plan and its maps will resolve the problem, since allocation of uses can then be determined beforehand. The form and content of the Land Use Plan, however, both as a statute and as a planning document, will become extremely important if it is to effectively regulate land use to achieve or maintain the environmental quality treasured by Vermont.

The provisions in this section that affect settlement patterns demonstrate this basic problem and also raise some more specific issues. The "Impact of Growth" provision in Section 6086(a)(9)(A) is the primary vehicle of settlement policy. Although it lists numerous and extensive issues to be taken into consideration with respect to population growth, these considerations are broadly phrased and offer little as substantive guidelines on state settlement policy. In addition, these matters are only to be "taken into consideration" by the Commissions, unlike the substantive standards of the other paragraphs of this section, which are put in the form of conditions that must be met by the applicant if a permit is to be granted. The regulatory impact of the state's settlement policy is further diluted by the provision that the burden of showing an adverse impact of growth on the locality's financial capacities is shifted to those opposing the permit.

Paragraph (H) offers a clearer, albeit indirect, method of effectuating a settlement policy against scattered development by requiring a showing that the additional costs of providing municipal services to outlying developments will be outweighed by the public benefits, such as increased employment opportunities, generated by the development. Section (L) is also somewhat more straightforward than Section (A) in imposing a policy of controlled expansion in rural growth areas, although it is also extremely general in its substantive standards.

Although a concern with settlement patterns is appropriate under the language of Section 6042 of Act 250 and was given considerable impetus from the citizen Task Forces appointed by the governor to supplement the statutory hearings on the proposed Capability and Development Plan, the enacted provisions are somewhat disappointing. Both the reports of these groups and the results of the hearings revealed a general concern over the continuing loss of agricultural and other open lands to development.[159] The diminished role of settlement policy in the adopted Plan is regretted by some of those involved in its formulation, especially since the statutory provision that the Land Use Plan be based on the Capability Plan may limit the extent to which settlement policy can be incorporated in the final plan in the series.[160]

Since the economy of the state is largely dependent upon agriculture, forestry, and scenic beauty, the legislature understandably enacted more stringent and well-defined conditions for the granting of permits affecting areas of the state's environment related to these functions. Thus if a proposed development would reduce the agricultural potential of prime agricultural soils, the applicant must show that there is no other way to realize a return on the land, that he has no other land suited to development, that the development has been planned to minimize the reduction in agricultural potential, and that the development will not reduce the actual or potential agricultural use of adjoining lands.[161]

Coordination of State, Local, and
Regional Planning

Originally, Act 250 presented an anomalous situation in that it required that District Commission decisions conform with local plans, but there was no requirement that local plans be created, nor any provision for integration of the state and local planning policies. Consequently, early proposals for the Capability and Development Plan suggested making local plans mandatory by a certain date, with state-level review to ensure that they were consistent with state policy in areas in which both were relevant. Although the effectiveness of the permanent plans as tools for maintaining the quality of the environment in Vermont is obviously dependent upon the state's ability to enforce its policies across jurisdictional lines and to achieve consistency in land use decisions at every level of government, the recent amendments to Act 250 considerably reduce its ability to do so.

The amendment of Section 6043 governing the permanent Land Use Plan strictly limits the authority of the Plan to developments that fall within Act 250 permit jurisdiction, thus greatly diminishing the Plan's potential usefulness in implementing state land use policy. In the important area of conformity between state and local planning, the legislature clarified the respective roles of the two levels of planning by enlarging the role of local plans. Thus local and regional plans are now to be taken into account in the development of the Land Use Plan.[162] Although the introduction to the printed form of the amendments, which was drawn in part from the legislative findings, asserts that the planning principles of the Capability Plan are intended as guides to public planning activities at all levels of government,[163] the sole statutory bow to the authoritativeness of the state plans is contained in an amendment to Section 6046(b). Here it is provided that only in the case of a specific showing that the proposed use will have a significant impact on surrounding towns or regions or on an overriding interest of the state may a District Commission or the Environmental Board issue a permit inconsistent with local plans.[164] This clarification of the authority of the state and local plans is not very likely to result in consistent advancement of statewide environmental goals. In addition, it does little to diminish the impact of the concurrent restriction of the authority of the Land Use Plan to developments falling within the jurisdiction of Act 250 permit review.

One state planner felt, at least before the recent amendments, that the structure of Act 250, even without state review of local plans, was adequate to ensure control of major developments.[165] The legislature, in any event, has made it clear that it does not intend to provide any mechanism for the certification of regional and local plans under the Act 250 plans. It remains to be seen whether this viewpoint will change if events prove that statewide environmental goals cannot be met without such policy coordination.

Apparently, despite the dual systems of planning and permit review of new construction under state and regional plans, the problem of a conflict between the two has not yet arisen.[166] It is not inconceivable that if there were such a conflict a case could be made in the courts that the state plans or environmental criteria might be considered binding upon local standards. Some Vermont Supreme Court decisions have held that the state standards (in one case, standards of environmental quality) were, in effect, conditions upon the state's

delegation of zoning power to local government.[167] One wonders
whether a solution to the political problems involved in getting state
legislatures to provide state administrative review of local planning
decisions might not be to provide by statute that the state delegation
of zoning and planning power is conditioned upon meeting state environmental standards and to provide for judicial review of nonconforming
plans or ordinances. Although such a course might be more palatable
to local groups, the burden on the courts and on the state to undertake
the procedure might weigh against it, and so might the difficulty of
comparing plans that might not be commensurable in scale. State
planners feel that the precise nature of the Land Use Plan's authority
will not really appear until it has been adopted by the legislature and
that the moral and practical force of such an adoption may well serve
to overcome some of the anomalous aspects of Act 250's provisions
on this point.[168]

Nonetheless, there are clearly several issues which will have
to be resolved. Although the lack of coordination between state and
local planning may not by itself be critical, in conjunction with the
now limited jurisdiction of the final plan and with the uncertain character of the land use classifications to be delineated by the Land Use
Plan, the effectiveness of the permanent plans as instruments of
state policy may be in doubt. Since Vermont has shown considerable
ingenuity and efficiency in finding administrative solutions for some
of the unforeseen anomalies created by the statute, there may be no
issue. However, if statutes attempting to maintain the quality of the
environment through state-level land use control are to be adopted
in states with more complex environmental problems and bureaucratic
structure, clear-cut statutory solutions may be required.

Planning Under the Maine Statutes

It would be extremely difficult to compare the provisions of the
Maine Land Use Regulation statute's planning provisions with Vermont's, at least on a practical basis, since no plans have been promulgated and the interim districts and land use guidance standards
have just been developed. It is interesting to note a few statutory
points of difference, however. The Maine statute leaves no room to
question its binding effect on almost anything. It provides that

> whenever the requirements of an adopted land use guid-
> ance standard are at variance with the requirements of
> any other lawfully adopted rules, regulations, standards,
> ordinances, deed restrictions or covenants, the more
> protective of existing natural, recreation and historic
> resources shall govern.[169]

In addition, as indicated above, the standards of the Commission will continue to govern any portion of a district that subsequently organizes until it shall adopt land use plans and regulations no less protective of these resources. Clearly, such provisions will greatly enhance the ability of the state to ensure that its environmental policies receive uniform and adequate implementation. Although such a technique might be applied in Vermont to those municipalities that have not adopted zoning ordinances (as well as to the small number of areas that have not yet incorporated), the practical difficulties involved in attempting to superimpose zoning ordinances upon existing plans and ordinances might be very great indeed.

Unlike the Vermont statute, there is explicit provision for invalidating plat recordings made in violation of the statute,[170] and unlike Vermont there is also a further explicit provision for invalidating conveyances.[171] The most striking difference in the statutes, aside from the greater specificity of the statutory definitions of the land use districts in the Maine statute and its inclusion of the power to set performance standards to minimize the impact of incompatible uses, is the clear delegation of zoning powers to the Land Use Commission.[172] The Commission may classify and draw district boundaries and prescribe the standards for and restraints upon the use of air, lands, and waters in the various districts (see Appendix B).[173] This clear power to limit uses is in great contrast to the language of Act 250.

Another noteworthy difference lies in the lack of any requirement in the Maine statute that the comprehensive plan be submitted to the legislature.[174] The Comprehensive Land Use Guidance Plan would appear roughly to correspond to the Vermont Capability and Development Plan, but the Land Use Guidance Districts are designated solely by the Commission and require no legislative approval. The only level at which the Vermont Environmental Board and the Maine Land Use Regulation Commission seem to have the same degree of freedom in determining the use to which a given area may be put lies in the power of the Land Use Commission to set guidance standards for each type of district and the corresponding power in the Environmental Board to promulgate rules effectuating the permanent plans.

Despite this lack of parallelism in the statutes, some very general conclusions can be suggested. The clearly defined scope of the Maine Commission's authority, the more precise definition of the authoritativeness of the districts and standards once developed, and the less ambiguous standards for permit review will make administration of the Maine statute somewhat easier and probably somewhat less open to attack in the courts.[175] The language of the Maine statute may also offer some advantages over that of Vermont by providing greater integration of the planning and regulatory functions. Although the Comprehensive Plan in Maine need only serve as a "guide" to the Commission in drawing district boundaries, the clear power to draw such boundaries and the provision that development permits must conform to the Land Use Guidance Standards (rather than the Plans) not only makes the meaning of "in conformance" considerably less vague but also conceivably makes implementation of the policies embodied in the designation of districts a tighter and more direct process. Nevertheless, Vermont officials believe that some of the looseness in the Vermont statute leaves room for a desirable administrative ingenuity and substantive flexibility in the decisions of the District Commissions.[176]

The Maine statutes also offer an advantage in that air quality considerations are directly incorporated in the land use statutes. Both the Land Use Regulation Statute and the Site Location Law use state air pollution standards as explicit criteria for the granting of permits, and the Land Use Regulation statute expressly requires that the guidance standards for each district shall reduce air pollution.[177] However, the administrators of Act 250 in Vermont have achieved roughly the same effect by administrative referral of permits to the air pollution control officer for review. The only difference would seem to lie in the substantive rules of decision which may be developed for permit review once each statute has a plan in actual operation to guide permit review.

EVALUATION

This review of the statutory and administrative structure of state land use control in Vermont and Maine leads to a few broad conclusions when analyzed in the light of current approaches to air quality management. More important, it indicates the areas in which issues are open and solutions will have to be found if state land use control is to achieve wider acceptance or be put to more varied uses, such as air pollution control. The generalizations that can be made about these statutes, as well as the unresolved problems they present, can be grouped around the following issues:

1. The machinery of control, its form, scope, standards of sanctions, adequacy, and effectiveness, and the practical and legal issues in horizontal and vertical integration of authority over land use control.
2. The role of land use planning, its function, scope, nature, and authority.
3. Problems involved in incorporating air quality issues into both the planning and regulatory processes.
4. State-level zoning: is it necessary, possible, useful, or are there alternative methods of accomplishing the same goals?

It appears undeniable that the comprehensive plan with its permit system for reviewing new or expanded uses of land provides an effective and flexible tool for identifying and gaining control of development.

Thus it is fairly clear that the permit review system in Vermont and Maine is an excellent method of ensuring that sizable development schemes will receive adequate site planning and attention to compliance with state environmental regulations. Whether such a system can also ensure that any given development will conform to the broader land use goals of the community is less clear. The usefulness of the state-level review of land use decisions to guarantee fulfillment of environmental and developmental needs of a more than local significance depends not only upon the appropriateness and adequacy of the permit review machinery but also upon whether that machinery can be harnessed to effectuate the land management goals of the state.

Machinery of Control

The threshold issue in assessing a regulatory mechanism is whether it fully extends to all those involved in the evil to be cured. In Vermont, it is felt that the 10-acre, 10-unit dragnet of Act 250 identifies most developments likely to have a significant influence on the environment.[178] Although strip developments caused by haphazard small-scale undertakings represent some problems in this area, they may to some extent be controlled through the "areas of scenic significance" criterion,[179] although it might be preferable simply to spell out legislatively an extension of the law's coverage to smaller parcels along scenic corridors. The Site Location Law in Maine, on the other hand, permits any development of fewer than 20 acres to escape regulation, and this problem is exacerbated by the administrative interpretation of the law to apply to 20 acres "disturbed" by the development rather than 20 acres "involved," as in Vermont.

On the other hand, very-fine-level regulation, as in Maine's Land Use Law, could not very well be extended beyond unincorporated areas, since it would represent a serious invasion of local control of development that does not create a significant impact on the environment of the state as a whole. Presumably, the dragnet should vary with the type and density of development to be expected in the region concerned as well as with the political organization being affected.

The sanctions applied by these laws seem to be satisfactory. The only caveat would be that penal sanctions do not appear to be particularly appropriate in this context, and they are not invoked in Vermont at all. Invalidating conveyances made in contravention of the law would presumably be particularly effective when one of the major evils to be remedied is the commercial exploitation of land. This penalty would especially be effective if tied to the recording system. The same comment cannot be made about unenforced criminal sanctions. If the technique of invalidating conveyances is used, it should perhaps be expressed in clear statutory language, as in the Maine Land Use Law, rather than left to administrative legislation or interpretation. Although it is assumed that conveyances in violation of the Vermont law will be found void, this penalty is left to judicial interpretation, and the actual penalties for violation of the property tax transfer law are related to violation of transfer formalities rather than of the transfer itself. This is an awkward approach to voiding the conveyance.

The problem raised by limitations on the power to obtain injunctions has already been discussed. The other major practical issue affecting the efficacy of the control machinery arises from the lack of funds and personnel not only for field evaluation of developments and efficient administrative processing but also for follow-up procedures. At the moment, relatively little opportunity exists in Vermont to discover whether permit conditions are in fact being met.

Additional tools in the hands of the agency responsible for plan implementation are also valuable. The provision in the Maine Site Location Law for hearings initiated by the Commission on development proposals that fail to file a notice of intent[180] is clearly useful, although the same purpose might be served indirectly by voiding conveyances. The power to acquire conservation easements or to purchase land outright would also be influential in guiding land use patterns, but the lack of sufficient financial resources in most states precludes its widespread use. Possibly the most influential and far-reaching proposal for new land use control tools lies in the suggestion that tax assessment be adjusted to reflect the designations of the state plans. Maine has already moved in this direction[181] by providing that the land use guidance maps be filed with the state Assessor, although they do not go so far as to require adjustments.

Questions have also been raised about the scope of the statutory criteria adopted by these laws. Many of those concerned with the operation of the law in Vermont favor broad statutory standards of permit review on the theory that such language permits the greatest flexibility in assessing a given proposal and tailoring the permit conditions innovatively to the needs of the community and the developer. This viewpoint is certainly appealing. On the other hand, practical considerations might favor clear and specific standards of decision, the meaning of which would be well known to those affected before they undertook to act. Clarity in statutory standards might also foster uniformity and consistency in decisions, either across a state or within a district.[182]

J. Walter's study of these three laws emphasized the due process and equal protection issues raised by vague statutory standards and criticized the Vermont statutory criterion that protects "rare and irreplaceable" areas[183] and its application (to a project that would have involved the draining of a beaver pond) as an unjustified exercise of state power in the absence of a plan designating the area as rare and irreplaceable before the permit was applied for. In this connection, Walter preferred the provision in Maine's Land Use Law for hearings on adoption of districts and standards to which affected property owners were party, on the theory that procedural due process is better served when the classification process is statutorily prescribed and can be protested by those affected.[184]

The issues are potentially important. To some extent, the form of the statutory criteria for permit review is a question of draftsmanship, of devising language that is clear and unambiguous yet sufficiently general to allow for flexibility and for opportunities to take local variables into account. But when the use of development permits is considered not only as a means of guiding land use but also of prohibiting certain uses in certain places, there is a great burden on the law and its administrators to ensure an opportunity to be heard and a rational relationship between the prohibition and the interests of the state.

As we have emphasized, the agencies and techniques of administration of statewide land use laws are at least as important as the substantive provisions of the statute. One member[185] of the Maine Environmental Improvement Commission, in discussing the value of state-level review as against regional-level review of development permits, noted the likelihood that local bodies would be more vulnerable to the needs of the local tax base and employment pool. The sensitivity of regulatory agencies to the feelings of their constituents is a commonplace of American official life, but the importance of incorporating local interests and considerations that might be unnoticed or submerged in a state-level decision cannot be ignored.

The Vermont experience so far does not seem to warrant fears that the District Commissions will be seduced by the development needs of their region, although it is probably too early in the implementation of the law to reach a definite conclusion on this point. Certainly the expert assessment of interested state regulatory agencies is a useful check on district-level decisions, which might tend to be biased in favor of local needs. Undue local influence can also be filtered out while retaining local input to permit decisions by controlling the composition of the local reviewing bodies and preventing, by statutory command or intelligent appointments, excessive representation from those most likely to be affected by the application of the law.

The elimination of administrative overlap among state-level agencies and of jurisdictional overlap between state-level and local controls on land use is also an important issue because such overlaps result in inefficiency for the state and impose an extra burden on those regulated. The current tendency to coalesce state agencies concerned with environmental controls is one step in this direction, but as the Vermont experience shows, this alone does not solve the problems presented by multiple procedural requirements and varying review standards. The fact that many kinds of control over the use of land have been exercised by the states for many years and the fact that environmental concerns have reached the public consciousness in a piecemeal fashion have combined to create a hodgepodge of agencies and controls concerned with land use. Merely housing the concerned state agencies under one roof does not necessarily result in a streamlined and uniform approach to land use decisions. Legislative fragmentation of environmental authority does appear to have been handled well administratively in Vermont. But it is easy to see that a larger and better entrenched bureaucracy, or one more heavily burdened by a great volume of construction or development proposals, might suffer more severely from a lack of coordination and integration of environmental regulatory mechanisms.

Similarly, the concurrent jurisdictions of state, region, and municipality over land use decisions must be clarified and assigned rational roles relative to each other. Putting aside for the moment the question how much of the actual land use control power should be returned to the state under such land use laws, it must be made clear which plans are binding upon local reviewing or planning bodies. The most appealing solution is that of the Maine Land Use Law, which makes state standards minimum requirements for local ordinances, but the limitations of such an approach when applied to developed and previously incorporated areas are fairly obvious. On the other hand, the anomaly resulting from Vermont's protectiveness of local control—that is, from the fact that regional and municipal plans are binding on the District Commissions but need not themselves conform to the state land use plan which the District Commissions implements— is clearly unacceptable. A simple requirement that local and regional plans be "consistent" with state plans might suffice to be binding without limiting local flexibility.

It is conceivable that coordination of state and local planning and land use control can come about indirectly, as in the case of the Vermont decision that the state's zoning authority is delegated to local agencies on condition that the state standards are to be met in the event that there is a conflict between state and local standards. But the importance of defining the local rule within a statewide system of land use control suggests that local powers will be defined explicitly and not left to judicial implication. Undoubtedly, numerous legal arguments could be marshalled in support of the obligation of local zoning bodies to legislate with an eye to statewide concerns, and it is probably safe to say that the power of the states to regulate local effects of state environment goals is limited as much by political realities as by legal ones.

The Role of Planning

The need to articulate the nature and scope of the authority of comprehensive state plans over regulatory permit decisions poses one of the more difficult and important issues in a state land use control statute such as that of Maine or Vermont. If a statute such as Vermont's confers broadly based control powers on the state, many would argue that the state should be permitted to prohibit or limit uses of land only pursuant to a plan that reflects legitimate goals to be reached by the exercise of the police power. Most limitations on uses that produce adverse environmental effects can be legally supported, but the scope and meaning of such provisions as Vermont's requirement of a finding that there will be no undue adverse effect on sites of particular natural, historical, or aesthetic significance should probably be better defined as such and supported by a well-articulated plan defining such areas in order to avoid unfairness to property owners and consequent challenges in the courts.

Whether a state plan should be required before state land use controls can be exercised is an issue that has gained in importance as statewide controls have received increasing consideration nationally, though not all statutory proposals condition the exercise of statewide land use control powers on a state plan. A state plan is not required as the basis for the exercise of state land use control powers in the Florida statute, for example, and this approach is being given consideration in other states.

The notion that the criteria which serve as the standards of permit review of development permits should be founded on a definite though general plan has at least three bases. First, fairness to those regulated requires that persons similarly situated be similarly treated, but it is hard to establish such regularity of enforcement when decisions are made and management of property limited on an ad hoc basis. Second, if the permit review process is to make a substantive contribution to land use control and the reviewing agency is to serve as more than a clearinghouse for the substantive standards of other agencies, then a plan is essential to justify any limitations on private action imposed by the state. Third, a plan is essential for practical reasons, since the simple application of across-the-board regulations may neither reflect nor enhance achievement of the environmental goals of the community if the size or type of undertaking involved is simply inappropriate to the needs of the community at that point.[186]

Adoption of statewide or at least regional land use plans might be desirable for the regulation of air quality because of the regional basis for air quality control and the federal requirement that state control strategies have a statewide implementation base. The issue is tied to some extent with the mechanics of the land use control process as applied to air quality objectives. The state plan cum permit review system of environmental control can be used to manage air quality simply by using the permit as a means of gaining control of the proposed development and then applying the regulations already in existence under the air pollution control program. In this case, incorporating air quality considerations is largely a matter of administrative logistics. The use of the state land use review mechanism rather than a permit system administered wholly within an air pollution control agency will be dictated more by questions of efficiency than by any inherent virtue of the land use review statute, since the result in either case is source-by-source regulation.

As soon as air quality controls based on the location and density of sources are to be implemented, however, the state plan cum permit review mechanism for land use proposals offers substantial advantages. The ability to prohibit certain uses in certain places and to vary at-the-stack controls according to the location of the source are essential and valuable powers in air quality control. But this type of control should be based on planning that takes into account the future of all community activities and development patterns that will produce pollution directly or indirectly. Without a link to general state land use policy, the air quality control agency will not be able to influence the general pattern of future source location and density and ordinarily will influence only certain types or sizes of industry rather than a complex of industrial, residential, and transportation sources creating pollution.

Thus, if Vermont had a more severe air pollution problem, or envisioned greater industrial or population growth in the future, the types of control available under its air pollution statute would not allow it to guard adequately against the concentration of industry near transportation or against the concentration of home building in valleys. If the state plan, independently of air quality considerations, encouraged future residential and commercial development to cluster in order to preserve prime agricultural and forest land, then rather severe air quality consequences might ensue, especially in a state whose topography encourages small pockets of pollution (Vermont has numerous valleys and chains of valleys). It is not difficult to see that in a state with a higher level of development the technique of reviewing land use proposals for conformance with state environmental goals might be essential to effective control of air pollution.

In this case, the planning level of the land use review process rather than the regulatory mechanism would be the locus of air quality control, and state emission standards could be applied either within the land use review process or within a separate air quality control agency, depending on questions of administrative efficiency. As long as the air quality effects of alternative plans are assessed by an expert agency and the per source regulations appropriate to the plan actually adopted are used,[187] the application of the regulations within the permit review process has certain procedural advantages. In fact, given the technical complexity of air pollution regulations and the actual machinery of source controls, it is probably preferable to have such regulations administered by the expert agency and to have, as in Vermont, review by the technical agency when emission controls are to be attached as a condition of permit approval. Thus the danger can perhaps be avoided of ultimate delegation of the prescriptive and enforcement powers to the emittor himself, which occurred in one area because of the extreme technicality of the information and evaluation involved.[188]

The major legal issue affecting the form of the plans themselves would appear to be a need for policies and standards that are general in substance and application, but not vague. If the plans are to provide an adequate basis for the review of new development proposals, whether or not the Vermont practice of particularizing them in administrative rules is followed, then the plans should embody policies and standards that are enforceable. Little is gained by plans that cannot be translated into actual prohibitions or limitations of uses because it is difficult or impossible to determine whether or how their constraints apply to a particular proposal. The problem of finding an appropriate level of detail for generalized land use plans has been difficult to resolve. More experimentation is required if statewide plans are to play a meaningful role in environmental protection through the control of land use.

STATEWIDE REGULATION

It is difficult to draw any unqualified conclusions about the value of statewide "zoning" as a tool of environmental control. What is considered state-level zoning varies with the prejudices of the observer, and what can be accomplished by state-level decision making varies with the subject matter. There is no great dispute over the need for state-level land use regulation in areas where there is no local control over environmental depredations. Where local controls do exist, the need for policy making on issues that cannot be confined within jurisdictional lines must be balanced against the interest of local bodies in controlling land use decisions that may radically affect the economic and social life of its citizens.

There are several possible ways of achieving an optimum balance of power. They range from true statewide zoning, in which the state agency delineates the permissible location of various categories of land use and decides in each case whether a given use conforms to the statewide scheme (as in Maine's provisions for unorganized areas) to an arrangement by which the state establishes planning goals for land use controls which are to be implemented entirely at the local level. An intermediate solution could be a statutory structure such as Vermont's Act 250, in which both local and state standards are administratively coalesced in a state-level regulation process, which could be simplified by making the state standards binding on local standards. Another intermediate solution is a system like that embodied in the Maine Site Location Law, which depends solely on state regulatory mechanisms but whose state review machinery is entirely dependent on local plans and criteria or on existing state regulations. Such a system would probably be the least effective mechanism for rational control of the environment, but it represents an interim solution in situations where existing control machinery is fragmented by subject matter or jurisdiction and where the impact of large-scale development proposals is clearly of concern to the state as a whole. Such a system could also be used on a limited jurisdictional basis, reviewing proposals only in designated areas of critical state concern or affecting only particular resources. This is the Florida statutory solution. Conceivably, a simple and locally acceptable solution would be the development of state plans of some specificity whose policies would then be binding on local and regional plans and which would also be sufficiently specific and sophisticated to provide guidance for local zoning decisions.

It is difficult to be specific about the best structure for comprehensive state control of land use, but one clear general conclusion seems warranted by the preceding discussion: If the control of land use patterns is to be an effective tool of air quality management, the impact of individual developments on air quality standards cannot be considered in isolation. Some method must be found to link decisions on individual developments to regional and statewide air quality standards. Whether this effort will require statewide planning or whether it can be accomplished by statewide regulation without the benefit of such planning can only be determined through further experimentation with land use controls at the state level.

NOTES

1. For an analysis of similar legislation in these and other states see E. Haskell, Managing the Environment: Nine States Look for the Answers (1971), hereinafter cited as Haskell.

2. Vt. Stat. Ann. Tit. 10, Secs. 6001-6091 (Supp. 1972).

3. F. Bosselman and D. Callies, The Quiet Revolution in Land Use Control 55 (1971), hereinafter cited as Bosselman; Haskell, 34.

4. Sec. 6086(a) 1-4.

5. Sec. 6088.

6. J. H. Marshall, The Efficacy of Vermont's Act 250, at 2 (1971), hereinafter cited as Marshall.

7. Sec. 6086(a)(10).

8. Sec. 6021.

9. Sec. 6022.

10. Sec. 6023.

11. Sec. 6024.

12. Sec. 6025.

13. Section 6041 provided that the Interim Plan, which was not adopted until February of 1972, shall expire in July 1972.

14. Sec. 6042.

15. Sec. 6043.

16. Sec. 6044a.

17. Sec. 6044c.

18. Sec. 6045.

19. Sec. 6046.

20. Sec. 6046, as amended 1973, No. 85, Sec. 5, eff. July 1, 1973.

21. Sec. 6031.

22. Sec. 6042.

23. Sec. 6043.

24. Sec. 6043, as amended 1973, No. 85, Sec. 4, eff. July 1, 1973.

25. Sec. 6089. That is, the Board hears the case as if it were a case of first instance. A case now pending in the Vt. Supreme Court (Land/Tech Corporation, Stowe, Vt., Application No. 10036), appealing a denial of a permit granted by a District Commission, has challenged several Environmental Board rulings on what constitutes a de novo hearing. In an earlier Vermont Supreme Court decision it was held that the same parties who appeared before the District Commission may appear in the appeal to the Board. In re Preseault, Vt., 292 A.2d 832 (1972).

26. See Sec. 6085(b)(c).

27. Sec. 6089.

28. Sec. 6089, as amended 1973, No. 85, eff. July 1, 1973.

29. Sec. 6081.

30. Sec. 6001.

31. Sec. 6083.

32. Sec. 6084(a).

33. Sec. 6084(b).

34. Sec. 6085(a).

35. Sec. 6085(b).

36. Sec. 6085(c).

37. Sec. 6085(d).

38. Sec. 6027(f), as amended 1973, No. 85, Sec. 3, eff. July 1, 1975.

39. Sec. 6086(a).

40. Sec. 6088.

41. Sec. 6086, as amended 1973, No. 85, Sec. 10, eff. July 1, 1970.

42. Sec. 6086(c).

43. Sec. 6089.

44. Sec. 6003.

45. Vt. Stat. Ann. Tit. 3, Sec. 2822 (Supp. 1972).

46. Sec. 2822(c)(1)(2).

47. Sec. 2822(c)(3).

48. Sec. 2822(c)(4).

49. Vt. Stat. Ann. Tit. 3, Sec. 2802 (1972).

50. Me. Rev. Stat. Tit. 38, Secs. 481-488 (Supp. 1972).

51. Tit. 38, Sec. 361.

52. Sec. 482.

53. Sec. 483.

54. Sec. 485.

55. Sec. 486.

56. Sec. 487.

57. Sec. 488.

58. King Resources Co. v. Environmental Improvement Comm'n, Me., 270 A.2d 863 (1970). The opinion held that appeal was to the Supreme Judicial Court sitting as the Law court, and that a development that was operational on the cutoff date was exempt from the law's coverage, even though it was not actually operating.

59. Tit. 12, Secs. 681 to 685-C (Supp. 1972).

60. Sec. 685-A(1)(A-D).

61. Sec. 685-A(4).

62. Sec. 685-C.

63. Sec. 685-B(1)(A-C).

64. Sec. 685-B(3).

65. Sec. 685-B(7).

66. Sec. 685-B(8)(9).

67. Sec. 685-C(4)(6).

68. The law makes the lack of "undue air pollution" a criterion of permit approval. Tit. 20, Sec. 6086(a)(1).

69. Tit. 12, Sec. 685-A(3)(B).

70. Letter from James Haskell, Jr., Executive Director.

71. Vt. Stat. Ann. Tit. 3, Sec. 2802 (1972).

72. Sec. 2803.

73. Sec. 2874.

74. Bosselman, 61.

75. Interview with Jonathan Bump, Land Use Administrator, July 13, 1972.

76. Marshall, 72; Bosselman, 63.

77. Id.

78. Interview with Donald Webster, Director, Division of Protection, July 13, 1972.

79. It was not until June of 1972 that the legislature transferred the rule-making authority as well as the administrative functions of

the Board of Health regarding air pollution control to the Environmental Conservation Agency.

80. Interview with Kenneth Senecal, Executive Director, Environmental Board, July 13, 1972.

81. Bosselman, 89.

82. Interview with Richard Valentinetti, Air Pollution Control Officer, July 13, 1973.

83. Interview with Kenneth Senecal, Executive Director, Environmental Board, July 13, 1973.

84. This figure is partly accounted for by the fact that the Board of Health had not yet promulgated regulations concerning building permits under the air pollution law, and these rule-making powers were but recently transferred to the Environmental Conservation Agency.

85. Vermont Agency of Environmental Conservation, statistics on Act 250 Applications, June 1, 1973.

86. Interview with Kenneth Senecal, supra note 83.

87. Id.

88. Marshall, 52.

89. Bosselman, Appendix A.

90. Vermont Agency of Environmental Conservation, statistics on Act 250 Applications, June 1, 1972 and June 1, 1973.

91. Interview with Donald Webster, Director, Division of Protection, July 13, 1972.

92. Interview with Steven Seuse, Land Use Administrator (replacing Jonathan Bump), July 13, 1973.

93. Bump interview, supra note 75.

94. Senecal interview, supra note 83.

95. Only about 15 are issued each year under all programs. Webster interview, supra note 91.

96. Senecal interview, supra note 83.

97. Id.

98. Bump interview, supra note 75.

99. Seuse interview, supra note 92.

100. Bosselman, 68.

101. Webster interview, supra note 91.

102. Senecal interview, supra note 83.

103. Id.

104. Marshall, 66.

105. Id.

106. Re L. M. Pike and Son, Inc.

107. Marshall, 86.

108. Letter from Richard Valentinetti, Air Pollution Control Officer, to L. M. Pike and Son, April 21, 1972.

109. See Sec. 5-488.

110. Interview with Richard Valentinetti, Air Pollution Control Officer, Division of Protection, July 13, 1972.

111. Air Pollution Regulations Sec. 5-487(15).

112. Tit. 10, Sec. 356(a) (Supp. 1972).

113. Vt. Stat. Ann. Tit. 10, Secs. 355, 358 (Supp. 1972).

114. See text at note 47 supra.

115. Valentinetti interview, supra note 109.

116. Valentinetti interview, July 13, 1973.

117. National Resources Defense Council v. Environmental Protection Agency, and Ruckelshaus v. Sierra Club, aff'd sub nom. Fri v. Sierra Club, slip opinion, No. 72-804, June 11, 1973. The first case was subsequently dismissed by the Tenth Circuit for want of standing (June 18), 1973). The latter case was a Court of Appeals (D.C.) opinion supporting an interpretation of the Federal Clean Air Act as requiring state implementation plans to prevent "significant degradation" of air quality. It was affirmed by an equally divided Court without opinion, leaving not only the language but also the legal status of the holding rather uncertain.

118. 38 F. R. 18986, July 16, 1973.

119. Valentinetti interview, supra note 115.

120. Bosselman, 192.

121. Only 4 out of 136 applications were wholly denied in the first year of operation. Bosselman, 192.

122. Bosselman, 193.

123. Interview with Orlando Delogu, Maine Environmental Improvement Commission, July 24, 1972.

124. Id.

125. Id.

126. The original reference to "residential" developments was dropped, although the commission still considers that the law applies to major commercial residential developments.

127. Bosselman, 196.

128. Letter from James Haskell, Executive Director, July 31, 1972.

129. Id.

130. Bosselman, 199.

131. Delogu interview, supra note 112.

132. Bosselman, 199.

133. This contention is not supported by some of the legislative history reported in Marshall, 36.

134. Interview with David Heeter, Consultant to the Vermont Environmental Board, July 13, 1972; Senecal interview, supra note 89.

135. Sec. 6043.

136. However, the last sentence of that section clearly distinguishes "zoning" at the local level from whatever it is that the land use maps are expected to accomplish.

137. Sec. 6047.

138. These boundaries are designated under Sec 6043.

139. These are designated under Sec. 6041.

140. For petitions relating to Sec. 6041 he must also show that the land is capable of sustaining the use proposed.

141. Secs. 6041-6043.

142. Bosselman, 74.

143. Id.

144. Bump interview, supra note 75.

145. Sec. 6086(a)(8).

146. See Walter, "The Law of the Land: Development Legislation in Maine and Vermont," 23 Me. L. Rev. 315 (1971).

147. Interview with Bernard Johnson, Vermont State Planner, July 13, 1972.

148. Heeter interview, supra note 133.

149. See Sec. 6042, which requires that the final plans shall be "consistent with" the Interim Plans. Johnson interview, supra note 146.

150. Plan, 2.

151. E.g. Johnson interview, supra note 146. Heeter interview, July 13, 1973.

152. Sec. 6042, Sec. 6043.

153. Senecal interview, supra note 83.

154. Sec. 6043, as amended, 1973, No. 85, Sec. 4, eff. July 1, 1973.

155. Heeter interview, July 13, 1973.

156. Sec. 6086(a)(9), as amended, 1973.

157. Walter, supra note 145.

158. Heeter interview, supra note 154.

159. The provisions for altering tax practices also reflect a departure from earlier hopes. The Task Forces and statutory hearings on The Capability and Development Plan (Notes, Vermont Capability and Development Plan, Vermont State Planning Office, June, 1972) revealed a general concern over the extent to which taxation practices accelerated the continuing loss of agricultural and other open lands. The new legislation refers to taxing practices only as a possible recommendation to be made under the permanent Land Use Plan (Sec. 6043, as amended 1973). The legislative findings did recommend that land should be appraised according to uses of the land consistent with the Act, and this goal was embodied in some adjustments in the tax statute. However the latter provisions were intended less as a tool for gaining conformity with the policies of the

Plans than as a protection to landowners suffering reduced development potential (Senecal interview, supra note 83).

160. Heeter interview, supra note 154.

161. Sec. 6086(a)(9)(B), as amended, 1973.

162. Sec. 6043, as amended, 1973.

163. Introduction to Vermont's Land Use and Development Law, State Planning Office, Montpelier, Vermont, June 1973, p. 1.

164. Sec. 6046(b), as amended, 1973, No. 85, Sec. 5, eff. July 1, 1973.

165. Johnson interview, supra note 146.

166. In fact, local and regional plans have been useful in defending challenges to state restrictions on permits (Senecal interview, supra note 83).

167. Kedroff v. Town of Springfield, 127 Vt. 624, 256 A.2d 457 (1969), and Thompson v. Smith, 119 Vt. 488, 129 A.2d 638 (1957).

168. Johnson interview, supra note 146.

169. Sec. 685-A(4).

170. The Vermont statute penalizes such recordings, but does not explicitly void them.

171. It is assumed in Vermont that such illicit conveyances would themselves be held void by the courts, but this decision would be based upon general legal principles rather than the statute.

172. Sec. 685-A(3)(E).

173. Sec. 685-A(3).

174. Only the governor's approval is necessary, (Sec. 685-C(1)), although the regional planning commissions must have the opportunity to comment.

175. Note Walter's criticism of the Vermont statute as lacking the provision for a hearing to which property owners are party, prior to adoption of the plans, and his praise of such provisions in the Maine statute as removing some of the procedural due process objections to land use control. See Walter, supra note 145.

176. Webster interview, supra note 78.

177. Sec. 685-A(3)(B).

178. Bosselman, 81, however, feels that the lot size is not appropriate and allows too many developments to escape.

179. Sec. 6086(a)(8).

180. Sec. 485.

181. Sec. 685-C(6).

182. Note that the uniformity problem can also be improved by clarifying the role of the comprehensive state plans in permit review, as discussed below.

183. Walter, supra note 135, at 328.

184. Id. at 341.

185. Delogu interview, supra note 112.

186. Walter seems to suggest that due process also requires a plan, on the grounds that otherwise the property owner has no notice of the limitations on his use of the land. Walter, supra note 135, at 341-3.

187. However, as plans are revised the assessments of their air quality impacts will have to be similarly revised.

188. See Goldstein and Ford, "The Management of Air Quality: Legal Structures and Official Behavior," 21 Buff. L. Rev. 1, 33-4 (1971).

4

ADMINISTRATIVE
REVIEW PROCEDURES

One of the major conclusions of Chapters 2 and 3 is that administrative procedures for relating land use planning to air quality management must take their place among a large group of other concerns in the state land use and permit review process. This chapter reviews the nature of popular review procedures and permit systems, including the environmental impact statement requirement under the National Environmental Policy Act (NEPA) of 1969, the A-95 review process under Office of Management and Budget (OMB) Circular No. A-95, the permit system utilized by many air pollution agencies, and the "complex source" regulations of the Environmental Protection Agency (EPA). The focus is on the value of the procedures for relating air quality management to land use planning.

The National Environmental Policy Act requires the introduction of environmental considerations into the decision making of all federal agencies. As it was enacted, NEPA had three main thrusts: The first, which follows an enacting clause and a statement of purpose, was a declaration of a national policy on the environment, emphasizing the promotion of the general welfare, the fostering of productive harmony between man and nature, and the fulfilling of the social, economic, and other needs of the present and future. The second thrust of the law, found in Section 102, was the establishment of a series of mandates and procedures compelling all agencies of the federal government to implement the policy declared in Section 101. The third thrust, found in Title II, was the establishment of a statutory three-person Council on Environmental Quality (CEQ) in the Executive Office of the President, with responsibilities to advise the President, gather information on conditions and trends in environmental quality, and to review and appraise the various programs and activities of the federal government in the light of the policy set forth in Title I of the Act and to make recommendations to the President with respect thereto.[1]

The scope of Section 102 is such that environmental impact statements are being prepared on projects and programs involving a total of more than $16 billion annually. By 1973, over 250 lawsuits, about 50 of which have resulted in injunctions, had been filed in courts in all parts of the country against federal agencies, alleging violation of Section 102. Most of these cases have involved federally assisted highway or airport projects, Corps of Engineers water resource projects, management activities of the Interior and Agriculture departments, licenses for nuclear power plants, and federally assisted housing projects. Court decisions have consistently upheld the Act, stressed its application to projects begun before the Act was passed, required strict procedural compliance, and required that statements be substantively adequate rather than perfunctory. At least 10 states and Puerto Rico have followed the federal example in enacting laws requiring environmental impact statements (the states are Arizona, California, Delaware, Hawaii, Indiana, Montana, New Mexico, North Carolina, Washington, and Wisconsin).

The Office of Management and Budget Circular No. A-95 has established a process to aid in the review of federally funded projects and programs and in their coordination with state, regional, and local planning.[2] Although the Section 102 statements and the A-95 review process are concerned with the sum of environmental impacts, for the purpose of this discussion emphasis will be on those impacts related to air quality.

The permit system of concern here is administered by the state or local air pollution control agency and usually involves the authority to construct and operate facilities emitting a minimum of 100 tons per year of air pollutants. Although the air pollution control permit system typically has as its goal the application of "state of the art" control technology to emission sources, the potential application of the system for relating land use decisions to air quality management is great. The complex source regulations, in many ways derivative from the permit system approach, were promulgated by EPA in 1973 to deal with indirect sources of air pollution. For the most part these regulations deal with facilities that generate considerable amounts of automobile traffic.

THE NATIONAL ENVIRONMENTAL POLICY ACT

Section 102(2)(C) of the National Environmental Policy Act of 1969 stipulates that all agencies of the federal government shall:

... include in every recommendation or report on proposals for legislation and other major Federal actions significantly affecting the quality of the human environment, a detailed statement by the responsible official on:

   (i)   the environmental impacts of the proposed action,
   (ii) any adverse environmental effects which cannot be avoided should the proposal be implemented,
   (iii) alternatives to the proposed action,
   (iv) the relationship between local short-term uses of man's environment and the maintenance and enhancement of long-term productivity, and
   (v)   any irreversible and irretrievable commitments of resources which would be involved in the proposed action should it be implemented.

Prior to making any detailed statement, the responsible federal official shall consult with and obtain the comments of any federal agency which has jurisdiction by law or special expertise with respect to any environmental impact involved. Copies of such statements and the comments and views of the appropriate federal, state, and local agencies, which are authorized to develop and enforce environmental standards, shall be made available to the President, Council on Environmental Quality and to the public as provided by Section 552 of Title 5, United States Code, and shall accompany the proposal through the existing agency review process.[3]

The use of these Section 102 statements as a means of introducing environmental considerations into the decision-making process of federal agencies has had three basic impacts: It has given community and national environmental groups greater access to the courts, and successful litigation on their part has served to strengthen NEPA.[4] The requirement for the development of Section 102 statements has forced federal agencies to consider environmental concerns along with other project goals. Even though the consideration of the environmental impact of a project may be in conflict with other goals, the Section 102 statements theoretically assure consideration of all goals on an equal basis. Finally, the burden of proof on environmental matters has shifted somewhat from the public—or at least the public interest groups—to agencies responsible for environmental impact.[5]

CEQ GUIDELINES FOR
PRODUCING 102 STATEMENTS

The Procedures

The Council on Environmental Quality, established under NEPA, serves as the body that supervises the Section 102 process. In its capacity as supervisor, the CEQ oversees agency compliance with NEPA and CEQ guidelines for implementing the Act, and reviews "draft" and final Section 102 statements, but it has no authority to reject statements or procedures established by the various agencies in regard to Section 102 statements.[6] The extent to which government officials utilize the information obtained in an impact statement is not always clear: Once a procedurally correct statement has been completed, the law has been satisfied—the law does not specify that an agency is obligated to incorporate the findings of a statement into its decision making.[7]

Although the CEQ has no legislative or veto powers, it can exert considerable influence upon agencies through its review of completed impact statements. If a CEQ staff member believes that a Section 102 statement has been inadequately prepared, suggestions for improving the statement are offered to the agency responsible for the statement. Should the agency still neglect to satisfy the CEQ guidelines, the Council refers the matter to the President.[8] It is through such informal functionings of the system that agencies are encouraged to consider environmental impacts in their decision making.

The development of detailed procedures to implement Section 102(2)(C), outlined very generally in the CEQ guidelines, rested with the agencies themselves. Basic procedural considerations developed by agencies in compliance with Section 102(2)(C) included outlining agency actions requiring impact statements, determining the appropriate time prior to decision making for obtaining the required consultations, and obtaining the necessary information for preparing the Section 102 statement. Section 102(2)(C) applies to all federal agencies involved in preparing recommendations or reports on proposals for legislation and "other major federal actions significantly affecting the quality of the human environment."[9] These "actions" should be considered in the light of their cumulative effect and must deal with beneficial as well as adverse effects.

The CEQ guidelines state that the 102 statement of a particular project or pending legislation should be made "as early as possible" and definitely prior to agency decision. Alternative actions that would minimize the adverse impact of a program should be evaluated along with the long-term implications to "man, his physical and social surroundings, and to nature."[10] In a project with multiple agency involvement, the agency that is first involved will be the first to evaluate its environmental effects. This is usually a state agency that formulates or approves a proposal before sending it on for federal action. For example, state and local agencies initiate proposals for construction of sewage treatment plants and recommend the proposals to EPA for funding. If state law requires an environmental analysis, the appropriate state or local agency will usually complete the analysis before referring the proposal to EPA.

The sponsoring agency uses all comments to modify its plans (where deemed necessary) and to prepare a final statement.[11] Where state or regional review of a proposed action is necessary, copies of the draft statement are sent either to clearinghouses established under the A-95 Review Process (discussed in the next section) or directly to state or local agencies having responsibility to develop and enforce environmental standards.[12]

The CEQ outlines the following distribution of environmental impact statements: ten copies of draft statements, when prepared, are sent to the CEQ; ten copies of all comments made on the final impact statement likewise are sent to the CEQ; and ten copies of the final 102 statement go to CEQ including all comments from federal, state, and local agencies, private organizations, and individuals. The CEQ guidelines recommend that the draft statement should be submitted to the CEQ "early enough in the agency review process to permit meaningful consideration"[13] of the possible environmental impacts.

The guidelines also propose that no administrative action shall be taken on a project sooner than 90 days after a draft statement has been circulated for comment, submitted to the Council, and, "except where advance public disclosure will result in significantly increased costs of procurement to the Government, made available to the public."[14] Neither should action be taken before 45 days after the final text of a statement has been made available to the CEQ and to the public. In instances where the time periods cannot be observed, the agency proposing action should consult with the Council.[15]

Problems with the 102 Process

Although the 102 process has necessitated a rethinking of the manner in which a federally funded project is approached and implemented, there are problems with the process that hinder its effectiveness. Many of these deficiencies result from the relatively short time in which NEPA has been in existence, from uncertainties and inconsistencies in its interpretation, and from varying degrees of willingness among the affected agencies to comply with the Act. For instance, notification to the public concerning a project has been left largely to the discretion of the agency; often the public has been informed at a late stage in the consideration of a project. Because decisions are sometimes made at the city or county levels of government, it is important that public groups have access to agency comments and can participate in the evaluation of a project before major decisions are made.[16] In the cases of a local sewer project or the location of a highway, for instance, issues of growth and land use are of central importance. Decisions concerning projects such as these are often made by individuals or groups who exercise economic or political influence in the community. According to a federal aide involved in the operation of NEPA, developers influence the local agencies, "but the only people who know that are the local people you don't get comments from."[17]

The time at which comments regarding the 102 statement are made available to the public was initially unclear; neither the Act nor the original CEQ guidelines clarified the situation. The time element is a key factor relating to the effectiveness of the 102 statement; a statement completed in the earlier stages of decision making will have greater impact than one distributed in the later stages of project development. Since the statute requires only that the final statement be made available to the public under the Freedom of Information Act,[18] the question of the point in the review process at which this information will be released was open to the discretion of the various agencies. This poorly defined policy resulted in inconsistent procedures among agencies. The Department of Transportation, for example, developed a general policy of not releasing comments on 102 statements to the public piecemeal but rather as a package once they were all received.[19] The argument in favor of releasing comments as a unit is that the public should examine all views at one time and not over an extended period. But where a project has been under consideration for an extended period of time, it would seem that the public would have little impact upon the project were it to see the comments after considerable time, expense, and planning had been invested in it.

It seems clear that 102 statements would have a greater impact in the decision-making process if the completed statements were available at all organizational review levels of a proposal and at the earliest stages of decision making. The availability of a completed statement at all review levels would serve three main functions: Each level would have the opportunity to consider the environmental views of others before reaching a decision. Second, early availability would encourage decision makers to take environmental considerations into account when deciding upon the need for a particular project.

Finally, "because each stage of decision making may result in an action that could have a significant effect upon the environment, it may be necessary at each stage to update the statement."[20]

The first revision in the guidelines in 1971 was a new emphasis on "building environmental considerations into the planning process."[21] Where the interim guidelines had directed the agencies to assess environmental impact before taking major actions, the revision ordered them to do so "as early as possible, and in all cases prior to agency decision." The President had already stated this policy but the change in the guidelines both reiterated the President's policy and emphasized that environmental considerations were to be integrated into existing planning processes rather than merely written up in after-the-fact paperwork exercises. Since preexisting procedures determined all actions of the agencies except the production of environmental impact statements, the change in emphasis was an important one.[22]

The revised guidelines also directed that all environmental impact statements be submitted to the appropriate state, regional, and metropolitan clearinghouses under the procedures of OMB Circular A-95 rather than merely listed as being available in the Federal Register, as was the case earlier. As noted below, the A-95 coordinative device was designed to ensure awareness of federal activities on the part of affected state and local officials. The requirement that environmental statements go through these channels thus substantially increased the certainty that such officials were aware of them.

Another point of confusion arose from the original CEQ guidelines in regard to the "draft" environmental impact statement. The statute itself does not mention the draft statement; the CEQ developed the concept as a means of implementing the process outlined in Section 102(2)(C), which states that "prior to making any detailed statement, the responsible Federal official shall consult with and obtain the comments of any Federal agency which has jurisdiction . . . with respect to any environmental impact involved." The circulation of this initial statement is among agencies and groups having an interest in the applicant's project; there was no requirement that a public group have access to the statement at this point.

In an attempt to establish a standard procedure, the guidelines state that draft statements must be made public at the same time that they are circulated for comment to other federal agencies. The guidelines also require that the statement must be made public 90 days before administrative action is taken and that the comments of other agencies must be released to the public as they are received.[23]

Another ambiguity related to the timing of 102 statements concerns the interpretation of the phrase "major federal action" in the statute that calls for the preparation of statements. Various state highway departments, for instance, have held that "major federal action" applies to the location of a highway, an interpretation that has often been used in the past. Highway opponents, on the other hand, have argued that "major federal action" relates to federal approval of any aspect of the project until construction begins. The question of when an impact statement is necessary was raised in the case of Morningside-Lenox Park Association v. Volpe (F. Supp.—3 ERC 1327, N.D. Ga. 1971). The court ruled that a 102 statement would be required on any ongoing federal project on which "substantial actions" remained to be taken. As a result of this case, an impact statement was required on an interstate highway project in Atlanta for which planning had been completed and hearings held before January 1, 1970.[24]

The scope of evaluation contained in an environmental impact statement often varies, and greater emphasis has been placed upon the "primary" rather than the "secondary" effects of a project.[25] Essentially, primary effects are those resulting directly from the project, while secondary effects may not develop as an immediate result of the project. An impact statement may evaluate the primary effect of a highway project by examining the projected auto usage and resulting emission levels, but neglect such long-range secondary effects as future growth patterns, social implications, and the effect on the area in terms of aesthetic considerations. The Federal Highway Administration (FHWA), for example, has not prepared statements on programs that cover large areas (such as a state or a metropolitan region), arguing that impact statements prepared on a program basis would be so broad and contain so many generalities that they would be meaningless and that coordination with other agencies would be extremely difficult.[26]

An examination of the possible secondary effects of a project would consider the environmental interrelationships both in the vicinity of the project and over the larger geographical area that ultimately might be affected. A new highway may be an inducement for the development of industrial, commercial, residential, or recreational uses, each of which would have additional environmental impacts.[27]

A thorough consideration of primary and secondary effects clearly requires not only coordination and cooperation among agencies but personnel with expertise in varied fields. It is doubtful whether an agency sponsoring a project has the personnel with sufficiently varied backgrounds to evaluate these effects. The statute therefore encourages agencies in the process of preparing 102 statements to consult with other agencies and individuals who do possess the expertise needed to fully evaluate all possible impacts. To date, greater emphasis has been placed upon the primary rather than the secondary effects.

It seems clear, however, that there is already increasing pressure to examine secondary effects. A case in point is the requirement by EPA that the states have in their air quality implementation plans procedures for evaluating what are in essence the secondary effects of such "complex sources" as shopping centers, sport complexes, and amusement parks. By and large these effects would be automobile-generated air pollution.

Indeed, in an additional set of revisions to the guidelines proposed by the CEQ in May 1973, increased attention is given to secondary effects. The proposed revisions state:

> Secondary, as well as primary consequences for the en-
> vironment should be included in the analysis. Many major
> Federal actions, in particular those that involve the con-
> struction or licensing of intrastructure investments (e.g.,
> highways, airports, sewer systems, water resource proj-
> ects, etc.), stimulate or induce secondary effects in the
> form of associated investments and changed patterns of
> social and economic activities. Such secondary effects,
> through their impacts on existing community facilities
> and activities, may often be even more substantial than
> the primary effects of the original action itself. . . .
> Such population and growth impacts should be estimated
> if expected to be significant and an assessment made of
> the effect of any possible change in population patterns
> or growth upon the resource base, including land use,
> water and public services, of the area in question.[28]

The final revisions provide that an impact statement must discuss the relationship of the proposed action to land use plans, policies, and controls for the affected area and that if any proposed action would conflict with any provision of any federal, state, or local land use plan, the statement should describe the extent to which the agency has reconciled its proposed action with the plan, and should explain why the agency decided to proceed despite the conflict.[29]

While it is important that an agency examine the range of impacts a project may foster, it is equally important that agencies be able to discern those projects that require 102 statements. A detailed evaluation of every project would result in a massive amount of paper work, which could hinder the effectiveness of the review process. In order to facilitate a more comprehensive approach and to promote efficiency, agencies should examine the environmental impacts of complete programs rather than individual projects related to the program. Such an approach would necessitate cooperation among agencies but could result in a more effectively designed program containing fewer projects that have adverse impacts.[30]

The various inconsistencies among the different agencies' approaches to the 102 statement suggest that the value of the statement is clearly a function of the manner in which it is prepared. An objective consideration and evaluation of possible environmental impacts resulting from a project and an investigation of alternatives to the proposed action should be the heart of a 102 statement. These inputs into the statement, made before and during the period in which decisions concerning the project are being made, should not be composed, as has often been the case, at the end of the decision-making process simply to satisfy the requirements of NEPA. The consideration of alternatives has been a particularly weak point in most statements, partly because the implementation of alternatives might be the responsibility of other agencies. In any case, the proposed revisions call for a "rigorous exploration and objective evaluation of the environmental impacts of all reasonable alternative actions, particularly those that might avoid some or all of the adverse environmental effects."[31]

That the burden of proof rests heavily upon the agency sponsoring the project seems to be a mixed blessing. While the agency is now required by law to consider and evaluate environmental impacts, one can argue that the sponsoring agency might be less than objective and that this might result in situations where analyses may be manipulated to justify predetermined goals.

The interpretation of NEPA and Section 102(2)(C) in the judicial process is clearly of primary importance in determining the ultimate effectiveness of 102 statements. It has been argued that it may be necessary for the courts to move beyond insurance of the mechanical functioning of Section 102(2)(C) to a point where the agency actively considers and initiates review of 102 statements at various stages of project development.[32] If the courts were to interpret the merits of an administrative decision, this "would have the effect of forcing new substance into agency decision making or . . . of permitting environmentalists to challenge a decision successfully on grounds that it contradicts the thrust of the impact statement."[33] Traditionally, the court does not judge the merits of an administrative decision unless the plaintiff can show an "arbitrary or capricious" action, or one not supported by "substantial evidence." But it appears likely that the courts will bring NEPA to bear even more directly on the substance of agency decision making.[34] If this is the case, many new issues will need to be resolved. Several district and circuit court opinions have held that NEPA imposes substantive duties on agencies to make environmentally sound decisions. Although the latitude of agency discretion is still quite wide, the process of circumscribing it through legal interpretation seems to be continuing.

Information deficiencies have remained even though the quality of environmental impact statements has improved over time. The lack of before ("base line") and after data from previous projects sponsored by an agency greatly impedes the forecasting of impacts of projects under consideration. The lack of base line data for present projects threatens to perpetuate this problem. An example of this type of problem is the attempt to determine the impact on air quality of a new major highway in a suburban or rural area when the background readings for the major air pollutants are inadequate, if they exist at all.

Finally, it should be noted that an apparent premise of NEPA's environmental statement requirement was that it would result in better decisions from an environmental standpoint. Yet while such information would seem to be a prerequisite for better decisions, it obviously does not guarantee them. Indeed, both Richard N. L. Andrews and Robert Gillette, writing in 1972, argued that neither the federal agencies nor their respective oversight committees appeared to have significantly changed their criteria for decision making as a result of the new information gathered.[35]

THE A-95 REVIEW PROCESS

OMB Circular No. A-95 provides the structure for implementing sections of three Acts: Title IV of the Intergovernmental Cooperation Act of 1968, Section 204 of the Demonstration Cities and Metropolitan Development Policy Act of 1966, and Section 102(2)(C) of NEPA.[36] These sections share a similar goal—the coordination of federal programs and projects with those envisioned by state, regional, and local governmental agencies. Among other things, the A-95 Review Process provides the mechanism whereby state and local agencies authorized to "develop and enforce environmental quality standards"[37] may assess the environmental impact of a project for which an application for federal funding will be submitted. Although the A-95 process may be used to obtain state and local comment on the 102 statement itself, the actual A-95 reviews occur prior to application for funding, while the impact statement itself is prepared and submitted for review by the federal granting agency subsequent to the application.

Project Notification and Review System

The Project Notification and Review System (PNRS) of A-95 attempts to encourage coordination by providing a system whereby applicants for federal monetary assistance must notify both the state and regional or metropolitan clearinghouses of intent to apply for a grant. State, regional, and metropolitan comprehensive planning agencies are designated as clearinghouses; those on the state and regional level are designated by the governor, while a metropolitan clearinghouse is recognized as such by OMB. While Section 204 requires the establishment of metropolitan clearinghouses, governors are not required to designate state or regional clearinghouses under the A-95 process. Nevertheless, state clearinghouses have been established in every state as well as in the District of Columbia and Puerto Rico. A majority of states have designated regional clearinghouses.[38] A clearinghouse has thirty days to indicate an interest in a project and to arrange for consultation with the applicant. If the clearinghouse indicates no interest in the proposed project, the applicant needs no further consultation with the clearinghouse. Should the clearinghouse wish to confer with the applicant, a conference is arranged during which issues and possible conflicts are discussed. By the time the application is completed, conflicting issues will have been identified, and, if these issues have not been resolved, the clearinghouse's comments will accompany the application.[39] The primary purpose of clearinghouses is to aid applicants to develop the best possible project that does not conflict with plans or programs of other jurisdictions or agencies. The reviews are strictly advisory, although a negative review can be influential in determining the outcome of an application.[40]

PNRS provides for an input to 102 statements by state and local agencies authorized to develop environmental quality standards. It is the responsibility of clearinghouses to identify state or local environmental agencies, inform them of proposed projects that may have an impact upon the environment, and give them the opportunity to make appropriate comments. The clearinghouse itself may possess the expertise to comment upon the environmental impact, and it may assist the applicant in preparing impact data or it may undertake other action to facilitate input into the 102 statements.[41]

Direct Federal Development

Part II of Circular A-95 requires that federal agencies sponsoring the development of federal projects consult with state and local governments that might be affected by these projects. Concerning the preparation of 102 statements, agencies are required to seek the comments of state and local environmental agencies. The clearinghouses identify the agencies that may have an interest in the environmental impact of a project; thus, the clearinghouses are the channel through which the CEQ receives the required state and local comments on the environmental impacts of projects.[42]

State Plans

Certain federal assistance programs, such as those involving the development of land use for housing, industrial, governmental, or other purposes, or the development and conservation of natural resources, require the submission of state plans. Part III of Circular A-95 gives the governor the opportunity to review such plans and to relate development strategies among the various federally supported state programs to each other and to strategies developed through the state planning process.[43] The review should be part of an ongoing planning process and should relate this process to specific regional and local projects.[44]

Coordination of Planning in Multijurisdictional Areas

The primary purpose of Part IV of the Circular is to coordinate geographically and functionally all federally funded programs encompassing a regional area. Fulfilling this requirement necessitates bringing the boundaries of federally funded planning and development districts into conformity with each other and with state districts. Applicants for federal assistance for projects covering a multijurisdictional area must coordinate their planning with other related programs. Applicants are encouraged to identify related planning activities and point out what attempts at coordination are being established. Although this section does not specify techniques that can be used to further coordination and prevent overlapping and duplication of projects, such measures as joint staffing, research and data gathering, and utilization of common statistics and projections are recommended.[45]

Accomplishments and Shortcomings of A-95 Review

Perhaps the most significant accomplishment of the A-95 Review Process has been to provide a structure for increased comprehensive planning through a strengthened communications network between jurisdictions and various governmental levels.[46] A well-staffed clearinghouse has the potential of initiating an effective clearance system whereby various individuals and agencies in an area are alerted to potential federal action. The clearinghouses provide a forum for discussing a proposed project and enable the applicant to outline his proposal in a way that maximizes his objectives while taking into account other regional goals.[47]

When local officials and clearinghouse staffs are alert to the clearinghouse function, the process can be used to inform local government on the availability and potential of categorical programs. The procedure also provides the basis for supplying localities with technical assistance. In the past, a local government would be reluctant to request such assistance from the federal government because in doing so "it is likely to expose its weaknesses, therefore hurting its competitive position for federal funds."[48] The clearinghouses have a more neutral or supportive relationship with local government and often possess the expertise to assist localities with planning activities.

The A-95 process has also exhibited several general shortcomings. In attempting to evaluate an application on the basis of conformity with regional planning, most clearinghouses discover that regional plans do not exist. This situation makes it difficult to evaluate the impacts of plans or programs relating to a region. Furthermore, the quality and expertise of the clearinghouse staff varies. Some clearinghouses have been in existence for years and have secured strong local support and competent personnel while others do not have their own staffs and have been created only recently to implement A-95.[49] Another shortcoming of A-95 review concerns its acceptance by regional federal agencies. Many agencies have exhibited a lack of interest in the process, uncertainty with the procedure and its requirements, and, at times, a failure to respond to clearinghouse comments on applications.[50]

When the clearinghouse is also a Council of Government (COG), the A-95 process provides the COG with what is essentially its only authority. In attempting to coordinate and evaluate regional activities on the basis of regional planning goals, the COG clearinghouse often finds itself in an awkward position in relation to its member governments, from which it receives its legitimacy, and to the federal government. The member governments tend not to view the role of the clearinghouse as one of influencing regional policy but rather as one of coordination; they tend to think of the clearinghouse more as a "communications forum, and an insurance device for the continued flow of federal funds to local governments."[51] The federal government, on the other hand, encourages the COG to develop a regional planning perspective, although such planning generally does not exist.

Changes in budgetary policies under the Nixon Administration have had a significant effect upon both the clearinghouses and A-95 review. Categorical grant programs, along with the Department of Housing and Urban Development's 701 planning program, are the basis for the existence of the COG clearinghouses and A-95; uncertainty about the continuation of part of these funds places the future of both in some doubt. The curtailment of categorical grant programs essentially removes the sanctions for A-95 review, and the review process is central to the clearinghouses' existence. Although the impacts of the budgetary changes are uncertain, it is clear that federal resources in the form of categorical grants will be reduced. Not only will the restructuring of federal monetary resources and their availability restrict the A-95 process as it now exists but it also carries implications for the future role of clearinghouses and A-95 as steps toward rational comprehensive planning on a regional level.

Possibly because of this impact on the clearinghouses, the Office of Management and Budget published in the Federal Register of November 28, 1973, revisions in the A-95 guidelines. The new guidelines were effective January 1, 1974. There are four major changes (it is, however, too early to judge their full impact).[52]

1. In Part I, if a clearinghouse recommends against a program and the federal agency approves it, the federal agency must now explain its action to the clearinghouse in writing.

2. In Part III, provision is made to provide federal agencies with information about federally funded state programs and multisource programs. The multisource programs are those funded by two or more federal agencies, including the Environmental Protection Consolidated Program Grants.

3. In Part IV, the original guidelines said that area planning should be coordinated with the comprehensive planning agencies. The revision requires the coordination and sets up a procedure for such coordination.

4. The list of programs affected by the revision has been expanded from 100 to 146.

NEPA, A-95 Review, and Air Quality

Richard N. L. Andrews has concluded that further progress in the achievement of NEPA's purposes will probably require four elements: (1) preservation of the broadened legal recourse secured by NEPA, in order to guarantee administrative accountability to all public groups affected by a project; (2) development of a more sophisticated evaluation framework for impacts and their alternatives; (3) refinement of the means of identifying, comparing, and trading off conflicting objectives; and (4) development of more effective ways for incorporating the preference of all persons affected by administrative actions into the process of planning and project selection.[53]

It is important to note these elements because the environmental impact statement is not a single action-forcing mechanism, but rather a dual process: the procedure of interagency review and comment, and the procedure of making the statement and the comments available for direct public review, comment, and legal action. It is often argued that interagency coordination has not been very effective in bringing about administrative changes that would encourage the consideration of environmental values rather than nonfederal pressures (law suits). The increased availability of judicial review as a resource, for example, has lent new effectiveness to the participation of nonfederal individuals and groups whose environmental values are at odds with those traditionally reflected in the agencies' policies.

Still, interagency review has a latent potential which has not been fully utilized. A variety of approaches have been suggested; these include general rule making, umbrella program statements, overview statements, and "lead agency" statements. Although NEPA requires an agency to balance all competing factors and to consider all reasonable alternatives, it does not dictate that this be done entirely anew in each decision, without the assistance of general rules and past experience. Decision makers are permitted to cut their more complicated decisions down to manageable size. Advance determination of program policy through rule making can implement NEPA and at the same time avoid repetitious reexamination of basic principles in the context of each individual action. Since many federal agency programs involve a multiplicity of individual actions, such as grants or permits, administered under relatively uniform policies, NEPA's requirements can often best be implemented by writing environmental policies into the general rules governing a program.

Indeed, the final CEQ guidelines released August 1, 1973, contain stricter requirements for agency preparation of impact statements concerning an entire program rather than only individual actions. The guidelines call on agencies to give special attention to determining which action would most appropriately serve as the subject of the statement and note that in many cases broad program statements will be required to assess the environmental effects of a number of individual actions or to assess environmental impacts that are associated with a series of agency actions.[54]

Thus in the future more attention will be given to the preparation of a single statement on a program as a whole than to the filing of separate environmental impact statements on individual actions. An umbrella program environmental impact statement affords an occasion for a more comprehensive look at effects and alternatives than is practicable in a statement on an individual action. The strongest feature of such a program is that it ensures the consideration of cumulative impacts likely to be slighted in a case-by-case analysis.

An overview statement, prepared jointly by a number of agencies, is appropriate for new policy initiatives at an interagency level. When shaping the policy on a major issue with environmental implications, it is necessary to explore a broad range of alternative actions that fall outside the jurisdiction of any one agency; in such a case an overview statement can theoretically reveal deficiencies early enough so that the program can be modified or abandoned.

"Lead agency" statements are potentially the most significant with regard to the relationship of air quality to land use planning. Under this approach, a lead agency is selected and assigned the responsibility for preparing a statement prior to implementing a program or policy. This approach is most appropriate when the action is a single project in which multiple agencies are involved by virtue of their separate legal authorities. Each agency's decision may relate to only a part of the project, but the impact statement would have to consider the cumulative impact. The CEQ guidelines provide that the lead agency is the federal agency that has primary authority for committing the federal government to a course of action. Three major factors are involved in the selection of the lead agency: (1) which agency became involved in the project first, (2) which has the heaviest involvement, and (3) which is the most expert with respect to the project's environmental effects.

EPA's responsibilities are clearly stated in Section 309 of the Clean Air Act:

> (a) The Administrator shall review and comment in writing on the environmental impact of any matter relating to duties and responsibilities granted pursuant to this Act or other provisions of the authority of the Administrator, contained in any (1) legislation proposed by any Federal department or agency, (2) newly authorized Federal projects for construction and any major Federal agency action other than a project for construction to which section 102(2)(C) of Public Law 91-190 applies, and (3) proposed regulations published by any department or agency of the Federal Government. Such written comment shall be made public at the conclusion of any such review.
>
> (b) In the event the Administrator determines that any such legislation, action, or regulation is unsatisfactory from the standpoint of public health or welfare or environmental quality, he shall publish his determination and the matter shall be referred to the Council on Environmental Quality.[55]

It is important to note that in almost all projects having an air pollution potential, EPA is not the lead agency since it is not the sponsoring one. It is therefore incumbent on EPA to develop clear, concise guidelines for project evaluations relating to air quality, since in most cases EPA's review will be late in the process and the initial evaluation will be done by other agencies. The guidelines should suggest that the statement describe the environmental properties of the area to be affected by the project before changes occur and that it indicate anticipated short-range and long-range primary and secondary effects. The statement should consider vegetation, topography, meteorological conditions, and present and future land use. Regarding the dispersion of pollutants, the statement should identify each pollutant, the vectors of transport, the quantities dispersed, and the areas to which they will be dispersed. The agency preparing the impact statement should consult with state or regional air pollution control agencies to determine whether the proposed action will be in conformance with air pollution control regulations and the state implementation plan and whether the action will result in the emission of a hazardous pollutant as defined in the Clean Air Act, Section 112.

Due to limitations mentioned earlier, input into air quality decision making through A-95 appears to be rather slight at this time; but, although the 102 statement often lacks the weight and consistency of evaluation that those concerned with environmental quality would prefer, it is a concept which, through sincere and objective application, could produce significant impact.

In evaluating the A-95 process as a means of introducing air quality considerations into urban planning, it is well to bear in mind that the thrust of Circular A-95 is toward coordination among various levels of government; its primary goal is the avoidance of conflicting projects and programs. A prerequisite for coordination is the establishment of channels through which contact and communication can take place; the A-95 process provides these channels. This system provides an opportunity for the development of improved projects and programs and for increased efficiency through planning. The systematic communication between the federal government and state and local governments involved in related planning and development activities should result in more effective and economical development. With regard to environmental quality, Circular A-95, particularly Parts I and II, essentially provides the structure whereby state, regional, and local comments may be attached to an environmental impact statement; the preparation of the statement itself is the responsibility of the applicant.

Although the A-95 process has established a structure through which inputs regarding air quality may be introduced into the decision-making process, certain limitations reduce its effectiveness for this purpose. Since only federally funded projects may be reviewed under A-95, projects not receiving federal assistance, although possibly having a very significant impact upon air quality, are exempt from review. An agency's ability to comment upon the air quality impact of a project also varies. An adverse impact is most severe in the immediate vicinity of the pollution source, but the city or regional planning agency charged with reviewing a project often does not possess the expertise to evaluate its impact upon air quality. Perhaps the most fundamental reason why concern with water quality, sewage treatment facilities, and land use predominates over air quality considerations is that planners traditionally concerned themselves with these interests and developed plans accordingly. Few planning agencies possess a fully developed air resources plan or the data and personnel necessary to evaluate air quality. As noted earlier, few regional agencies even have a detailed comprehensive land use plan.

Finally, most agencies have limited procedures for obtaining environmental expertise available in other agencies. A systematic approach is needed to ensure that such expertise is identified and utilized to the fullest extent possible. One approach might be for the agency to outline those aspects of its activities for which outside evaluation should be sought. The agency could then select the federal, state, or local agency that could best furnish the needed knowledge and make arrangements for obtaining it. As a final consideration, an agency should develop procedures to ensure that agencies possessing expertise review and comment on relevant impact statements.

THE PERMIT SYSTEM

The permit system is a technique for implementing that part of air pollution regulations which applies to point source emissions. In issuing permits to construct and certificates to operate, the department or agency in charge of enforcing air pollution regulations considers such items as design, operation, and maintenance of equipment used in controlling point source emissions. In general, the permit system provides for agency review of plans for construction, modification, or operation of source equipment or processes that have the potential of emitting pollutants. Before commencing such construction, modification, or operation the industry (or owner of the equipment) must apply for a permit. The applicant usually provides information necessary to evaluate the estimated emissions from the source. Permits to construct, install, and operate this equipment will usually be issued if the reviewing agency determines that emissions will conform to applicable standards.

The registration system is sometimes considered as an alternative to the permit system and requires less administrative capability. Under the registration system, those planning to build a facility emitting air pollutants are required to submit to a designated body information relating to the location of the proposed operation, a general description of its functioning, and the nature of the expected emissions. The body to which the plan is submitted does not, as under the permit system, approve or disapprove the operation; reliance is placed upon the applicant for meeting emission requirements.[56] Under the requirements of the Clean Air Act the registration system has been deemphasized in favor of the permit system.

In actual practice the permit system operates as follows: An applicant must apply for a construction permit before work begins on the installation. After the permit is issued an inspector visits the construction site to check the equipment against the submitted plans; if performance standards must be met, source testing will be done before the permit to operate is issued. In the event that inspection reveals noncompliance with the plans or violation of an air pollution ordinance, notice is given to the operator of the deficient equipment as well as a designated time by which to correct the problem. Reinspection is then made and action taken according to the policy of the specific agency.[57]

The complexity of applications for construction permits varies according to the size of the proposed installation. Plans submitted to an agency are usually drawings showing the general arrangement of the operation and should include control devices. For industrial process equipment, stack heights and the distance to the nearest receptors are considered useful for evaluation purposes. The plan should include "sufficient data" to allow the reviewing agency to evaluate the equipment against local ordinance criteria.[58] The interpretation of "sufficient data" has traditionally been left to the local agency.

An effective permit system obviously requires that the air pollution control agency possess the necessary expertise to determine from plans and specifications whether a proposed installation will meet emissions limitations.[59] The conventional opinion has been that in areas with a population of fewer than 100,000 the plan examination process could be performed in conjunction with other governmental reviews; in larger urban areas, the review should be performed to a greater extent by an air pollution control engineer. "Cooperation and coordination" of other departmental units that may be affected by the air pollution impact of the proposed construction has been considered essential to the system. All concerned agencies should have reviewed the project before the permit is granted.[60]

The Los Angeles Permit System

In 1947 the California legislature enacted a bill authorizing counties to establish air pollution control districts. These districts were given the power to administer a permit system requiring a permit to construct and a permit to operate. The Los Angeles County Air Pollution Control District (APCD) was activated in October 1947. The rules for the Los Angeles County program prescribe that an Authority to Construct be obtained before "construction, alteration, or replacement of any equipment capable of emitting or controlling air contaminants."[61] The Permit to Operate must be obtained before operation of the equipment begins. Not all equipment emitting pollutants falls under permit system review; some, notably vehicles,

116

are exempt by state law, while other equipment is exempted by the District. However, equipment not included under the permit system must still be operated in compliance with emission standards.

The system is administered by engineers who are responsible for evaluating permit applications, determining whether the proposed installation will be in compliance with air pollution laws, and approving or denying permits. Instead of requiring a separate application and permit for each individual equipment item, the APCD has developed a "permit unit" concept which groups items operating as a functional unit into one application and one permit.

The APCD has adopted a series of rules or "prohibitions" that provide emission standards for equipment, specify certain equipment and fuels for various operations, and prohibit specific operations. Some of these rules limit and define darkness and opacity for a visible emission plume; limit the discharge of particulates, sulfur compounds, and combustion contaminants; specify control for petroleum products storage tanks; and prohibit "public nuisances," open fires, and single chamber incinerators.

The operation permit is granted only when the emissions from installations have been controlled to the standards established by law and it remains valid only as long as its conditions are met. The District asserts that the system enables it to inventory emissions and their sources and to determine the effect of new programs and proposed installations upon air quality. By requiring approval to construct before work is begun, the District believes it saves industry the expense of installing equipment and then having to replace inadequate control equipment.[62]

The APCD has stated that an inventory of pollutants emitting from stationary sources indicated that the permit system has prevented 5,560 tons of pollutants from entering the air each day. The permit system alone, according to the District, has been responsible for achieving control of more than 78 percent of all emissions from stationary sources.[63]

The Permit System as a Locational Control Technique

In addition to meeting the formal objective of compliance with the regulations of the air pollution control agency, the permit system aids in the development and maintenance of an inventory which provides data on industries, equipment, and processes that emit air pollutants in a given jurisdiction. Such emission data usually includes the fuel usage by specification and quantity, estimated emission rates, actual emission rates from stack tests, location of equipment, and the period of time in which the equipment is in operation. Since the evaluation of an application for a permit is normally based on engineering calculations by the air pollution control officer, this information is of considerable utility.

There is evidence, however, of a trend towards introducing land use planning considerations into the decision along with the engineering calculations. In addition to requiring that a facility or equipment meet certain specified emission rates, it is becoming the rule that the permit will be issued only if the installation and operation of the equipment will not prevent the attainment or maintenance of applicable air quality standards.[64] This changing interpretation of the use of the permit system is extremely significant. If the permit required only that applicable emission standards be met, sources could continue to concentrate in a certain location and, even though each source would emit relatively few pollutants, the sheer number of point sources concentrated at one place would exceed the assimilative capacity of the ambient air, thereby violating the air quality standards. The existence of such "hot spots" is fairly common, since industries often concentrate to take advantage of available low-cost transportation (water, rail, or highway), water supply, and other factors.

With a new locational constraint in operation, it is obvious that the permit system will influence industrial location. Most likely, the long-range impact of the system will be to spread point sources over a region—at least more so than in the past—to increase the assimilative capacity of the air. Thus, the system becomes a land use planning tool in addition to a pro forma engineering calculation. Although it is often stated that the air pollution control program should "interface with zoning and planning, particularly in the areas of meteorology, emissions inventory, air monitoring, air pollution modeling, the permit system and enforcement,"[65] this interaction is not operating effectively at present.[66] It is expected, however, that over the next few years the permit system can join the NEPA and A-95 review process as a potentially effective means of relating land use planning to air quality management.

COMPLEX SOURCES

In April 1973 EPA proposed revised regulations for the preparation, adoption, and submission of state implementation plans pursuant to the Clean Air Act Amendments of 1970; the revised regulations would require increased consideration of air quality in the design and location of new stationary sources. The original guidelines for the preparation of state implementation plans, discussed earlier, required states to establish procedures for reviewing new stationary sources of air pollution to determine if the construction of such a source would inhibit the state from achieving or maintaining the national ambient air quality standards specified under the 1970 Act. A stationary source of air pollution has traditionally been defined as one that emits its own pollutants and directly influences air quality and thus is regulated under the permit system. However, the EPA proposal extended this definition to include facilities that "may affect air quality by indirect means, primarily by means of the mobile source activity associated with them."[67] Such "complex sources" would include airports, shopping centers, amusement parks, highways, sports complexes, and other facilities that may have an indirect impact on achieving and maintaining the national ambient air quality standards. The proposal would thus necessitate greater consideration of design and locational factors that might affect air quality. Each state would also be required to develop legally enforceable procedures for reviewing the location and design of these complex sources before construction is initiated and for preventing construction if the facility "cannot be made compatible with air quality requirements."[68]

The final regulations, released in June 1973,[69] were essentially unchanged except that a requirement was added for the identification of such areas as counties, urbanized areas, and standard metropolitan statistical areas with a potential for exceeding national air quality standards during the next 10 years. Identification of these areas was to be completed by May 1974. By August 1975, states must submit to EPA an analysis of projected growth impacts on air quality for each potential problem area. Where necessary, the states must submit a plan describing measures that will be taken to insure the maintenance of the national air quality standards for 10 years. The analysis will have to deal with all the significant air quality implications of growth and development, including not only the increased air pollution arising directly from new commercial, industrial, and residential development but also that arising from increases in demand for electricity and heat, motor vehicle traffic, and production of solid waste.

The complex source—or more accurately, "indirect source"—regulations are a logical extension of the changing view on the use of the permit system. In this case, the regulations are aimed primarily at carbon monoxide emissions. Carbon monoxide, a fairly stable pollutant, does not contribute significantly to photochemical reactions but clearly achieves high concentrations around the indirect sources. Although the states have not promulgated their regulations as of this writing, one can conclude that they will have to work out an accommodation with other required federal reviews. For example, Section 102(C) of the National Environmental Policy Act, discussed earlier, and Section 109(j) of the Federal-Aid Highway Act impose similar requirements with respect to certain types of facilities, notably highways and airports. To avoid jurisdictional conflicts and duplication of data gathering and analysis, the states will have to work out a well-defined process for integrating reviews, and this will inevitably lead them closer to a comprehensive state planning mechanism.

NOTES

1. National Environmental Policy Act, 42 U.S.C. Sec. 202 (1969).

2. Office of Management and Budget Circular No. A-95 (revised), hereinafter cited as OMB Circular No. A-95.

3. National Environmental Policy Act, 42 U.S.C. Sec. 102(2)(c).

4. Robert Gillette, "National Environmental Policy Act: How Well Is It Working?" 176 Science 146 (April 14, 1972), hereinafter cited as Gillette.

5. "Courts Say NEPA is a Law for All People," 6 Fed. Report 210 (No. 3 March 1972). Although NEPA created a judicially cognizable interest in environmental matters that is capable of being enforced by the suit of private citizens, that interest often is severely curtailed if these public interest representatives are required to develop the burden of proof. The private citizen often enters late in the decision-making process and the applicant for Federal approval usually has the advantage of expertise and financial resources which may be unavailable to the citizen. In regard to the concept of public interest, therefore, 102 statements require Federal agencies to fulfill "their responsibility of actively protecting those interests." See Eva H. Hanks and John L. Hanks, "An Environmental Bill of Rights: The Citizen Suit and the National Environmental Policy Act of 1969," in Environment Law Review 1971 189-90 (H. Floyd Sherrod ed. 1971).

6. "NEPA Challenges the Nation's Plans and Priorities," The Conservation Foundation Letter 5 (Rice Odell ed. May 1972).

7. Gillette, 148.

8. Lee M. Talbot, "Environmental Impact Statements at the Federal Level," in Proceedings of the Symposium on Environmental Assessment of Resources Development 12 (June 1, 1971).

9. 36 Fed. Reg. 7724 (1971).

10. 36 Fed. Reg. 7724 (1971).

11. Id.

12. Council on Environmental Quality, Environmental Impact Statements, 1 102 Monitor 4 (No. 10 November 1971). A clearinghouse is a planning agency capable of identifying the relationship of a federal project to the plans of state or local governments. There are three types of designated clearinghouses: state, regional and metropolitan. The state and regional clearinghouses are designated by the state governor; a metropolitan clearinghouse is recognized as such by the

Office of Management and Budget for the purposes of implementing Section 204 of the Demonstration Cities and Metropolitan Development Act of 1966.

13. 36 Fed. Reg. 7726 (1971).

14. Id.

15. 38 Fed. Reg. 10856 (1973).

16. Supra note 6, at 5-7.

17. Id. at 7.

18. Administration of the National Environmental Policy Act, Hearings Before the Subcommittee on Fisheries and Wildlife Conservation of the Committee on Merchant Marine and Fisheries 20 (No. 91-41 December 1970).

19. Id. at 142.

20. "Improvements Needed in Federal Efforts to Implement the National Environmental Policy Act of 1969," Report to the Subcommittee on Fisheries and Wildlife Conservation of the Committee on Merchant Marine and Fisheries 19 (May 1972).

21. 36 Fed. Reg. 7724 (1971).

22. Richard N. L. Andrews, Environmental Policy and Administrative Change: The National Environmental Policy Act of 1969, 1970-1971 129 (dissertation U. of N.C. 1972), hereinafter cited as Andrews.

23. 38 Fed. Reg. 10856 (1973).

24. Angus Macbeth and Peter W. Sly, "Federal-Aid Highways: Public Participation in the Administrative Stages," 1 Natural Resources Defense Council Newsletter 13 (No. 3 1971).

25. Supra note 6, at 7-8.

26. Supra note 20, 23.

27. United States Environmental Protection Agency, Guidelines for Preparation of Environmental Statements for Reviewing and Commenting on Environmental Statements Prepared by Other Federal Agencies 17-18 (rev. ed. 1973).

28. 38 Fed. Reg. 10856 (1973).

29. 38 Fed. Reg. 20549 (1973).

30. Supra note 6, at 8.

31. 38 Fed. Reg. 10856 (1973).

32. Supra note 6, at 4-5.

33. Id. at 4. In a case involving the Calvert Cliffs nuclear plant in Maryland, the court stated that "purely mechanical compliance" with NEPA is not adequate, but there must be "full good faith consideration of the environment." See Calvert Cliffs Coordinating v. Atomic Energy Commission, 449 F. 2d 1109, D.C. Cir. (1971).

34. See Frederick R. Anderson, NEPA in the Courts: A Legal Analysis of the National Environmental Policy Act (1973).

35. Andrews, 461; Gillette, 147.

36. Intergovernmental Cooperation Act, 40 U.S.C. Sec. 531-35, 42 U.S.C. Sec. 4201, 4211-14, 4221-25, 4231-33, 4241-44 (1968). Demonstration Cities and Metropolitan Development Act, 42 U.S.C. Sec. 3301 (1966). National Environmental Policy Act, 42 U.S.C. Sec. 4321 (1969).

37. "The Impact of Environmental Impacts Statements," 38 Planning ASPO Newsletter 89 (June 5, 1972). See also, OMB Circular No. A-95.

38. William K. Brussat, "A-95: Evaluating the Process of Review," Planning 1971 (1971), at 58 hereinafter cited as Brussat.

39. OMB Circular No. A-95 2-3.

40. Brussat, 59.

41. OMB Circular No. A-95 6-7.

42. Id. at 8-9.

43. Id. at 10.

44. Vincent T. Smith, "The Intergovernmental Cooperation Act of 1968: Opportunity for State Government," Planning 1971, 63 (1971).

45. OMB Circular No. A-95 12.

46. Brussat, 59.

47. Melvin B. Mogulof, "Regional Planning, Clearance, and Evaluation: A Look at the A-95 Process," 37 J. Amer. Inst. of Planners 420 (No. 6 November 1971), hereinafter cited as Mogulof.

48. Id.

49. Brussat, 59.

50. Mogulof, 421.

51. Id. at 419.

52. 38 Fed. Reg. 32873 (1973).

53. Andrews, 463.

54. 38 Fed. Reg. 20549 (1973).

55. Clean Air Act, 42 U.S.C. Sec. 1857 et seq. (1970).

56. Jean J. Schueneman, "Air Pollution Control Administration," in Air Pollution 779 (III 2d. ed. Arthur C. Stern ed. 1968), hereinafter cited as Schueneman.

57. Charles W. Gruber, "Source Inspection, Registration, and Approval," in Air Pollution 579-80 (II 2d ed. Arthur C. Stern ed. 1968), hereinafter cited as Gruber.

58. Gruber, 592.

59. Schueneman, 778.

60. Gruber, 592-4.

61. Robert G. Lunche et al., "Administration of a Permit System," 19 J. Air Pollution Control Ass'n 10 (January 1969).

62. Id. at 9-14.

63. Id. at 14.

64. Pacific Environmental Services, "Guide to Engineering Permit Processing" 4.1 (prepared for EPA, Office of Air Programs

1972). For requirements under the Clean Air Act, see Chapter 2 and 37 Fed. Reg. 10842 (1972); 37 Fed. Reg. 15082 (1972).

65. Pacific Environmental Services, at 4.14.

66. See Chapter 9 for a discussion of a potentially effective program.

67. 38 Fed. Reg. 9599 (1973).

68. Id.

69. 38 Fed. Reg. 15834 (1973).

5

BUFFER ZONES AS
A CONTROL OVER
AIR POLLUTION:
AN APPLICATION OF
THE EMINENT DOMAIN
AND ZONING POWERS

The utility of buffer zones to minimize the adverse impacts of one type of land use upon another depends to a great extent upon the fact that this impact is reduced as the distance from the source increases. The relationship between the source, the transfer medium (the atmosphere), and the receptor is a complex one. Consideration must be given to such variables as the nature of the "negative externality"—its intensity, frequency, and duration—physical and meteorological properties of the location, and relationships between differing externalities generated from the same source. The quantitative information available is inadequate for the formulation of meaningful policy guidelines, and vague generalizations and inconsistencies are common in the literature. In this chapter we discuss the "state of the art" of reducing the impact of air pollution and noise through the use of buffer zones and the legal tools available to accomplish this end. Distance is the primary consideration, although attention is also given to the physical properties of trees and vegetation as "absorption devices" and to the tradeoffs one might make between distance and the erection of physical barriers. A distinction must also be made between the use of a buffer zone to minimize the impact from point sources and from line sources. A point source is stationary while a line source refers to a corridor containing mobile emitters (a highway, for example). Four major components of the environment are examined: air pollution, microclimate, water quantity and quality, and noise.

Particular attention is given to the use of buffers along highways since the automobile is such a pervasive polluter in the urban environment. The internal combustion engine of the automobile produces fuel consumption by-products (carbon monoxide, hydrocarbons, and oxides of nitrogen) which, when emitted into the atmosphere through the automobile's exhaust system, become a major source of degradation of air quality. The automobile's adverse environmental impact is particularly acute alongside heavily traveled major highways. However, this adverse impact can be made less severe if the highway is lined on each side with a buffer zone that would separate emitters from receptors. These zones can act to counter the effect of automobile emissions in a number of ways. First, a zone of open space in public ownership necessarily precludes any private development of lands immediately adjacent to the highway. The significance of keeping these adjacent areas free from development is threefold: (1) If there are no buildings lining the highway, the automobile's pollutive emissions will disperse more rapidly and effectively, thus reducing the pollution concentration in the immediate highway area. When a highway is built among buildings, especially tall ones, this dilution of pollutants is rendered more difficult.[1] Buildings surrounding a highway create a canyon effect which cuts down the speed of the surface wind and prevents an updraft of air movement, thus keeping the pollutants from dispersing rapidly. By using buffer zones to keep the area adjacent to the highway open, this canyon effect is prevented. (2) The restriction of development along the highway corridor will also act to separate the polluting automobiles from any receptors that are, or would be, located in the area immediately adjoining the site of a present or proposed highway. If, for example, there are no residences or businesses in areas contiguous to highways, few or no people will be exposed to the full impact of the pollutive emissions. (3) The vegetation in the buffer zones has properties that help reduce the impact of automobile emissions. As noted in more detail below, vegetation absorbs moisture from the air and helps maintain a cooler surface temperature than is found in barren areas. By creating this cool, humid surface, vegetation helps certain types of pollutants to settle out of the air. An associated characteristic is that trees increase local turbulence, thereby increasing the dispersion of vehicular emissions.[2]

Proposals for the use of buffer zones to minimize the adverse impact of pollutants upon a receptor require consideration of two properties of the buffer itself—its size and the type of vegetation in the buffer zone. In order to estimate the distance needed between a source and the receptor, one must determine the dispersion characteristics of a particular pollutant. Although research findings differ concerning the distance that should be allowed for pollutant dispersion, the state of the art seems to be more advanced in regard to optimum buffer size than in regard to the role of vegetation in reducing pollutant concentration.

DISPERSION AND VEGETATION

Pollutants may be classified as gases or aerosols (more commonly termed particulates). The dispersion characteristics of gases and aerosols are important in evaluating the use of a particular type of buffer to minimize the impacts of a specific air pollution situation. Although there are numerous substances belonging to the general classification of aerosols and gases, we will discuss general dispersion characteristics of aerosols and the basic dispersion qualities of a particular gas, carbon monoxide.

Dispersion Characteristics of Aerosols

Aerosols range in size from approximately 1/16,660 to 1,000 micrograms per cubic meter.[3] The transport of aerosols through the atmosphere is a function of time aloft and weather conditions and is also dependent upon the microclimate of a particular area. Larger particles settle quickly because of their high rate of sedimentation; smaller particles have a great degree of mobility and may become electrically charged, often resulting in their attachment to other particles.[4] The principal means by which particles are removed from the atmosphere is by gravitational settling, which prevents the larger particulate matter, such as fly ash and soil, from traveling far from their sources. Smaller matter may be removed from the air by striking obstacles such as buildings and trees. Precipitation is effective in removing particles smaller than two micrograms in diameter; some matter as large as ten micrograms may be kept airborne by turbulence for extended periods of time.[5] Wind direction and velocity are therefore primary factors to be considered in determining the transport and dispersion of particulate matter. The actual direction of transport is determined by large-scale circulation in the atmosphere as well as by the local influence of breezes, the surface features of a specific area, heat sources (such as the higher temperatures observed over urban areas), and air masses of differing densities.[6]

Numerous studies have found that particulate dispersion is directly related to the distance between source and receptor. It is difficult, however, to establish a specific distance as a guideline for buffer width, since dispersion depends upon factors other than distance alone. A study by A. L. Page et al. examined lead concentrations in 27 varieties of vegetation along highways. They found a direct relation between lead content in the plants and distance from the roadway, although the relationship was most significant at distances less than 150 meters from the highway. Lead content was also found to be influenced by prevailing winds.[7]

Peter C. Rydell and Gretchen Schwarz cite a Russian study which concludes that "the concentration of pollution decreased by about half over 500 meters of open space, and by two-thirds to five-sixths over 500 meters of planted land."[8] I. A. Singer also notes a 75 percent reduction in dust particle count over a strip of open space 600 feet wide.[9]

Other studies have attempted to estimate the buffer zone size necessary to minimize pollutant impact. Frank L. Cross determined the size requirements for a buffer zone to protect citrus groves from fluoride emitted from a phosphate plant gypsum pond. Based upon a standard where 75 parts per million of fluoride in citrus leaves was considered to be evidence of pollution, a half-mile buffer strip was established around the pond to alleviate the fluoride effect.[10] In another case, Cross defined a zone for suspended particulates emitted from a dolomite processing plant, and concluded that to reduce the adverse impact of settling particles upon nearby residents, a buffer of 1,500-feet radius around the plant site would be required.[11] A third study by Cross investigated the buffer width needed to restrict ambient air particulate concentrations from a hot-mix asphalt plant to 100 micrograms per cubic meter. Results indicated that a buffer zone of one-mile radius reduced particulate concentration to the determined level.[12]

General Dispersion Characteristics of Carbon Monoxide:
A Case Study

A study by the General Electric Company (GE) for the New York City Department of Air Resources measured traffic-generated air pollutant concentration and dispersion patterns for five major roadway configurations.[13] In attempting to determine the behavior of carbon monoxide, hydrocarbons, and particulates along highways, GE contributed data that may prove useful in evaluating the type of buffer most effective for minimizing pollutant impact from a particular highway configuration. The study monitored six variables: carbon monoxide, hydrocarbons, particulates, wind speed, wind azimuth and elevation angles, and the sigmas of wind azimuth and elevation. Sites were divided into five categories based upon roadway design: open cut, tunnels, cantilever covered, open, and intermittently covered.

Summarizing the findings regarding carbon monoxide, GE found that the gas exhibits the expected exponential decay with distance, providing that the path of the pollutant is not obstructed. Vehicle-induced turbulence also affects the dispersion of carbon monoxide along a highway. A negative linear relationship exists between the concentration at the automobile exhaust level and traffic speed. Thus, higher average traffic velocities result in lower carbon monoxide concentrations due to increased vehicle operating efficiency and increased turbulence.[14] While the decay of the concentration with distance from the vehicular source has been substantiated by measurement, the role of traffic-generated turbulence in providing a diffusive mechanism for the gas is not clear and quantitative expression of this phenomenon is in the formative stages.[15] Another factor influencing the dispersion of carbon monoxide is the "canyon effect" created by buildings along a street. The width and height of the buildings have been shown to affect the wind and pattern velocity within the canyon. Density and design characteristics of buildings also influence dispersion of the gas irrespective of wind velocity.[16]

Results of the carbon monoxide horizontal profiles from the GE study indicate peak values at impermeable walls because the pollutant accumulates at these points. In an open-cut roadway, for instance, maximum concentration occurs at the two walls and a minimum was observed at the center of the highway.[17] The magnitudes of the carbon monoxide concentration are directly related to traffic volume on each side of the highway.[18] The horizontal profile at a site with a wall on one side of the road and the other side open to ventilation indicates maximum concentration at the wall.[19] At a site open to ventilation on both sides, maximum concentration occurs at the middle of the road and decays in both directions across the roadway.[20]

Measurement of the relationship between indoor and outdoor concentrations of carbon monoxide at five sites revealed that the concentrations closely correlated with each other. The outdoor levels tended to be higher, but the difference did not usually exceed four parts per million. In the case of air-tight structures, weekend indoor levels were higher than outdoor levels due to increased cooking and other household activities.[21]

Vegetation as a Pollutant Absorption Device

The literature concerning the effectiveness of vegetation in reducing pollutant levels is sparse; results are inconclusive and in some respects conflicting. Generalizations about the usefulness of vegetation in absorbing pollutants are difficult to formulate because of the complexity of interrelated variables, such as type of vegetation and density required, pollutant type and concentration, and seasonal variations. Various studies indicate that trees remove certain aerosol and gaseous pollutants from the atmosphere and that the leaves are probably the most effective means of removal. Coniferous species would therefore seem to be most effective in improving air quality. Kohout and

Materna experimented with the uptake of sulfur dioxide by plants and discovered that of the six species used, the sulfur dioxide penetrated the leaf tissue in only two species. These results suggest that gaseous pollutants can be removed by plants without penetrating the leaf.[22] Particulate matter seems to have minimal harmful effect upon vegetation, although it has been shown that several gaseous pollutants can injure plants.[23] The relation between the pollutant concentration and the amount of a substance that conifers are capable of removing without sustaining injury is still uncertain. It is not clear, for instance, whether the absorption of gaseous pollutants by vegetation "appreciably lessens" pollutant concentration prior to the point when the plant is harmed; a damaged plant has a reduced capacity to absorb additional pollutants.[24] Leaves exposed to low levels of sulfur dioxide are capable of transforming the pollutant into sulfate, a substance less injurious to the organism. When exposed to high levels of the pollutant, however, the leaves may be damaged before being able to transform sulfur dioxide to sulfate.[25] In general, research findings indicate that forest belts are ineffective in significantly reducing sulfur dioxide concentrations, although certain species of trees demonstrate an ability to reduce concentrations of dust particles as well as solid and gaseous radioactive substances.[26]

Studies of the ability of plants to absorb ozone and thus reduce smog levels have concluded that vegetation can "reduce appreciably the amount of ozone in polluted air."[27] The assimilation of ozone by foliage can "significantly" aid in cleansing the polluted air to about the same extent that photosynthesis decreases the carbon dioxide concentration in the air.[28] George P. Hanson and Linda Thorne have concluded that petunias and bougainvillea are respectively "efficient" and "intermediate" ozone absorbers. They discovered, however, that in order for the leaf stomates to remain open and trap the pollutant, concentrations must be kept at a reduced level; therefore, the effectiveness of these plants in reducing smog levels depends upon the maintenance of a certain ozone level.[29]

MICROCLIMATE

When evaluating the effectiveness of vegetated buffer zones in improving air quality, one must consider the extent to which these zones affect area microclimatology. Trees influence three basic elements of the microclimate: temperature, humidity, and wind.[30]

Vegetated areas usually have narrower temperature ranges than open areas. The lower summer temperature in a forest is due primarily to the amount of radiation that is transformed into energy used for evaporation rather than for transformation into sensible heat

(heat added to a body when its temperature is changed). A study by
F. W. Went concluded that the amount of radiation reflected by a forest
may be similar to the amount reflected by an urban area but that the
forest may use as much as 60 to 70 percent of the incoming radiation
for evaporation heat rather than for transformation into sensible heat.
The reduced energy available for conversion into sensible heat results
in a lower temperature.[31] The temperature over vegetated surfaces
on sunny summer days may be 10 to 14 degrees cooler than over
barren soil. There can be 1500 British thermal units (BTU) per square
foot less heat per season over grassy surfaces; this cooler, more
humid air reduces dust formation.[32]

Vegetated areas tend to be more humid than barren spaces
because of the transpiration of the foliage. Absolute humidities are
normally highest near the ground level of a tree cluster, and the humidity decreases with altitude. Once again, the greater humidity of vegetated areas lowers particulate dust formation.[33]

Numerous studies indicate that trees influence wind velocities
of a specific area; the use of trees as windbreaks is a common form
of microclimatic alteration. Wind velocities are reduced within a
forest owing to the retarding of wind speed by friction, although this
effect does not extend great distances beyond the forest or shelter
belt. Studies have demonstrated that the reduction of wind speed is
proportional to tree height: a 10 percent reduction in speed may result over a distance three times the tree height to the windward and
twenty times to the leeward.[34] However, dense plantings tend to create
turbulence and the retarding effect may be negated downwind.[35]

WATER

Forested areas have an effect upon the quantity and quality of
the water and upon flooding. A forest reduces the water yield of an
area by causing a considerable portion of the precipitation to be evap-
orated or transpired. Water quality tends to be improved in regions
where forests are present. The vegetation cover conditions the structure of the soil so that when precipitation occurs, it penetrates the
soil surface without causing great disturbance to the surface. Soils
without vegetation may not have suitable structure and stability; precipitation may flow overland and carry quantities of materials, which
results in low-quality water. A study of the Wissahickon Valley watershed near Philadelphia revealed that the average depth of water in-
filtrated per minute was 0.58 inches for wooded areas, 0.28 inches
for fields, and 0.10 inches for suburban lawns.[36] Other benefits related to underground runoff of forested areas include more uniform
streamflow, less need for artificial storage, less erosion in steep

areas, removal of salts from the soil, and enhanced degradation of rock into soil components.[37] H. E. Heggestad points out that soil, apart from vegetation, is important in removing pollutants from the atmosphere, especially gaseous substances such as carbon monoxide and ethylene which are not absorbed by green plants. Fungal microflora in the soil are primary absorbers of carbon monoxide; it has been estimated that the total soil area of the continental United States is capable of removing more than twice the amount of carbon monoxide produced annually in the world by man. The soil is also a sink for hydrocarbons, a major automotive pollutant.[38] Forests may also reduce the damage caused by minor floods, but since they become saturated they have little impact upon major flooding.

The effects of trees upon water are not constant; variations occur with the character of the soil, type of weather, and nature of the forest. For instance, the water yield from a deciduous forest was found to be 2.7 inches greater than from a forest of jack pine and 3.0 inches greater than from a mixture of pine and oak.[39]

NOISE

The use of a buffer zone to minimize the impact of noise upon a receptor involves two primary factors: distance between the noise source and the receptor, and absorption of noise by vegetation. Although there are various scales for measuring sound, for the purposes of this discussion noise quality will be represented by frequency, or cycles per second (cps), and noise intensity will be indicated by decibels (db). Reference will be made to the "A" scale of measuring intensity. This scale emphasizes frequency components of sound in the range of 800 to 8,000 cps and corresponds to the perception of sound by the human ear, which is capable of detecting sound in the frequency range from approximately 20 to 20,000 cps. Generally, intensity greater than 120 dbA may cause pain and an intensity of 160 dbA may cause physical damage, especially with prolonged exposure. Sound diminishes with distance; in an unobstructed path, the sound level is reduced by six decibels as distance is doubled. Noise is defined as unwanted sound, whether it is perceived as a nuisance or causes physical damage to a receptor.

Noise standards developed by the Federal Highway Administration (FHWA) have been incorporated into the Federal-Aid Highway Act of 1970. The standards are used by state highway agencies and FHWA offices in the planning and design of highways receiving Federal funds. The standards contain design noise levels that are applied to developed lands, various exterior land uses, and certain interior uses. The levels are based upon subjective annoyance criteria and interference with speech communication. A 70 dbA level has been established for school and residential exteriors, and this standard may not be exceeded more than 10 percent of the time during the hour of the day exhibiting the greatest noise intensity.

The standards require that "noise sensitive" land uses in the vicinity of highway projects be identified; if anticipated dbA levels exceed the standard, the guidelines stipulate that "corrective measures are to be taken to the extent feasible." Highway agencies are required to make available to local officials projected noise levels for highway improvements and any other information that will aid local governments to minimize future traffic-generated noise.[40]

Vegetation absorbs sound. William H. Smith notes a study by T. F. W. Embleton which reveals that coniferous trees result in greater noise attenuation than deciduous species.[41] Many investigators have observed greater vegetative sound attenuation as frequency increases, but Embleton suggests that attenuation is independent of frequency within the 200 to 2,000 cps band for all tree types (providing that deciduous varieties are in full leaf).[42] Gerhard Reethof concluded that a growth of tall trees (40 to 50 feet) planted at a depth of 100 feet can reduce noise by 5 to 8 db. Reethof's data support Embleton's conclusion that there are no major differences in attenuation between species.[43] Other studies point out the difficulty of making definitive statements concerning the value of trees in reducing noise. For instance, assuming that noise reduction in the 300 to 800 cps range is desirable and that a 25 dbA reduction is required, based upon Embleton's data a dense coniferous growth approximately 400 feet wide would be needed; data compiled by F. M. Wiener and D. N. Keast indicate that a 1,900-foot-wide belt would be necessary for the same reduction.[44]

The efficiency of trees in affecting sound transmission depends upon height, width, and density rather than upon differences in leaf size and shape and branching characteristics. Taller trees present a greater surface to block a sound wave, which gives them a greater opportunity for absorption and diffusion. The greater depth of a belt offers an increased number of absorbing structures to intercept the sound wave; density provides more elements per unit volume, resulting in greater absorption and more complete diffusion.[45] In a study of the effect of vegetation in reducing traffic noise, F. J. Meister notes that a "relatively dense woods" would reduce traffic noise between 0.16 and 0.18 db per meter and suggests that a residential development would have "low" traffic noise if it were separated from the highway by 200 meters.[46] Embleton and G. J. Thiessen estimate that 1,000 feet of "dense forest" are needed to obtain a 15 db reduction of the most significant band of diesel freight-train noise.[47] David I. Cook and David F. Van Haverbeke cite a study by Peter Durk which indicates that the sound absorption of trees increases with the frequency of the sound wave.[48] The Durk study also concludes that a 50-meter-wide park can result in a 20 to 30 db reduction of noise below its source level.

Cook and Van Haverbeke maintain that the value of trees in reducing noise level is a function of proper place, density, tree height, and belt width for each specific application. Belt widths from 75 to 100 feet are desirable, as is the use of evergreens for the tree type. A 20- to 25-foot-wide belt of shrubs and trees that are 15 to 30 feet high might be adequate for noise screening in a residential area, but this could have negligible impact in an area where trucks and buses are the main noise sources. Thus, although the vegetation configuration necessary to reduce noise varies among locations, some general guidelines may be proposed. For instance, when compared to pavement surface over distances of 225 feet or more, a combination of trees, shrubs, and grass usually results in an 8 to 12 db greater reduction. Cook and Van Haverbeke suggest that trees be placed closer to the noise source than to the receiver.[49]

Cook and Van Haverbeke include two specific recommendations whereby noise could be reduced by 5 to 15 db.[50] To achieve reduction of high-speed automobile and truck noise, they recommend planting 65- to 100-foot-wide belts of trees and shrubs, with the edge of the belt within 50 to 80 feet of the center of the nearest lane of traffic. Trees in the center row should be 45 feet or more. In urban areas, where moderate-speed traffic results in tire-road interaction noise, they recommend planting 20- to 50-foot-wide belts of trees and shrubs, with the edge of the belt from 20 to 50 feet from the center of the nearest traffic lane. Shrubs should be 6 to 8 feet tall next to the traffic lane and backup rows of trees should be 15 to 30 feet tall.[51]

Following are the results of two control situations from the Cook and Van Haverbeke study:

10 row belt, 10 feet between rows; in-row spacing of 8 feet; width 120 feet; 58 feet height: 130 feet from the tree belt, there was a 6 db reduction in truck noise beyond a test situation where there were no trees.[52]

4 row belt; 12 feet between rows; in-row spacing 8 feet; width 45 feet; 30 feet height: 155 feet from the tree belt, there was an approximate 7 db attenuation from truck noise beyond a test situation where there were no trees.[53]

GENERAL OBSERVATIONS ON
THE UTILITY OF BUFFERS

This brief review has done little to advance specific proposals for the use of buffer zones as means of improving environmental quality. As was mentioned earlier, it is difficult to make quantitative evaluations and definitive statements due to lack of data and inconsistent conclusions among researchers. Nevertheless, certain general observations may be ventured. The available evidence indicates the usefulness of vegetated buffer zones to reduce the impacts of air and noise pollution, although the extent of this reduction depends upon numerous factors. The unique nature of various geographic locations and pollution problems increases the difficulty of recommending general solutions that may be applied to all situations. Quantitative analyses regarding the use of vegetated buffers in minimizing air pollution impacts seem less precise than studies concerned with noise. Moreover, the transmission of noise seems to be somewhat less affected by variables, such as meteorological conditions, that influence the dispersion of air pollutants.

The use of a buffer zone may be related to three air quality objectives: the reduction of human exposure to a point or line pollution source, the reduction of average pollutant concentrations, and the reduction of total emissions in the atmosphere. Two characteristics of the buffer contribute to the accomplishment of these objectives. Distance between source and receptor allows for pollutant dispersion, thereby minimizing human exposure and reducing concentration. The use of vegetation in the buffer zone as a filtering device can, to a limited and as yet undetermined extent, improve air quality by lowering total emissions. Vegetation may also indirectly influence air quality by altering the microclimate of an area; however, the most significant use of a buffer zone directly related to air pollution would seem to be in minimizing adverse impacts of pollutants upon a specific receptor rather than in controlling ambient air quality. Difficulties encountered in attempting to formulate recommendations for the use of a buffer zone include variations in meteorological conditions, the different properties of different types of pollutants, determining the effectiveness of specific types of vegetation as filters, and the lack of quantitative data concerning the level of pollutant reduction achieved by a given amount of a space and vegetation.

Mention should also be made of the economic feasibility of using buffer zones to improve environmental quality. Air and noise pollution are most severe in densely populated urban areas, where land values are usually high. In many instances the reduction in pollution level that could be brought about by a buffer would probably not justify the cost of land acquisition necessary to achieve these reduction. It is more realistic to advocate the use of the buffer zone in future planning and design criteria than in already developed areas.

BUFFER ZONES AND THE HIGHWAY

Under design standards applicable to most highway construction, setbacks from the right-of-way are ordinarily required. For the setback, or buffer, to act as an effective absorbent of pollution emissions, however, this highway buffer will in most cases have to be expanded beyond the width that is at present usually required as a conventional part of highway design. Securing this expanded buffer area will therefore require the adaptation of legal tools that are presently utilized to buffer highways from adjacent land developments. Either this additional buffer area will have to be acquired and placed in public use or it will have to be secured against development through use of the police power. In the latter case, there will be no compensation for the extra burden the widened highway buffer imposes on landowners.

Either approach imposes costs and burdens on the public land acquisition and regulatory machinery. In the first instance, the direct costs of acquisition must be borne either by the highway agency or by some other governmental agency that assumes responsibility for the highway corridor program. These costs are substantial, and since they must be borne by the entire taxpaying public while the benefits of the corridor buffer program are largely enjoyed by property owners who are adjacent to the highway, this cost burden may well be resisted.

On the other hand, utilization of the regulatory system to achieve appropriate highway buffers concentrates the entire cost of the program on adjacent property owners to the extent that these owners are uncompensated for the loss of use of all or a portion of their land. Although much of the benefit from the uncompensated highway setback may flow to these same property owners, there is no direct correlation of benefit and burden, so that courts may resist giving sanction to overextensive highway setbacks.

In addition to the high costs of acquisition and the difficulties of regulation, an expanded highway setback program imposes other costs on the metropolitan development structure. Since the effect of the expanded setback program is to remove considerable amounts of potentially developable land from development, other land that might not have been used for development will have to be used instead. Overall densities may to some extent be reduced, and the spread of urban development may be extended. These effects may be desirable or undesirable, either from an urban planning or air pollution control viewpoint, but they need to be carefully considered as part of an expanded highway buffer program.

These considerations also suggest that alternative control methods may also be utilized to reduce the level of pollution emissions along highway corridors. For example, setbacks may remain the same, but buildings along the freeway may be built so as to protect their occupants from pollution effects. To the extent that this approach requires windowless structures and a greater use of interior air conditioning, this cost may be accepted as part of the cost of highway construction in lieu of the additional costs of expanded setback acquisition. Some highway departments have already taken steps in this direction by providing funds for the sound conditioning of buildings adjacent to expressways.

These observations suggest that caution is warranted in the utilization of highway buffer programs as an attempt to reduce the impact of air pollution along highway networks. Moreover, improvements in the technology of automobile engines, changes in the pattern of highway systems in urban areas, and increasing reliance on urban mass transit may reduce the need for protective buffer strips. Nevertheless, although perhaps of limited use as a means for alleviating the impacts of air pollution on a comprehensive regional scale, the highway buffer strip still deserves consideration as a method of controlling the impact of air pollution in areas of the region where pollution levels are critically high and where a program of this kind can have significant beneficial effects.

Certain legal issues related to the use of buffer zones remain to be analyzed. The first issue deals with the authority of the state or political subdivision to utilize the power of eminent domain to acquire protective buffers in order to neutralize the effects of air pollution along highway corridors. The second is the use of the police power by the state or its political subdivision to accomplish the same purpose.

USE OF THE EMINENT DOMAIN POWER
TO ACQUIRE PROTECTIVE BUFFERS

The legal problems posed by the use of the eminent domain power to acquire protective buffer strips center on two issues:

(1) Can a state or its political subdivisions acquire, through exercise of its eminent domain power, land alongside a highway in order to neutralize air pollution in this highway area?

(2) Can a state condemn this contiguous land with the purpose of reselling it in order to minimize the cost of the land acquisition if, upon resale, appropriate restrictions are put upon the use of the

property so as to insure that the original purpose of the condemnation (that is, neutralization of air pollution) is carried out? Alternatively, may the state condemn easements in this contiguous land that require it to be kept open and properly planted and maintained in order that the effects of air pollution may be neutralized?

Extensive research has failed to discover any case to date in which the eminent domain power was used for pollution abatement purposes along highways. Thus, this analysis will focus on analogous cases and statutory law and will attempt to extract principles from these sources that will allow their extended application to the automobile emission problem. One factor that may tend to mitigate the persuasiveness of the following analysis must be kept in mind, however. Even though the power of eminent domain has been universally recognized as an inherent power of a sovereign entity, and even though courts are liberally construing the concept of public use, the eminent domain power conflicts with the landowner's constitutional right to own and enjoy property without governmental interference.[54] This limitation upon the owner's constitutional rights could make the courts hesitant to extend the eminent domain power to encompass new areas. However, courts have given no indication of such unwillingness to extend the doctrine, and the following analysis will show that the seeds of the extension of the eminent domain power to include its exercise to abate air pollution have already been planted.

Constitutionality of the Use of Excess Condemnation

There are various theories with which one can approach the use of the eminent domain power to acquire highway-corridor land. The first of these is the theory of "excess condemnation."[55] According to this doctrine the state (or condemning agency) may condemn more land than is needed for the improvement provided the excess land is to be used to protect the improvement, to improve its utility, to extend its usefulness, or to secure the desirable development of its surroundings. Thus when the state condemned land for a highway it might also be able to condemn the adjacent land for use as buffer zones.

The power to exercise this type of protective excess condemnation has been recognized constitutionally, statutorily, and judicially. The following New Jersey constitutional provision is representative of similar provisions and statutes of other states:[56]

> Any agency . . . of the state which may be empowered to take or acquire private property for any public highway, may be authorized by law to take abutting property to preserve and protect the public highway.[57]

Protective excess condemnation also has much case law support. In City of Tacoma v. Welcker,[58] plaintiff was permitted to condemn the land surrounding the Green River, its principal source of water, to act as a buffer to protect this water supply from future pollution. In People v. Lagiss,[59] a California court allowed the state highway commission to condemn more land than was actually needed for the highway to use for drainage purposes and to improve visibility along the highway. In Cully v. Pearl River Industrial Commission,[60] a Mississippi court upheld defendant's power to condemn any land within a quarter-mile perimeter from its reservoir in order to preserve and protect said reservoir. Finally, in Illinois State Toll Highway Commission v. Eden Cemetery Assn.,[61] plaintiff was permitted to condemn an easement under defendant's cemetery property for sewer and water facilities to service a privately owned restaurant and gas station located alongside the highway, as these establishments were considered an integral part of the highway.

While excess condemnation to protect the improvement itself is permitted, our concern is whether the concept can be extended to protect adjacent lands from the adverse effects of a public improvement. The Lagiss case could imply that such an extension is not possible. In the Lagiss case the court stated that if the real purpose for the taking of adjacent lands was for a public use unrelated to the highway project, the excess taking would be in bad faith and an abuse of discretion and would be disallowed. However, various counterarguments may be available to rebut this statement. First, this statement was not necessary to the decision, as the Lagiss court upheld the excess taking in that case. Second, it may be argued that protecting adjacent areas from pollution emissions is related to the highway project. This argument has some case law support. In West Inc. v. United States,[62] defendant condemned land for a flood control project and also condemned additional land around the project site for use as a fish and wildlife preserve. In upholding this excess taking the court said:

> Provided that the [excess] land can be reasonably related to a public purpose, the United States in eminent domain proceedings is not limited to taking in fee only the amount of property which will be physically occupied by the public or actually submerged in a flood control operation. If the operation has some concomitant deleterious effects on the fish and the wildlife in the areas involved, the scope of the condemnation can include remedies to remove such deleterious effects.

Brown v. United States[63] also seems in point. In the Brown case, plaintiff's land was condemned in order to provide a new site to replace that part of a town that was to be flooded by defendant's reservoir. In upholding the condemnation the Supreme Court said:

> The acquisition of the town site was so closely connected with the acquisition of the land to be flooded, and so necessary to the carrying out of the project, that the public use of the reservoir covered the taking of the town site.

Similarly, in a later case, Culgar v. Power Authority of New York,[64] the New York Court of Appeals upheld defendant's power to condemn plaintiff's property in order to provide sites for the relocation of residences that were to be destroyed by a flooding that provided power to run defendant's power plant.

It may also be argued that whether the use of the excess land is "related" to the improvement is a moot issue so long as the excess property is put to any public use. There is support for this assertion. In United States v. 91.69 Acres of Land,[65] plaintiff condemned excess land around the dam and reservoir of a flood control project for recreational purposes. In upholding the taking the Fourth Circuit stated:

> Ordinarily the Government may take not only the land that will be flooded but such additional land as in the discretion of the condemning authority may be necessary or desirable to protect the lake or to permit incidental public use. [Emphasis added.]

Similarly in United States v. Agee,[66] upholding the government's power to condemn excess land in connection with the building of a dam, the Sixth Circuit said:

> It is well established that the federal government in eminent domain proceedings is not limited to precisely the amount of property which will be physically occupied by the public . . . In the construction of a dam, the government is not restricted to taking the land which will actually be submerged if the additional land can be reasonably related to a public purpose. [Emphasis added.]

Finally, in Winter v. Mackie,[67] defendant condemned the entire interest in plaintiff's land for a highway. Later gas and oil were discovered under this area. Plaintiff claimed that defendant should not be entitled to the gas and oil rights but rather should be restricted to the surface rights to the property, as only that estate was to be used for the highway. The Michigan court, upholding the fee simple acquisition, stated:

> Highway officers are authorized to condemn land in excess of the amount needed for the right of way proper <u>if the public interest will best be served by such taking,</u> and the discretion so vested will not be interfered with in the absence of a clear abuse of discretion. [Emphasis added.]

One is therefore led to the conclusion that there appears to be no reason why, on the basis of the above principles, excess land along the sides of an existing or proposed highway may not be taken through the eminent domain power to neutralize automobile emissions. Either the abatement of the adverse environmental impact of the highway upon the immediate area is sufficiently related to the operation of the highway itself so as to justify the excess condemnation, or the restriction of air pollution is itself a sufficient public use to justify the exercise of the eminent domain power in its absolute sense, without regard to the property's relation to the highway project per se. This latter point will be more fully explored below.

Statutory Authority for Excess Condemnation

Existing statutes also seem to provide the necessary framework for the extension of the excess condemnation doctrine. A Washington statute reads as follows:

> The state highway commission is authorized to acquire . . . title to any interest in real property adjacent to state highways for the preservation of natural beauty. . . . or to provide a visual or sound buffer between the highway and adjacent properties.[68]

The visual or sound buffer authorized by this statute would also be helpful in the control of air pollution. A California statute also seems encouraging:

> The [highway] department may condemn real property or any interest therein . . . along any state highway . . . constructed or to be constructed by the department, and may after the laying out and construction of such improvement, convey out any such property . . . thus acquired and not necessary for the improvement, with reservations concerning the future use and occupations of such property

140

so as to protect such public work and its environs, and to
preserve the view, appearance, light, air and usefulness
of such public work.[69] [Emphasis added.]

The key wording is that alluding to the protection of the environs of
the improvement. While this statute has never been judicially interpreted so as to encompass condemnation for air pollution control
purposes it could be forcefully argued that the language of the statute
does authorize such condemnation.

Indirect Control: Taking Property for Beautification

Buffer zones could also be secured through the eminent domain
power in a slightly roundabout manner. Statutes in a number of states
allow the condemnation of property adjacent to highways in order to
preserve and enhance the beauty of the highway and its surrounding
region. The Washington statute that provided for the sound buffer
also allows condemnation in order to enhance the aesthetic appeal
of the highway. A California statute provides as follows:

The [highway] department may acquire . . . any real property which it considers necessary for highway purposes.
[Real property for such purposes may be condemned for
any of the following uses]. (F) For the culture and support of trees which benefit any state highway by aiding
. . . in the maintenance of the attractiveness of the scenic
beauties of such highways.[70]

In a recent New Jersey case, West Outdoor Advertising Co. v. Gold-
berg,[71] defendant's transportation department condemned plaintiff's
land located adjacent to a highway, pursuant to a New Jersey statute
similar to those authorizing a taking for highway beautification purposes.[72] In upholding the constitutionality of the statute and the validity of the taking, the New Jersey court stated:

We have no hesitancy in stating that the restoration, preservation, and enhancement of scenic beauty adjacent to
public highways is a public use for the public welfare,
filling a special need of our time. Therefore, the power
to acquire land for that purpose is beyond judicial interference.

A similar result was reached in a Wisconsin case, Kamrowski v.
State.[73] In this case the state highway commission condemned a

141

"scenic easement" in plaintiff's property to a depth of 350 feet from the highway. Defendant's action was authorized by a Wisconsin statute74 allowing the highway commission to acquire, by eminent domain, negative easements in lands adjoining the state highways preventing the landowner from dumping any garbage or erecting any signs or billboards. The statute also permitted the acquisition of a negative easement forcing the owner, if he used or leased the land for residential purposes, to maintain a frontage of not less than 300 feet from the highway for each residence. The state justified the taking of these easements as a necessary means of preserving and protecting, for scenic purposes, the natural beauty of the areas adjoining the highway. The Wisconsin court upheld the constitutionality of the statute (and hence the taking) by ruling that the public's enjoyment of the scenic beauty of a highway is a public use for which land, or an easement in land, can be validly taken.

Thus it seems clear that a condemning authority can acquire the needed buffers along the highway simply by condemning the land for highway beautification purposes. Although the justification would only partially explain the true purpose for the taking, it does not seem that such condemnation would be in bad faith or an abuse of discretion. By condemning this corridor area for use as a buffer, the condemning authority is indeed enhancing the beauty of this region. Fields of trees and shrubbery, especially if they are well maintained, are most pleasing aesthetically. In fact, some of the beautification statutes, such as the California statute, expressly provide for the maintenance of vegetation as a means of preserving the beauty of the highway right of way. The fact that vegetation serves the important concomitant function of neutralizing vehicular emissions by no means detracts from its beautification function.

Direct Control:
Taking Property to Abate Air Pollution

Notwithstanding the above analysis, it may be possible to examine these eminent domain issues in a different perspective. Instead of dealing with the problem as one of "excess" condemnation, a taking of highway corridor land may be viewed merely as an exercise of the eminent domain power in its purest sense. The eminent domain power is a power inherent in any sovereign entity, such as a state, and the state can delegate this power to any of its agencies—a highway commission, for example. The only limitations on the exercise of the eminent domain power are: (1) the land taken must be put to a public use, and (2) the condemning authority must justly compensate the owner for the taking of his property. The condemnation problem presented here may be visualized as follows: the state highway commission, acting pursuant to power delegated to it by the state, condemns a certain amount of land for a highway. This taking is easily justified as a taking for a public use. As the Supreme Court said in Rindge Co. v. Los Angeles County,[75] "A taking for a highway is universally recognized as a public use." The highway commission also condemns land on each side of the proposed highway. This taking is rationalized as a taking for the public use of abating the air pollution in the highway corridor caused by automobile emissions. Can this excess taking be legally justified in this manner? This question has two components which must be examined separately: (1) Is a taking to abate air pollution in general a taking for a public use? (2) Is a taking to protect potential receptors located in the highway area a taking for a public or for a private use?

The solution to the first question is relatively simple. Although it has never been held that land may be constitutionally taken in order to abate air pollution, by viewing cases in which analogous takings have been upheld the necessary connection can be made. In City of Tacoma v. Welcker the Washington court upheld a taking of land to protect the town's water supply from pollution. In so holding the court stated that since it is the function of a governmental body to ensure that the town's water is pollution free, an exercise of the eminent domain power to accomplish this end is justifiable as being for a public use. The holding and reasoning of the Welcker case should apply with equal force to a taking to protect the town's air quality from pollution.

Since pollution of the air breathed by the public is a menace to the public's health, safety, and welfare, a taking of property to eliminate this menace is also supported by ample case law precedent. In New York City Housing Authority v. Muller,[76] the court upheld plaintiff's taking of defendant's property for the purpose of redeveloping slum-ridden areas and providing decent, sanitary housing for low-income families. The court justified the taking as one to promote the public health, safety, and welfare by eliminating unsanitary housing and rehabilitating unsafe neighborhoods. In so ruling the court used the following language, which could equally apply to the situation discussed in this chapter:

> To take for the maintenance and promotion of public health is a public purpose. . . . The fundamental purpose of government is to protect the health, safety, and welfare of the public. Its ammunition to accomplish these ends [includes] the power of eminent domain. Whenever there arises in the state a condition of affairs holding a substantial menace to the public health, safety, or welfare,

it becomes the duty of the government to apply whatever
power is necessary and appropriate to check it.

In a Supreme Court case, Berman v. Parker,[77] the validity of a taking
to promote public health, safety, and welfare received the highest
sanction possible. The facts in the Berman case were similar to those
in the Muller case—private property was taken for purposes of redeveloping blighted areas. The Court upheld the taking, stating in
conclusive language that the improvement of public health is a con-
spicuous example of the traditional application of the eminent domain
power.

Upon viewing some of the cases in which a taking has been upheld as being for a public purpose, it is clear that a taking to abate
air pollution should also be sanctioned. In United States v. 1,972 Acres
of Land,[78] the court held that a taking of land for use as a wildlife
preserve is a proper taking for public purposes. In County of Los
Angeles v. Anthony,[79] a California court held that plaintiff's taking
of defendant's property for eventual use as a television and movie
museum was a valid taking for a public purpose. In Schank v. City
and County of Honolulu,[80] the court held it constitutional for a municipal government to exercise the eminent domain power to acquire
private property for use as off-street parking facilities. If the takings
in these cases were valid as being for public uses, how much the more
justified would be a taking to neutralize the harmful effects of air
pollution.

The second issue presents a thornier problem, however. If the
condemning authority tries to exercise its eminent power to acquire
the corridor area, the landowner could contest the taking on the grounds
that the property taken would not be put to a public use. He could
argue that, since the land is being taken only to protect those people
in the immediate highway area from the harmful vehicular emissions,
the entire public will not be able to "use" the land taken, and therefore the proposed use of the property is private. As one of the under-
pinnings of the exercise of the eminent domain power is lacking, he
argues, his land may not be taken in this situation.

Each state has its own definition of what is and what is not a
public use and of how far a use must extend before it can be considered public. Any attempt to synthesize these rules would be fruitless.
It suffices to say that there is ample support for the proposition that
the use of the land taken does not have to be shared by the entire
public to be considered a public use. For example, in County of Los
Angeles v. Anthony the California court, in sustaining a taking for
museum purposes, stated:

144

There have been two different interpretations of public use
in this country, one the broader meaning of public utility
or advantage, the other a narrower one of use or right of
use by the public. In California the courts have followed
the broader definition of public use.

In Berman v. Parker the Supreme Court sustained a taking of land to
redevelop slum areas, even though the new housing to be built in the
condemned area would be occupied exclusively by low-income families
and would not be open to the public at large. In New York City Housing
Authority v. Muller, the New York court reached an identical decision,
stating:

> A use is not private just because the taking is to provide
> apartments to be rented to low income persons. Use of a
> proposed structure, facility, or service by everybody and
> anybody is one of the abandoned universal tests of public
> use.

In Sublett v. City of Tulsa[81] the Oklahoma court held that the development and improvement of harbors and ports is a public use for which
property may be condemned, notwithstanding the fact that the harbor
or port is not available for indiscriminate use by the public. In reaching this decision the court ruled that a public use did not have to be
a use by the entire public, but may be a use for the benefit of a restricted locality if such use is common to or available to all members of such locality on the same terms.

There is a series of cases in which courts have upheld an exercise of the eminent domain power in order to provide access roads
to a highway from properties rendered landlocked by construction
of that highway. These takings were sustained as being for a public
use, even though the immediate benefit of the roads built on the lands
taken inured only to those few individuals for whom they provided
access. In Arata v. Monsanto Chemical Co.[82] a Missouri court sustained such a taking, saying:

> In order to constitute a public use it is not necessary that
> the whole community or any large part of it should actually
> use or be benefited by a contemplated improvement. Bene-
> fit to any considerable number is sufficient. Nor does the
> fact that the advantage of a public improvement also inures
> to a particular individual or group of individuals deprive
> it of its public character.

145

In State Highway Commission v. Bush,[83] a New Jersey court sustained a similar taking in the following terms:

> A use is not denominated public or private simply by rely-
> ing on the number of people it serves. It has been stated
> that a use does not fail to be public upon the ground that
> the immediate enjoyment of it is limited to a small group
> or even to a single person.

Similar decisions have been reached in Illinois[84] and Ohio.[85]

On the basis of the above cases and principles, it seems clear that the taking of land to protect an area adjacent to a highway from air pollution should be considered a public use. The protection would not be provided to individuals as individuals but rather would be provided to all residents of a specific locality. Everyone located, or to be located, within the protected area would be equally entitled to share in the clean air on the same terms as all others located within this area. Hence the character of the use of the adjacent property appears to be public and its acquisition by the eminent domain power therefore permitted.

Since the issue of abating air pollution is most pressing and immediate it seems unlikely that a court will not expand its conception of public use to include pollution abatement in the face of current public demand for stricter environmental controls. The concept of public use is not static. In Katz v. Brandon,[86] the Connecticut court upheld a taking of land for a redevelopment project, stating:

> A public use defies absolute definition for it changes with
> varying conditions of society, new appliances in the sci-
> ences, changing conceptions of the scope and functions of
> government, and other differing circumstances brought
> about by an increase in population and new modes of com-
> munication and transportation.

It seems that the concept of public use we advance would easily fit within the confines of the above statement. In addition, it seems that public policy would support all the ideas postulated in the above discussion.

Finally, if the state by statute, or the condemning authority by resolution, declared that the taking of land adjacent to a highway for pollution abatement purposes was for a public use, the taking would have such a heavy presumption of validity that any doubts as to its public nature would be dispelled. It has long been held that a parcel is presumptively binding on the courts.[87] On the other hand, the issue of whether the use to which the property taken is to be put is indeed public is potentially justiciable in every case, legislative determinations notwithstanding. However, many courts, while giving lip service to this principle, attach a heavy presumption of validity to a legislative declaration of public use. Thus in New York City Housing Authority v. Muller the court said:

> Legislative determinations of public use are not conclusive on the courts, but they are entitled to at least great respect since they relate to public conditions concerning which the legislature both by necessity and duty must have known.

Also, in Berman v. Parker, the United States Supreme Court gave near judicial immunity to a legislative declaration of public use:

> Subject to specific constitutional limitations, when the legislature has spoken the public interest has been declared in terms well nigh conclusive. In such cases the legislature and not the judiciary is the main guardian of the public needs to be served by social legislation . . . This principle admits no exception merely because the power of eminent domain is involved. The role of the judiciary in determining whether that power is being exercised for a public purpose is an extremely narrow one.

Acquisition of Partial Interest

Instead of acquiring full title to corridor land, the condemning authority could acquire a negative easement in this land to restrict development in order to facilitate pollution abatement. The precedent for this type of acquisition was established in Kamrowski v. State. However, the cost of acquiring this easement could be nearly as great as the cost of acquiring title in fee, as the easement would disallow all development in the buffer area.

An alternative solution would be for the state to acquire the needed land and then sell it subject to appropriate restrictions to ensure its function as a pollution-neutralizing buffer. This subsequent resale could be used to recoup part of the cost of the original acquisition. Little difficulty in reselling land subject to be negative restrictions could be expected in rural areas, where the restricted section will usually form only a part of a much larger tract. In urban areas, assembling a tract of land large enough to absorb the restricted section may be more difficult. The land acquisition agency may have to settle for a lower price on the restricted portion in order to find a buyer willing to accept the restricted area as well.

147

Attempting to extend the law of eminent domain to include condemnation for resale is a most ambitious undertaking. Heretofore, this type of excess condemnation (called the recoupment theory, since the condemning authority attempts to "recoup" the cost of the improvement by selling the excess land) has been held unconstitutional as a taking for a private use (see Cincinnati v. Vester[88]). Recent trends, however, could indicate a departure from the judicial disfavor in which recoupment excess condemnation has been held. In a 1963 New York case, Courtesy Sandwich Shop v. Port of New York Authority,[89] defendant, in condemning land in Manhattan for the World Trade Center, condemned excess property to lease to private interests in order to produce revenue to help finance the cost of the project. The court upheld the excess taking on the grounds that the revenue produced by such leasing facilitated the building of the Trade Center, which itself was a public project. Similarly, in Southern Pacific Land Co. v. United States,[90] defendant, in condemning land for a naval air station, condemned full title, the land including its mineral interests, in order to enhance the marketability of the property if it ever decided to sell. The Ninth Circuit upheld the taking, ruling that the advantageous liquidation of a government investment is a legitimate consideration in determining the title to be condemned and that the appropriate liquidation of an investment which was for a public purpose is itself a public use.

Moreover, if the excess land is condemned under the "protective" excess condemnation theory, the argument for resale is strengthened, so long as appropriate restrictions are put on the use of the property so as to assure the antipollution purpose for which the land was originally acquired. The California protective condemnation statute specifically provides for such resale with appropriate restrictions. The relevant case law is also in accord. For example, in Cully v. Pearl River Industrial Commission, the court not only upheld defendant's taking of the land around its reservoir to protect it from contamination but also allowed the sale of this land so long as the deeds contained restrictions that the property would not be used in a manner inconsistent with the public purpose for which it was acquired.

The extension of a permitted "protective" resale to include the type of resale proposed here would be a considerable extension of the current law, as it would contradict the still disfavored recoupment theory of excess condemnation. However, a strong argument may be made that the recoupment theory is not as strongly disfavored as it once was and that the purposes proposed here are so closely analogous to permitted protective condemnation resales that the required extension may be made.

EMINENT DOMAIN: A SUMMARY

From the above discussion it seems clear that the eminent domain power may be used to acquire land alongside a highway for use as a buffer to reduce the adverse environmental impact of automobile emissions. We may also conclude that it is legally possible to acquire such land and later resell it to recoup the cost of the acquisition, so long as appropriate restrictions are placed on the property to ensure its function as a buffer. This latter conclusion, however, is an ambitious extension of current law and the support for it is far weaker than for the former conclusion.

Changes in state highway and in general condemnation statutes will also be needed if the acquisition of buffer areas along highways is to be made possible. While the nature of this legislation will vary depending on which agency is given the authority to acquire land for these purposes, a statute authorizing the state highway agency to condemn land for the purpose of creating buffer zones might read as follows:[91]

> The highway commission may acquire or condemn the
> whole or part of any interest in land adjacent to any high-
> way right of way for use as a buffer area to reduce the
> environmental impact of exhaust emissions from motor
> vehicles traveling on the highway. The commission may
> also convey or lease any land so acquired to its original
> owner or to any other person or entity subject to such re-
> servations, conditions, easements, covenants or other con-
> tractual arrangements as will preserve the use of the land
> for this purpose.

USE OF THE POLICE POWER TO REQUIRE
PROTECTIVE SETBACK AREAS
ALONG HIGHWAY CORRIDORS

As an alternative to the acquisition of protective buffer areas along highway corridors, setback areas can be required under the regulatory police power. Two major features would distinguish a setback requirement program from the direct acquisition of buffer areas. One has already been mentioned; setbacks would be set aside under the uncompensated exercise of the regulatory police power, and the land so set aside would remain in private ownership. The second important difference arises from the nature of the police power and the government agencies that would be authorized to exercise it. In most states, the power to impose setback controls rests with local government units rather than with the state highway department, although some statutes do confer this power on state highway agencies. When the power to impose setbacks rests with local governments, the ability to assure that the highway network will be adequately covered by setback requirements will depend on the extent to which the state air pollution or some other agency is able to convince local government units that such controls are necessary. Since coordination of this kind will be difficult to achieve, the argument for providing the state highway commission with statutory power to impose setbacks is strong.

Statutory questions are not as important in this area, however, as the constitutional issues. The following section therefore concentrates on the constitutional issues that are raised by setback requirements.

Constitutionality of Setback Requirements in General

The best way to approach the constitutional issue is to examine the judicial treatment of the setback requirement. Political units have established, either by separate ordinance or as part of a comprehensive zoning ordinance, requirements that businesses or residences fronting roads and highways be set back a required distance from the right of way. These ordinances are passed under the police power of the municipality as necessary to promote the health, safety, and welfare of the community. There appears to be no reason why these ordinances cannot also be used to provide the necessary distance between receptor and polluter along the highway to eliminate the adverse effects of vehicular emissions.

As indicated above, both local government units and state highway commissions have been authorized by statute to impose setbacks. At the local level, this requirement is sometimes made the subject of a separate ordinance, while in other instances it is included as part of a comprehensive local zoning ordinance. An example of the first approach is found in Illinois:

> In addition to existing powers and to the end that adequate light, _pure air_, or safety may be secured . . . the corporate authorities in each municipality have power by ordinance to establish, regulate, and limit the building or set back lines on or along any street, traffic way, drive or parkway . . . as may be deemed best suited to carry out these purposes. The powers given by this [section] shall not be exercised so as to deprive the owner of existing property of its use or maintenance for the purpose to which it is then lawfully devoted.[92] [Emphasis added.]

A Mississippi statute authorizes the state highway commission to impose setbacks.[93] An Oregon statute also applies to municipalities:

> The council or other governing body of any incorporated city under an exercise of its police powers may establish or alter building set back lines on private property adjacent to any alley, street, avenue, boulevard, highway or other public way in such city. It may make it unlawful and provide a penalty for erecting after said establishment any building or structure closer to the street line than such set back line except as may be expressly provided by the ordinance.[94]

An example of a statute authorizing the establishment of the setback requirement in a comprehensive zoning ordinance can be found in a Pennsylvania statute, now repealed:

> Council may establish classes of buildings, structures, and land for any or all of the purposes of zoning. Within the zones defined council may regulate and restrict according to the classes established by it: (i) The establishment, maintenance, or setting back of building lines upon streets.[95]

Cases arising under these and similar statutes have almost uniformly upheld the constitutional validity of the setback requirement. The landmark case in this area was a 1927 Supreme Court decision, Gorieb v. Fox,[96] in which the Court upheld a local ordinance establishing setback lines. In sustaining the constitutionality of the setback ordinance the Court used language equally applicable to our situation, the use of the setback to secure buffers for environmental protection along the highway:

> [The setback] rests for its justification upon the reasons which have risen in recent times as a result of the great increase and concentration of the population in urban communities and the vast changes in the extent and complexity of the problems of modern city life. State legislatures and city councils who deal with the situation from a practical standpoint are better qualified than the courts to determine the necessity, character, and degree of regulation which these new and perplexing conditions require; and their conclusions should not be disturbed by the courts unless clearly arbitrary and unreasonable. . . .

Frontyards afford room for lawns and trees, keep the
dwellings farther from the dust, noise, and fumes of the
street, add to the attractiveness and comfort of a residential district and create a better home environment.
. . . Set back requirements have a rational relation to
public safety, health, morals, and general welfare and
therefore can be sustained as a legitimate exercise of
the police power.

This somewhat lengthy quotation, although written in 1927, has
been reiterated both verbatim and in principle in later cases. Thus
a 1961 Texas case, Fisher v. City of Irving,[97] denied plaintiff a permit to build a gasoline station within the 80-foot setback line established by ordinance. The court upheld the validity of the setback
ordinance, stating that Irving as a home rule city had the authority
to pass any ordinance reasonably necessary for the protection of the
health, safety, comfort, or welfare of the public. Without the setback
ordinance, the court said, abutting property owners could and would
develop their property up to the street line. Since the Texas court
saw such development as injurious to the interests of abutting property owners, the ordinance advanced the public welfare, health, and
safety and was a valid exercise of the police power.

In Boardman v. Davis,[98] an Iowa court relied heavily on the
Gorieb case to validate a 50-foot setback requirement, forcing defendant to remove a house built 30 feet from the street in violation
of the ordinance. In Town of Atherton v. Templeton,[99] defendant was
enjoined from having a tennis court in his front yard in violation of
a zoning ordinance requiring residential dwellings to be set back 60
feet from the front property line and prohibiting structures in front
yard areas. The California court made two relevant points in upholding the zoning ordinance: (1) elimination of structures from front
yard areas is desirable in that it affords room for lawns and trees
which add to the attractiveness and comfort of a residential district;
and (2) every presumption will be indulged in favor of a zoning or
setback ordinance, and these ordinances will not be set aside unless
there is no reasonable relation between the regulations established
and the public welfare, or unless the physical facts show that there
has been an unreasonably oppressive interference with property
rights. This presumption is usually accorded to regulations of land
use. Similarly, in McCavis v. De Luca,[100] the Minnesota court had
little trouble validating a 15-foot setback ordinance enacted under
the police power, although not enacted as part of a zoning ordinance:

That set back lines may be established as part of a zoning
ordinance in the exercise of the city's police power

cannot now be in doubt. There is no reason why setback lines may not be adopted in the absence of a general ordinance providing for zoning as well as part of such ordinance.

Also, in French v. Town of Clintwood, [101] a Virginia court upheld the validity of a 10-foot setback provision in a zoning ordinance:

We have adopted the view that a municipal ordinance enacted in the interest of the health, safety and convenience of the public prohibiting an owner of property bordering on a public street to construct buildings nearer than a specific distance from the street line does not unconstitutionally deprive such owner of his property without due process of law.

Finally, Burgden Development Co. v. Kiefaber, [102] a 1960 Ohio case, seems to sum up the law in this area. In approving a zoning ordinance provision calling for a 60-foot setback, the court said:

That lot sizes, setback building lines, and yard sizes may be regulated by zoning ordinances in the proper exercise of the police power is no longer an open question. . . . Far larger yard spaces than involved here have consequently been approved and held valid.

Setbacks in Rural Areas

Thus it appears that there is little doubt about the constitutionality of setback requirements in general. Nevertheless, problems have arisen in the application of setback requirements in certain land use control settings.

First, there is a question whether setback regulations are valid at all in rural areas. As most new highways will be built in less developed areas it would seem most imperative to zone this as yet undeveloped land so that future receptors to be located in this area will not be adversely affected by the pollution from cars traveling on future highways. However, a 1957 Pennsylvania case, Schmalz v. Buckingham Township Zoning Board of Adjustment, [103] held that a zoning ordinance establishing a 50-foot setback line in a wholly agricultural and rural district was invalid as an unreasonable and improper exercise of the police power. The court held that even though the area involved might someday be nonagricultural, and even though setbacks are justified in urban areas, they are not necessarily reasonable in rural areas. Their reasonableness, the court held, had to be determined according to existing conditions, and the 50-foot setback served no justifiable function in the rural area.

This case could present grave problems for setback zoning in rural areas. However, the court's reasoning can be challenged. Perhaps the main basis of criticism, from our point of view, is that the court did not consider the use of setbacks for the purpose of alleviating the adverse effects of air pollution. If the level of traffic on a road is high, air pollution emissions can be dangerous to abutting property owners in rural as well as in urban areas. Earlier cases considering the constitutionality of setback ordinances did not explicitly take into account the air pollution problem, although the Gorieb case did mention protection from the "fumes" of passing vehicles as a basis for imposing setbacks in that case. Direct and more explicit consideration of the air pollution problem would thus seem to provide a reasonable basis for setback ordinances and would serve to justify their imposition in such circumstances as those presented in the opinion on the Schmalz case. What may be needed is more direct attention, both in the purpose clauses of enabling legislation and in the plan of the regulations, to the impact of the setback ordinance on the control of air pollution generated on highway corridors.

Permitted Depth of Setbacks

Another problem arises in deciding what the permitted depth of the setback should be. A setback of 200 feet or more might be required to significantly reduce the impact of vehicular emissions. Can an ordinance requiring a 200-foot setback be constitutionally defended? Extensive research has discovered no case in which such a deep setback requirement was validated either as part of a zoning ordinance or as an independent ordinance. The deepest permitted setback discovered was 80 feet from the edge of the property line.[104] This problem can be solved in one of three ways: (1) We could be satisfied with an 80-foot setback, since a buffer of such depth would allow for the diffusion of part of the emissions. However, a buffer that is 80 feet deep, while considerably better than no buffer at all, is still less than the optimum. (2) A mixture of the eminent domain and police powers could be employed. Thus, if 80 feet is the maximum depth of land that can be secured without cost through the police power, the remaining required land could be acquired through the exercise of the eminent domain power. (3) Perhaps the entire setback question could be reconceptualized to permit the required 200-foot setback from the highway.

The legal foundation for such a setback has been firmly established. The police power of a municipality may be exercised through the enactment of appropriate legislation to promote the health and safety of its inhabitants, so long as the means adopted are rationally related to the promotion of these objectives. It is also well established that polluted air is detrimental to the health and well-being of those that breathe it. Synthesizing these accepted principles, we can advance the following proposition: Appropriate legislation for pollution abatement purposes may be enacted under the police power as necessary to promote the health and welfare of the residents of the community. Since it has been shown that buffer strips 200 feet deep or more are often needed to effectively reduce the local impact of vehicular emissions, legislation providing for these buffers is a rational means of obtaining the desired end of pollution abatement. Hence businesses or residences may be required to set back 200 feet from major highways.

While the setback issue has heretofore never been presented in precisely this manner, the logic of this argument points to the extended application of setbacks. A somewhat analogous 1957 Wisconsin case, Highway 100 Auto Wreckers, Inc. v. City of West Allis,[105] provides support for this extended application. In the Auto Wreckers case the Wisconsin court upheld the validity of a Wisconsin statute requiring that all automobile junkyards be set back at least 210 feet from the center line of the highway. In sustaining the validity of this statute the Wisconsin court used the following language, which could also be used to sustain the validity of a 200-foot setback ordinance for antipollution purposes:

> In this day none will dispute that government in the exercise of its police powers may impose restrictions upon the use of property in the interest of public health, morals and safety. . . . The court will not interfere with the exercise of the police power by a municipality unless the illegality of the exercise is clear. We are dealing with one of the most essential powers of a government, one that is the least limitable, the police power. . . . The municipality is the judge of the necessity and reasonableness of its ordinance under the police power and its ordinance creates a prima facie presumption that it is reasonable.

Moreover, in a recent encouraging Illinois case, Brunhill Towers v. Chaddick,[106] a lower Illinois court recognized the use of the zoning ordinance for pollution abatement purposes. In the Chaddick case, plaintiff was forced to discontinue the use of his parking lot since it violated the town's zoning ordinance in that it was not surfaced with the required material. The court upheld the validity of the surfacing section of the ordinance and used the following language, which could signify an extended application of the police power in the pollution abatement area:

> We must note that the surfacing requirements of the zoning ordinance were in the comprehensive amendment in part as a measure to control dust pollution and that a municipality has extensive power to pass ordinances for the health, safety and welfare of the public provided that the public welfare requires such application and that property owners do not suffer unreasonable exactions as contrasted with the resulting public benefit. The parking lot in the instant case was covered only with rolled stone and cinders and the Zoning Administration apparently considered that the surface was inadequate to insure that antipollution protection necessary in high density residential areas. The resurfacing of plaintiff's lot will contribute in a small way to a lessening of the amount of pollution in the atmosphere.

The application of this quotation to the situation herein discussed is obvious.

Planting Requirements in Setbacks

Assuming that a 200-foot setback ordinance could be upheld, could the property owner be required to plant and maintain the needed vegetation in the area so as to most effectively utilize it as a buffer strip? Probably the landowner will keep the area green of his own volition for aesthetic purposes. Possibly the same antipollution rationale which justified the setback ordinance in the first place could also require that the setback area be kept in vegetation. The zoning of land so as to provide buffer zones covered with vegetations has recently received case law support. For example, a recent New Jersey case, State of New Jersey v. Gallop Building,[107] sustained that part of a zoning ordinance which forbade development for business purposes of land located in a business district, but within 50 feet of a neighboring residential district, unless the business use was screened by evergreen trees so as to hide it from the abutting residential district. The court upheld this provision and stated that the permitted business operation in this contiguous area had a potentially harmful influence requiring protection for abutting property owners

156

in the residential zone. The court also stated that such a buffer provision contained attributes similar in character to zoning ordinance
setback requirements, which, when reasonable in scope, have been
uniformly upheld as proper. Finally, the court held that the buffer
provision had a reasonable relationship to the public interest in that
it conserved the value of the abutting residential property and furthered
the aesthetics of the area.

Similarly, in a later New Jersey case, Quinton v. Edison Park
Development Corp.,[108] plaintiff questioned the validity of a provision
of a township zoning ordinance requiring a 100-foot buffer strip between a business use on an area of 10 acres or more (in this case a
shopping center) and adjacent residential areas. The buffer strip
was meant to provide a screen against light and noise that emanated
from the shopping center. The New Jersey court upheld the constitutionality of the provision, not only to protect the residents of the town
which passed the zoning ordinance but also to protect residents in an
adjoining town. In so holding, the court stated that shopping centers
bring disturbing noises, lights, fumes, and congestion and that the
buffer provision passed to protect nearby residents did promote the
public health, safety, and welfare and hence was a valid exercise of
the zoning power. An analogy is easily drawn to the use of buffers
to protect owners of land abutting highways from the dangerous and
irritating pollutants emitted from the cars traveling on these highways.

A somewhat contrary decision was reached in a 1970 Maryland
case, Spaid v. Board of County Commissioners for Prince George's
County.[109] In the Spaid case, plaintiff's land was zoned for residential
use even though it was most difficult economically to build a house on
this parcel, since it was located within an industrial zone. The purpose of this incongruous zoning was to prevent all development on
this parcel so as to utilize it as a buffer zone between industrial and
residential areas. The buffer zone was to prevent the industrial uses
from encroaching into the residential area and to prevent existing
and proposed residential areas from becoming more intensively developed. The court held that the zoning was unreasonable, discriminatory, and confiscatory and that it deprived plaintiff of his property
without due process of law in violation of the 14th Amendment. However, there are some factual differences that effectively distinguish
the Spaid case from the New Jersey cases and from the issue discussed
here. First, as plaintiff's entire parcel was zoned for residential
use, he was effectively denied the use of all of his land. In the New
Jersey cases the affected parties merely had to dedicate a portion
of their land for the buffer area, development being permitted on the
other portion of the property owner's land. Similarly, if a 200-foot
setback ordinance were enacted, all land more than 200 feet from
the edge of the highway would be available for development. On the

other hand, if the landowner owns less or slightly more than 200 feet of land along the highway so that a 200-foot setback ordinance effectively precludes all development and deprives the landowner of all reasonable use of his property, the ordinance will be confiscatory and hence unconstitutional. This point will be discussed more fully below. Second, the Maryland court stressed that the zoning of plaintiff's land for this buffer area would be used for the protection of others and was not for plaintiff's benefit. The court thought that this was unfair and felt that the protected parties' own land should be zoned to provide such protection to them. While the New Jersey cases allowed zoning for buffers to protect the property of others from the adverse effects of neighboring business uses, and thus are irreconcilable with the Spaid decision, the advocated setback requirement is meant to protect the receptors whose property is zoned, and may be unconstitutional under the Maryland holding.

Application of Setbacks to Individual Properties

While setback requirements are valid in general, it may be possible that the specific application of such an ordinance to a particular piece of property may be unreasonable, discriminatory, or confiscatory and hence may be unconstitutional as it affects that piece of property. If, as advocated, a zoning ordinance is passed or amended or a setback ordinance is passed requiring a 200-foot setback for properties fronting the highway, various problems will arise. The first of these problems was mentioned above; if an abutting landowner owns so little land that the setback requirements deprives him of all the use of his property, the ordinance may be confiscatory as it applies to this landowner, and hence invalid. For example, in Richards v. Zoning Board of Appeals of Malverne, [110] where setback restrictions on each side of a corner lot in a residential district reduced the usable portion by about one-fifth the size of the lot and limited construction of a dwelling to a width of 11 feet, the ordinance was deemed confiscatory and plaintiff was granted a variance permitting construction of a dwelling with a width of 21 feet. Similarly, in Householder v. Town of Grand Island, [111] a town ordinance prohibiting the erection of buildings fronting a highway within 90 feet of the right of way was declared unconstitutional and unenforceable as applied to plaintiff's property. Since the 90-foot setback, if observed, would have reached almost to the edge of a river, the setback prevented the plaintiff from building any structure whatever on his property and thus deprived him of all appropriate use and enjoyment of his property.

Finally in Foshour v. County of Contra Costa, [112] where setbacks on each side of plaintiff's triangular lot reduced the buildable portion to an area adequate for the construction of a doll's house, the ordinance was declared confiscatory and hence unconstitutional for depriving plaintiff of his property without due process of law. However, for a setback ordinance to be deemed confiscatory the landowner must be denied the use of his property for any and all reasonable purposes. Mere financial inconvenience is not enough. Thus, in Sierra Construction Co. v. Board of Appeals of the Town of Greece,[113] the New York Court of Appeals upheld the validity of an 82-foot setback requirement and stated that in order for the court to sustain an attack upon the validity of a setback ordinance an aggrieved property owner must show that if the ordinance is enforced the consequent restriction upon his property precludes its use for any purpose to which it is reasonably adapted. In this case, even with the 82-foot setback, plaintiff still had 150 feet left on which to build a house. Hence the ordinance was sustained. A similar decision was reached upon identical reasoning in Symonds v. Bucklin.[114]

Should the setback ordinance prove to be confiscatory a variance could be granted enabling the property owner to utilize enough of his property to avoid a holding of unconstitutionality. The buffer zone may still serve as a protection against pollution in these instances if the variance power is utilized to restrict uses in the buffer zone to those which would not be adversely affected by exhaust pollution. For example, residential uses might be prohibited in the buffer area, or permitted only if built and constructed to minimize the effect of air pollution on residents in the dwelling.

A second practical problem that arises when the setback ordinance is applied to specific property is that preexisting nonconforming uses must be permitted to remain, or at least given a reasonably lengthy amortization period before they are removed. This problem would be particularly acute in developed areas but practically nonexistent in undeveloped areas. On the basis of the zoning experience, however, it should be possible to develop some method for requiring the removal of nonconforming uses in buffer areas after a reasonable period of time.

The required buffers may be secured along the highway corridor through exercise of the police power at a minimal cost. Problems will arise in applying such setback ordinances to preexisting nonconforming uses and to very small parcels. However, these problems are not insurmountable, and it certainly appears that pollution abatement can be legally carried out in the highway area without a prohibitive cost through the use of the setback approach.

NOTES

1. Dabberdt, Ludwig, and Johnson, Urban Diffusion of Carbon Monoxide, in The Relationship of Land Use and Transportation Planning to Air Quality Management 62 (G. Hagevik ed. 1972).

2. Alan M. Voorhees and Associates, Inc., A Guide for Reducing Air Pollution Through Urban Planning 2-35 (1971).

3. Morton Corn, "Nonviable Particles in the Air," in 1 Air Pollution 49 (2d ed. Arthur C. Stern ed. 1968), hereinafter cited as Stern.

4. Id. at 60.

5. A. J. Haagen-Smit and Lowell G. Wayne, "Atmospheric Reactions and Scavenging Processes," in Stern, 182.

6. R. C. Wanta, "Meteorology and Air Pollution," in Stern, 207. For a more detailed analysis of particulate fallout characteristics see Stern, 211-9.

7. A. L. Page et al., "Lead Quantities in Plants, Soil and Air Near Some Major Highways in Southern California," 41 Hilgardia 1-31 (No. 1 July 1971).

8. D. N. Kalyuzhnyi et al., "Industrial Enterprises and Residential Quarters," in Peter C. Rydell and Gretchen Schwarz, "Air Pollution and Urban Form: A Review of Current Literature," 34 J. Amer. Inst. of Planners (March 1968), hereinafter cited as Rydell.

9. I. A. Singer, "An Objective Method for Site Evaluation," a paper presented at the annual meeting of the Air Pollution Control Association (1959).

10. Frank L. Cross, Jr. and Roger W. Ross, "New Developments in Fluoride Emissions from Phosphate Processing Plants," J. Air Pollution Control Assn. (January 1969), in Cross, "Community Air Pollution Protection Using Buffer Zones" 7-9 (unpublished manuscript n.d.), hereinafter cited as Cross.

11. Frank L. Cross, Jr., "Air Pollution at a Dolomite Plant, Minerals Processing" (November 1967), in Cross, 7, 9-10.

12. Frank L. Cross, Jr., "How One State Set Air Pollution Standards for Asphalt Plants, Roads and Streets" (June 1965), in Cross, 7, 11-2.

13. L. H. Dworetsky et al., "Report on Urban Expressway Air Pollution at Ten Sites in New York City," in The Relationship of Land Use and Transportation Planning to Air Quality Management 73 (G. Hagevik ed. 1972), hereinafter cited as Dworetsky.

14. General Electric Company, Final Report on Study of Air Pollution Aspects of Various Roadway Configurations 44 (June 1971).

15. Id. at 55.

16. NOAA Environmental Research Laboratories, "Air Pollution in the Locality of Buildings" 520 (1971), in H. W. Georgii, 40 Bulletin World Health Organization 624-35 (1969).

17. Dworetsky, 77, 81.

18. Dworetsky, 79, 99.

19. Dworetsky, 79, 83.

20. Dworetsky, 79, 84.

21. Dworetsky, 192-4. See also General Electric Company complete study; John Yocom et al., A Study of Indoor-Outdoor Air Pollutant Relationships (NTIS No. PB 195338 May 1970).

22. Saul Rich, "Effects of Trees and Forests in Reducing Air Pollution," in Trees and Forests in an Urbanizing Environment 32 (1971), hereinafter cited as Rich.

23. H.E. Heggestad, "How Plants Fight Man-Made Pollution," 39 The Science Teacher (No. 4 April 1972), hereinafter cited as Heggestad. See F. Elder and C. Hosler, Ragweed Pollen in the Atmosphere (1954); P. J. Zinke, "Forest Interception Studies in the United States," in Sopper and Lull, Forest Hydrology 137-61 (1967); N. C. Cassidy, "The Effect of Cyclic Salt in a Maritime Environment: The Absorption by Plants of Colloidal Atmospheric Salt," 28 Plant and Soil 390-406 (1968); F. H. Borman et al., "Fallout on the Vegetation of New England During the 1957 Atom Bomb Test Series," 39 Ecology 376-8 (1958); E. M. Romney et al., "Contamination of Plant Foliage with Radioactive Fallout," 44 Ecology 343-9 (1963); R. S. Russell, "An Introductory Review—Interception and Retention of Airborne Materials on Plants," 11 Health Physics 1305-15 (1965).

24. William H. Smith, "Trees in the City," 36 J. Amer. Inst. of Planners 431 (No. 6 November 1970), hereinafter cited as Smith.

25. Id.

26. A. Bernatsky, "The Importance of Protective Plantings Against Air Pollutants," in Air Pollution Proceedings 383-95, First European Conference on the Influence of Air Pollution on Plants and Animals (Trans. from German by Belov and Associates 1968).

27. Rich, 31.

28. Paul E. Waggoner, "Role of Plants in Improving the Environment," 1 J. Environmental Quality 123-7 (No. 2 1972).

29. George P. Hanson and Linda Thorne, "A Partial Pollution Solution: Plant Trees," 19 Lasca Leaves 35-6 (June 1970).

30. C. A. Federer, "Effects of Trees in Modifying the Urban Microclimate," in Trees and Forests in an Urbanizing Environment 23-7.

31. F. W. Went, "The Forest: What It Does and How It Is Established," in Smith, 432.

32. Victor Olgyay, "Design with Climate-Bioclimate Approach to Architectural Regionalism" (1963), in Rydell.

33. R. Geiger, "The Climate Near the Ground" (1965), in Smith, 432.

34. Id.

35. Panel on Weather and Climate Modification, Weather and Climate Modification: Problems and Prospects, 2 Research and Development (1966); N. J. Rosenberg, "The Influence and Implications of Windbreaks on Agriculture in Dry Regions," Ground Level Climatology (R. H. Shaw ed. 1967), in Smith, 433.

36. P. M. Felton and H. W. Lull, "Suburban Hydrology Can Improve Watershed Conditions," 94 Public Works (1963), in Smith, 433.

37. R. C. Newcomb, "Geologic Influence on Water Storage and Movement, Symposium of Forest Watershed Management" 57-8, in Smith, 434.

38. Heggestad.

39. D. H. Urie, "Influence of Forest Cover on Ground Water Recharge, Timing and Use," in Sopper and Lull, Forest Hydrology 313-24.

40. F. C. Turner, Noise Standards, 37 Fed. Reg. 11730 (1972).

41. Smith, 430.

42. T. F. W. Embleton, "Sound Propagation in Homogeneous Deciduous and Evergreen Woods," 35 J. Acoustical Soc. of Amer. 1119-25 (1963), in Smith, 431.

43. Gerhard Reethof, "Effect of Plantings on Radiation of Highway Noise," a paper presented at the annual meeting of the Air Pollution Control Assn. (1972).

44. Smith, 431. See also Embleton; F. M. Weiner and D. N. Keast. "Experimental Study of the Propagation of Sound Over Ground," 31 J. Acoustical Soc. of Amer. 724-33 (1959).

45. David I. Cook and David F. Van Haverbeke, "Trees and Shrubs for Noise Abatement," U.S. Dept. of Agric. Research Bulletin 56-7 (No. 246 July 1971), hereinafter cited as Cook and Haverbeke. See also Raymond E. Leonard, "Effects of Trees and Forests in Noise Abatement," in Trees and Forests in an Urbanizing Environment 35-38; Mary McLean, "Zoning Buffers: Solution or Panacea?" Planning Advisory Service, Amer. Soc. of Planning Officials (No. 133 1960); Kevin Lynch, Site Planning (2nd ed. 1971).

46. F. J. Meister, "Measurement of Traffic Noise in West Germany," 29 J. Acoustical Soc. of Amer. 81-4 (1957).

47. T. F. W. Embleton and G. J. Thiessen, "Propagation of Train Noise and Adjacent Land Use," 33 J. Acoustical Soc. of Amer. 1676 (1961).

48. Peter Durk, "The Influence of the Forest on the Health of Man," in Cook and Van Haverbeke, 5.

49. Cook and Van Haverbeke, 62-7.

50. Cook and Van Haverbeke, 62-3.

51. Cook and Van Haverbeke, 67.

52. Cook and Van Haverbeke, 24-5.

53. Cook and Van Haverbeke, 24-5.

53. Cook and Van Haverbeke, 27-8.

54. U.S. Const., Amend. V, XIV.

55. There are three types of theories that support excess condemnation. One is the "remnant theory," in which the condemning authority condemns more land than is needed for the improvement in order to prevent rendering the remaining remnant valueless and also to avoid excess severance damages. The state's power to exercise this type of excess condemnation has been judicially upheld in People v. the Superior Court of Mercer County, 68 Cal. 2d 206, 436 P, 2d 342 (1968). In a second type of excess condemnation the condemning authority condemns more land than is needed for the improvement in order to later resell it to realize the appreciation in value caused by the improvement's location nearby. This type of excess condemnation, appropriately called the recoupment theory, has been disallowed on the grounds that the excess land condemned will be put to no public use. Cincinnati v. Vester, 33 F. 2d 242 (6th Cir., 1929), aff'd on other grounds, 281 U.S. 439 (1930). However, this judicial disfavor of the recoupment theory is showing signs of changing, as will be explained in the text. The third type of excess condemnation is the protective or restrictive type. It is this type of excess condemnation that is generally discussed in the text, and the term excess condemnation as used in the text will always refer to this type unless the contrary is indicated. For recent articles exhaustively discussing the excess condemnation issue see Matheson, "Excess Condemnation in California: Proposals for Statutory and Constitutional Change," 42 So. Cal. L. Rev. 421 (1969); Note Excess Condemnation—To Take or not to Take: A Functional Analysis, 15 N.Y.L.F. 119 (1969).

56. For example, Missouri Const. Art. I, Sec. 27; New York General Municipal Law Sec. 36-A; Ohio Const. Art. XVIII, Sec. 10; Wisconsin Const. Art. II, Sec. 3A.

57. New Jersey Const. Article IV, Sec. 6(3).

58. 65 Wash, 2d 277, 399 P. 2d 330 (1965).

59. 223 Cal. App. 2d 23, 35 Cal. Rptr. 554 (1964).

60. 234 Miss. 788, 108 So. 2d 330 (1959).

61. 16 Ill. 2d 539, 158 N.E. 2d 766 (1959).

62. 374 F. 2d 218 (5th Cir., 1967).

63. 263 U.S. 78 (1923).

64. 3 N.Y. 2d 1006, 147 N.E. 2d 733 (1957).

65. 334 F. 2d 220, 221 (4th Cir., 1964).

66. 322 F. 2d 139 (6th Cir., 1963).

67. 376 Mich. 11, 135 N.W. 2d 364 (1965).

68. Wash. Rev. Code Ann. Sec. 47.12.250.

69. Calif. Streets and Highways Code Sec. 104.3 (1965).

70. Id., Sec. 104.

71. 55 N.J. 347, 262 A. 2d 199 (1970).

72. N.J. Stat. Ann. Tit. 27, Sec. 7-22.4 (Supp. 1972). "The [high-way] commissioner is hereby authorized to acquire by . . . condemnation real or personal property for landscape and roadside development appropriate for the restoration, preservation, and enhancement of scenic beauty adjacent to Federal Aid highways."

73. 31 Wis. 2d 256, 142 N.W. 2d 793 (1966).

74. Wis. Stats. Sec. 15.60 (1961).

75. 262 U.S. 700 (1923).

76. 270 N.Y. 333, 1 N.E. 2d 153 (1936).

77. 348 U.S. 26 (1954).

78. 297 F. Supp. 1137 (W.D. Okla. 1969).

79. 224 Cal. App. 2d 103, 36 Cal. Rptr. 308 (1964).

80. 41 Hawaii 219 (1955).

81. 405 P. 2d 185 (Okla. 1965).

82. 351 S.W. 2d 717 (Mo. 1969).

83. 34 N.J. Super. 84, 226 A. 2d 840 (App. Div. 1967).

84. Dept. of Public Works and Farina, 29 Ill. 2d 474, 194 N.E. 2d 209 (1963).

85. Tracey v. Preston, 172 Ohio St. 567, 178 N.E. 2d 923 (1962).

86. 156 Conn. 521, 245 A. 2d 579 (1968).

87. People v. County, 68 Cal. 2d 206, 436 P. 2d 342 (1968).

88. 33 F. 2d 242 (6th Cir., 1929), aff'd on other grounds, 281 U.S. 439 (1930).

89. 12 N.Y. 2d 379, 190 N.E. 2d 402 (1963).

90. 367 F. 2d 161 (9th Cir., 1966).

91. Some of the same problems that will arise in the acquisition of land for purposes of alleviating air pollution emissions along high-ways have also arisen in the highway scenic easement program, and experience in this program should also be consulted. See D.T. Sutte and R. A. Cunningham, Scenic Easements: Legal, Administrative, and Valuation Problems and Procedures (1968).

92. Ill. Ann. Stat. C. 24, Sec. 11-14.1 (1962).

93. Miss. Code Ann. Sec. 8038(n) (Supp. 1972).

94. Oregon Rev. Stats. Sec. 227.290.

95. Pa. Stats. Ann. Tit. 53, Sec. 39103 (1957).

96. 274 U.S. 603 (1927).

97. 345 S.W. 2d 547 (Texas Ct. Civ. App. 1961).

98. 231 Iowa 1227, 3 N.W. 2d 608 (1942).

99. 198 Cal. App. 2d 146, 17 Cal. Rptr. 680 (1961).

100. 233 Minn. 372, 46 N.W. 2d 873 (1951).

101. 203 Va. 562, 125 S.E. 2d 798 (1962).

102. 113 Ohio App. 523, 179 N.E. 2d 360 (1960).

103. 389 Pa. 295, 132 A. 2d 233 (1957).

104. E.g. Fisher v. City of Irving, supra; Galt v. Cook County, 405 Ill. 396, 91 N.E. 2d 395 (1950).

105. 6 Wis. 2d 637, 96 N.W. 2d 85 (1957).

106. 274 N. E. 2d 872 (Ill. App. 1971).

107. 103 N.J. Super. 367, 247 A. 2d 350 (App. Div. 1968).

108. 59 N. J. 571, 285 A. 2d 5 (1971).

109. 259 Md. 369, 269 A. 2d 797 (1920).

110. 285 App. Div. 287, 137 N.Y.S. 2d 603 (1955).

111. 202 Misc. 550, 115 N.Y.S. 2d 852 (Sup. Ct. 1951), aff'd, 305 N.Y. 805, 113 N.E. 2d 555 (1953).

112. 203 Cal. App. 2d 602, 21 Cal. Rptr. 714 (1962).

113. 12 N.Y. 2d 79, 187 N.E. 2d 123 (1962).

114. 197 F. Supp. 682 (D.C. Md. 1962).

6

SELECTED LOCAL CONTROLS

PERFORMANCE STANDARDS IN ZONING ORDINANCES

Performance standards in zoning ordinances provide a link between the direct pollutant-emissions controls typical of air pollution codes and the separation of incompatible land uses by means of zoning ordinances. Zoning ordinances have traditionally classified land uses on the basis of external characteristics that indicate whether certain uses would be considered incompatible in some areas of the community. For example, industrial uses have usually been excluded from residential areas. Additional distinctions are also made within general classes of land uses, and industrial uses, for example, are often subclassified into light, medium, and heavy. An industrial use placed in one of these categories is not usually allowed to locate in an area reserved for another of these categories.

Performance standards, on the other hand, are one of the traditional regulatory techniques used to control pollutant emissions. As defined in the provisions of the Clean Air Act of 1970, which authorize federal standards of performance for new stationary sources of pollution, a performance standard is "a standard for emissions of air pollutants which reflects the degree of emission limitation achievable through the application of the best system of emission reduction."[1]

Most of the zoning innovations introduced by the performance standards concept have been applied to industrial uses, and it is on these uses that we will concentrate here. The difficulty with industrial zoning is that the air pollution produced by each class of industry within zoning subclassifications is not taken into account when these subclassifications are created, even though the basis on which these land use distinctions are made includes the propensity of industries within these classifications to pollute the air. Traditional zoning has therefore ignored the obvious fact that it is not the character of an industry that determines whether it is more or less obnoxious to its environment (the rationale for segregation) but rather the extent to which it can control the external effects of its operations. Performance standards were introduced in zoning as a method of overcoming these limitations in the traditional zoning ordinance.

The Origins of Performance Standards Zoning

Dissatisfaction with the traditional use lists that preceded performance standards zoning arose for several reasons. There was no general agreement on where to draw the dividing line between light, medium, and heavy industries. It was difficult to include in a use list all possible new industries, so that new, well-qualified industries that did not happen to be listed in the zoning ordinance were kept out. Technological progress kept changing the characteristics of many existing industries, rendering the lists obsolete.

Another major shortcoming was the failure to take account of the fact that plants manufacturing the same product vary widely in their nuisance-producing characteristics, both at any given time and especially over any extended period of time. The size of the plant and the degree of modernization in its manufacturing operations greatly influence the extent of its environmental impact. Nor are most industrial nuisances associated directly with the product manufactured. The making of "electronic parts," for example, can be a nuisance-free operation, but it can also create some serious air pollution problems, as when magnet wire is made or electrical transformers are potted (soaked with plastic material).

The crude division of uses achieved by many zoning ordinances left many incompatible industries side by side and confined some industries that were compatible with light industry or even with commercial uses to heavy industry districts. Use lists provided no incentive to the older plant to modernize and update its operations so as to be less of a nuisance, for there was no guarantee that other nearby establishments would do the same.

The use of performance standards in zoning was originally conceived in 1951 by Dennis O'Harrow,[2] then director of the American Society of Planning Officials, as a means of overcoming these limitations in the traditional zoning ordinances.[3] Since industrial districts were primarily concerned with classification according to nuisance generation, it was felt that regulations phrased directly in these terms, if properly worked out and administered, would be more effective than regulations based upon use lists. Such regulations would encourage innovation by assuring manufacturing industries a better environment if they would eliminate or reduce the nuisance effects of their operations. There was also a desire to update "primitive" industrial zoning by using objective quantitative tests instead of such indefinite qualitative descriptions as "offensive" or "objectionable." Moreover, use of precision measurements would help lessen the rigidity of industrial classifications. "Effects" regulation is more reasonable and often less restrictive than regulation based upon use lists.

O'Harrow therefore suggested that the detailed and often inequitable catalogues of permitted uses in zoning ordinances be replaced with scientific standards by which one could measure the nuisance impact of an industry. While the threefold classification of industrial districts (light, medium, heavy) was retained, the basis for this classification was shifted from the control of use to the control of effect ("effects" zoning). Any use could be located in any industrial district if it could comply with measurable performance standards fixing the permissible level of environmental impact.

New York City's zoning ordinance (1961) illustrates this approach. Light, medium, and heavy manufacturing districts (called M1, M2, and M3 districts respectively) are also designated as "high performance," "medium performance," and "low performance" districts. The purpose of the M1 district is to provide for those manufacturing and related uses "which can conform to a high level of performance standards,"[4] while M3 districts "are designed to accommodate the essential heavy industrial uses which involve more objectionable influences and hazards, and which, therefore, can not reasonably be expected to conform to those performance standards which are appropriate for most other types of industrial development."[5] O'Harrow had listed 11 types of effects for which standards could be quantified,[6] and the American Society of Planning Officials (ASPO) subsequently expanded the list to 14.[7]

Chicago, in its 1957 amendment to the zoning ordinance, became the first city to incorporate industrial performance standards. Its ordinance regulates noise, vibration, smoke and particulate matter, toxic or noxious matter, odorous matter, fire and explosive hazards, and glare or heat. New York City's 1961 zoning ordinance also regulates humidity and radiation. More recent ordinances may consider such other external effects as sulfur oxides and waste matter.

Although performance standards were developed for industrial zoning and are so employed in almost all the ordinances that have adopted them, performance standards zoning can theoretically also be applied to residential and commercial uses. Some ordinances do apply fundamentally similar performance standards to all zoning districts. This is the case with the zoning ordinances of Marion County, Indiana.[8] In the proposed code for Virginia Beach, Virginia states that those standards which apply to the light industrial district "shall be applied to districts other than industrial."[9] A survey taken by ASPO in late 1970 showed that 19 percent of the respondents applied performance standards to commercial uses in their zoning ordinances, 15 percent applied them to residential uses, while 31 percent employed them to regulate industry.

The issue of extending performance standards to commercial and residential districts is beyond the scope of this chapter, which deals only with industrial performance zoning. Suffice it to note, however, that the extension of performance standards to other districts creates additional enforcement problems, that some of the standards essential to the measurement of industrial activities have little applicability to residential housing, and that there are some residential uses, such as lawn mowing, air conditioning, cooking malodorous foods, and outdoor cooking, which may not conform strictly to performance standards that might apply in a restricted industrial zone.

The drawback of performance standards zoning as applied to industrial uses also appears to lie primarily in the method by which they are administered. Performance zoning requires extra enforcement personnel with high technical ability, both to evaluate plans before construction and to enforce the standards after construction. Use lists have the virtues of certainty and ease of administration. Some industries are unwilling to locate in areas where they cannot determine their compliance with performance standards until after the plant is built. Furthermore, if it is concluded after the plant is built that the emission standards cannot be met, it is the rare local government that will tell the industry to relocate.

By classifying and grouping industries solely on the basis of external effects, performance standards should, in theory, render use lists obsolete, since any industry ought to be free to locate in any industrial district by demonstrating its ability to meet the standards for that district. In practice, no city has been bold enough to abandon traditional boundaries of use districts. Performance zoning is thus used as a supplement to rather than as a substitute for the older type of regulation, serving to provide a higher degree of differentiation among industrial districts and to allow the least noxious industrial uses close to residential districts.

Use lists in performance zoning ordinances can be applied to prohibit named industries without regard to performance standards otherwise applied. The Chicago ordinance lists 27 activities—including the storage or manufacture of dynamite, TNT, or nitroglycerin—which are excluded unless licensed by the Fire Prevention Bureau.[10] Use lists can also be utilized to designate those activities which are permitted in each manufacturing district "as of right," without regard to performance standards otherwise applied. Both the Chicago and New York zoning ordinances[11] do this to permit such uses as banks, restaurants, community facilities, and amusement establishments.

Finally, use lists can be applied to enumerate selected industries or groups of industries permitted to locate in a given industrial zone provided they comply with the performance standards for that zone. The New York City zoning ordinance imposes performance standards upon uses included in certain "use groups." Two such use groups are custom manufacturing activities and automotive and other necessary semiindustrial uses.

Performance Standards and Air Pollution

The environmental effects most commonly controlled by performance standards in a zoning ordinance are air pollution and various aspects thereof. Performance standards for air pollution have classically covered smoke, particulate matter, odors, and toxic matter. Recently some zoning ordinances have added sulfur oxides to this list. Widespread experience with smoke control ordinances and the more advanced state of research on standards for smoke pollution and dust, in comparison to other nuisance effects, account for the universal appearance of emission limitations on air contaminants in performance zoning.

Conceptually, there are two starting points to the establishment of performance standards—ambient standards and emission standards,[12] both ending in some form of source control. Almost all zoning ordinances use the latter approach, though in the proposed zoning ordinance for Puerto Rico ambient standards are used, at least in setting standards for particulate matter.

Under the ambient standards approach the community determines the level of a particular environmental contaminant that it will tolerate. The community then establishes the performance standards that will ensure that these levels are not exceeded. The criteria for determining ambient air standards may be based on the effects of particular contaminants on human health, vegetation and livestock, property, visibility, or other things, as in the federal air pollution control program under the 1970 Clean Air Act.

The alternate route to formulating performance standards, and the one generally followed by zoning ordinances, is the establishment of emission standards that deal with the technical capacity of desired industries to meet a specified nuisance output. In this case the starting point is source control rather than a predetermined ambient air level. No attempt is made to describe an acceptable air environment, that is, to define the "end state" aimed at by the emission rates, aside from a vague declaration that the standards are designed to promote and protect "the public health, safety, and general welfare" or to protect neighboring residential and commercial uses from "offensive" or "objectionable" influences.[13]

Smoke

Smoke is defined by the New York City ordinance as "any visible emission into the open air from any source, except emissions of an uncontaminated water vapor."[14] Smoke emissions are evaluated by means of the Ringelmann Chart, which contains graduated shades of gray varying in equal steps from white to black. The average performance standard prohibits or restricts for a specified time period the emission of smoke of a shade or density equal to or darker than a specified number on the chart, the numbers ranging from zero (all white or clear) to five (completely black or opaque).

New York's zoning ordinance is typical in setting the maximum permitted smoke emission standard at Ringelmann number 2: "In all Manufacturing Districts, the density of emission of smoke during normal operations shall not exceed Standard Smoke Chart number 2."[15] Some communities have tightened the requirements to Ringelmann number 1 and in some cases Ringelmann number 0. The proposed Auburn, New York, zoning ordinance (1971) prohibits the emission of smoke darker than Ringelmann number 1 in M1 and M2 districts, except that in the M2 districts "smoke of a shade not to exceed Ringelmann number 3 is permitted for up to 3 minutes total in any one 8 hour period."[16]

The New York City, Chicago, and Cook County, Illinois (1960) ordinances also limit smoke intensity and the duration of emission in terms of "smoke units," a measure which represents the product obtained by multiplying the Ringelmann Chart number by the emission time in minutes. The emission of smoke at density number 2 for 4 minutes equals 8 smoke units. New York City sets a maximum of 10 smoke units per hour per stack in M1 districts, 20 such units in M2 districts, and 30 such units in M3 districts.[17] These standards, which are tighter than those set in the earlier Chicago zoning ordinance, are applied in addition to the previously mentioned maximum density of Ringelmann number 2 which applies to all manufacturing districts. In addition, the performance standard zoning ordinances commonly contain a catchall provision declaring that the emission of smoke "in such manner or quantity as to be detrimental to or endanger the public health, safety, comfort, or welfare" constitutes "a public nuisance [which] shall henceforth be unlawful."[18]

It should be noted that the Ringelmann test is not particularly useful as a control over air pollution because it does not provide a measure of the actual amount of pollutants being released. The Ringelmann test is based on the appearance of the emission and does not indicate the quantity or type of air pollutant released.[19]

Dust and Other Particulate Matter

Particulate matter, the major visible ingredient of smoke, is defined as fine particles, either solid or liquid, that are small enough to be dispersed and carried in the air (dust is one sort of solid particulate matter). Particulate matter is usually divided into three classes: combustion products, made up of smoke, soot, and fly ash; industrial dust from foundries, paint spraying, steel mills, or rock crushing; and products of wind erosion from streets, alleys, playgrounds, vacant lots, and open fields.[20]

A distinction is often made between the particulate pollution of fuel burning equipment, refuse burning equipment, and manufacturing processes. Emission standards for particulate matter from manufacturing processes take various forms. The New York City zoning ordinance sets its standards in terms of pounds per hour per pounds of process weight, "process weight" being "the total weight of all materials used in any process which discharges dust into the atmosphere," but excepting liquid or gaseous fuels or combustion air.[21] Thus, in all manufacturing districts the maximum limit for manufacturing processes is 0.50 pounds per hour for 100,000 pounds of process weight.[22] In M1 or M2 districts a flat limit is placed on the amount of matter that may be emitted from all sources (that is, from manufacturing processes and combustion) from a single stack of 33 pounds per hour in the M1 district and 250 pounds per hour in the M2 district.[23]

Another approach, used by Cook County and Chicago, Illinois, relates the control of particulates to land area. The regulations in the zoning ordinance vary in the three industrial districts and set forth a maximum emission rate in pounds per hour per acre of property. Correction factors make allowances for the height of emissions and, in the Chicago ordinance, for the velocity and temperature of emissions. The total net rate of emission (determined by adding the emissions in pounds per hour from each source in the lot, then dividing by the number of acres in the lot to arrive at the gross hourly rate of emission in pounds per acre, and finally deducting from this the correction factors for stack height, temperature, and velocity) from all sources within the boundaries of the lot may not exceed 1 pound per acre of lot area during any one hour in the M1 district, 3 pounds in the M2 district, and 8 pounds in the M3 district.[24] The effect of this type of regulation is to benefit a plant with larger acreage and to penalize one with smaller acreage. At least one writer has questioned the reasonableness of this approach.[25] This type of regulation will make compliance with performance standards depend on whether the plant owner is willing and able to acquire additional acreage if it is needed. In fully developed industrial areas, expansion areas for existing sites may not be available.

Control of particulate emission can also start with ambient air quality standards, which are then related back to the emission point. Ground level concentrations of air pollutants can be mathematically related to the strength of an emission source with meteorological dispersion formulas. One of the basic meteorological dispersion formulas can be employed to define an emission rate of particulate matter in pounds per hour, given an acceptable air quality.

Thus far only the proposed Puerto Rico Land-Use Regulation (1969) incorporates a dispersion formula in the ordinance itself, allowing an industrial developer to calculate the allowable rate based on the particular characteristics of the proposed plant.[26] In the proposed Puerto Rico zoning ordinance, the maximum acceptable ground level concentration is 25 micrograms per cubic meter above background outside the zoning lot in the M1 district, 50 micrograms in the M2 district, and 100 micrograms in the M3 district, measured not outside the lot but rather in any other industrial district.[27]

It is worth noting that Puerto Rico rejected the approach of relating air pollution emissions to land area. The feeling was that since developable land on the island was extremely limited, such a method of regulation would appear to give the large landowner an unduly generous allowance for "air rights" to disperse air pollutants.[28]

As with smoke, zoning ordinances commonly add a general provision prohibiting the emission of particulate matter in such quantity or manner as to be detrimental to "public health, safety, comfort, or other aspects of the general welfare, or to cause damage or injury to property."[29] The zoning ordinance also generally specifies that dust and other wind-borne air pollution from storage areas, yards, service roads, or other untreated open areas, should be minimized by appropriate landscaping, oiling, or paving.[30]

Toxic or Noxious Matter[31]

Toxic matter is defined as any solid, liquid, or gaseous matter "containing properties which by chemical means are: (a) Inherently harmful and likely to destroy life or impair health, or (b) Capable of causing injury to the well-being of persons or damage to property."[32] Generally, the zoning ordinance restricts itself to a broad prohibition of "the discharge of toxic matter across lot lines in such concentrations as to be detrimental to or endanger the public health, safety, comfort, or welfare, or cause injury or damage to property or business."[33]

M. Salzenstein's proposed zoning ordinance for Auburn, New York, is more precise, incorporating the state ambient air quality standards and providing that, where toxic materials are not listed in the state's air quality standards, "the release of such materials shall be in accordance with the fractional quantities permitted below, of those toxic materials currently listed in the Threshold Limit Value adopted by the American Conference of Governmental Industrial Hygienists."[34] Threshold limit values are the maximum allowable concentrations of toxic materials for industrial workers inside industrial plants. The maximum is set at one-thirtieth of the threshold limit value across lot lines in the M1 district and at one-thirtieth of the threshold limit value beyond the district boundary line in the M2 district.

Sulfur Oxides

Zoning ordinances do not include sulfur oxides among the contaminants regulated. An exception again is the proposed Auburn ordinance which sets maximum limits on the emission of sulfur oxides in terms of pounds per hour per acre of lot area, 0.05 pounds per hour from all stacks per acre of lot area in the M1 district, and 1.5 pounds per hour in the M2 district.[35]

The Limitations of Performance Standards Zoning

The general consensus among writers who have considered the problem appears to be that if environmental control is desired it is better accomplished through comprehensive codes covering the particular nuisance involved: "The manner of controlling air pollution is not inherently or essentially a zoning problem. It is, rather a regulatory problem which can best and only be met in a comprehensive regulatory ordinance."[36] A report issued by the National Association of Counties Research Foundation reaches a similar conclusion: "Zoning laws should be an adjunct to air pollution control. They are too flexible a vehicle to be utilized as the basic method of control. Emission standards and other air pollution control standards belong to regulations relating to the specific subject."[37]

Performance standards were intended primarily as a zoning device (hence the term "performance zoning") and not as an air quality maintenance tool. This accounts for some of the basic inadequacies of zoning performance standards in air pollution control.

First, as most zoning ordinances incorporating performance standards were enacted before the recent surge in concern with air pollution, the emission standards contained in them are usually limited to particulates and toxic matter when, in fact, carbon monoxide, sulfur oxides, oxides of nitrogen, and hydrocarbons may be equally harmful to the health of surrounding households. More recent ordinances (for example, the proposed ordinance for Auburn, New York) have included sulfur oxides, but it is probably unreasonable to expect a zoning ordinance to lay down comprehensive controls for all harmful or potentially harmful air contaminants.

Second, the significant consideration in performance standards zoning has been the desire to prevent injurious effects from adjacent land uses, especially to protect residential districts from neighboring industries. The standards referring to emission rates have seldom been based on predetermined objectives of desirable ambient air quality. Among the specific purposes for the establishment of manufacturing districts enumerated in the New York City zoning ordinance one does not find any reference to the enhancement of ambient air quality, but one does find the desire "to protect adjacent residential and commercial areas, and to protect the labor force in other establishments engaged in less offensive types of manufacturing and related activities."[38]

Since zoning performance standards focus on the pollution source and gauge their controls to the ability of the industry to comply, the nuisance or environmental effect is not necessarily eliminated.[39] Indeed, the ambient air quality can be seriously threatened by the cumulative emissions of many industrial sources, even when each individual source meets the emission standard. In this sense it can be said that performance zoning has too localized a perspective to deal effectively with the broad problem of air pollution, which transcends district boundaries.

Third, performance standards for industrial zoning do not usually apply to all air polluters. There are many nonindustrial sources of air pollution, particularly "line" sources such as automobiles, which are not regulated by the zoning ordinance. Also, zoning ordinances cover only new uses and do not, except under special circumstances, eliminate previously existing sources of nuisance problems. With regard to a lawfully established existing use the ordinance usually states only that such use shall not be "so altered or modified as to conflict with, or further conflict with" the applicable performance standards.[40] Hence zoning performance standards cannot substitute for a comprehensive abatement program.

Fourth, performance zoning is administered by planners and it is doubtful whether planning or zoning agencies have the knowledge and experience to zone on an air pollution basis. For example, it is of critical importance when establishing such zones to consider such meteorological factors as prevailing wind speed and direction, turbulence, the prevalence of temperature inversions, precipitation, hours of sunshine, as well as all the various local surface features that can affect the microclimate and the atmospheric dilution capacity. Yet performance standards in the zoning ordinance were set without taking into account meteorological conditions, with the result that the actual air pollution impact may vary from plant to plant.[41] As one report has pithily remarked, "air pollution control specialists [are] needed to cope with . . . air pollution control."[42]

Fifth, it may be that zoning laws are too pliable to be an effective means of air pollution control. Economic and political pressures have long led to abuses of the variance-special-exception procedures. Zoning performance standards in particular are likely not to be enforced.[43] A comprehensive air pollution code not only gives added and necessary prominence to the air pollution problem but is also presumably less vulnerable to abuse. The New York City Air Pollution Control Code, for example, allows the administrator to grant a variance for "unreasonable hardship" for up to six months only upon condition that the recipient make "such periodic progress reports as the administrator shall specify." Extensions may be granted for periods up to six months only if "satisfactory progress" has been shown.[44]

The Zoning Ordinance and the Air Pollution Control Code

Once a governmental unit has enacted a comprehensive emission code and enforcement program, zoning performance standards relating to stationary emission sources need to be made compatible or else deleted from the ordinance. Under the 1967 Clean Air Act passed by the State of Washington, performance standards are superseded by the rules and standards promulgated by county, multicounty, or regional air pollution control authorities unless the zoning performance standards are more stringent.[45] The applicable statutory language provides as follows:

> The rules and regulations . . . adopted by an [air pollution] authority under the provisions of this chapter shall supersede the existing rules, regulations and ordinances of any of the component bodies included within said authority in all matters relating to the control and enforcement of air pollution as contemplated by this chapter. . . . Provided further, That nothing herein shall be construed . . . to affect . . . performance standards incorporated in zoning ordinances or resolutions of the component bodies where such standards relating to air pollution control or air quality containing [sic] requirements not less stringent than those of the authority [that is, the air pollution control agency].

Zoning ordinances themselves may explicitly delegate responsibilities in the field of air pollution to the local air pollution control agency. The industrial zoning ordinance of Marion County, Indiana

(Indianapolis area) does not specify performance standards but states simply that "The emission of smoke, particulate matter, or noxious or toxic gases shall conform to the standards and regulations of the Air Pollution Control Ordinance of the City of Indianapolis, Indiana (a copy of which is on file in the office of the Metropolitan Planning Department of Marion County, Indiana, and which standards and regulations are hereby incorporated by reference and made a part hereof)."[46] New York City's zoning ordinance does specify performance standards but it also declares, "In case of any conflict between the performance standards [and] the rules and regulations adopted by the Board of Air Pollution Control,[47] the more restrictive shall apply."[48]

At three points the New York City ordinance also provides for intervention in the zoning process by the air pollution authority. The section on smoke emission limitations reads:

"The method of measurement, additional limitations on the emission of smoke of a density not exceeding Standard Smoke Chart number 2, and the maximum permitted density and quantity of smoke during special operations such as . . . soot blowing, or process purging, shall be determined in accordance with rules and regulations adopted by the Board of Air Pollution Control."[49]

The section requiring certain procedures for minimizing windblown air pollution also adds, "or any other means as specified in rules and regulations adopted by the Board of Air Pollution Control."[50] Most significant, perhaps, for toxic or noxious matter the ordinance itself includes only a general prohibition against emissions that result in concentrations which endanger the public health or welfare, but precedes this with the statement that in all manufacturing districts, "the emission of toxic or noxious matter into the atmosphere shall be in accordance with limits established by the Board of Air Pollution Control."[51]

New York City has both performance zoning (1961 zoning ordinance) and an air pollution code enacted in 1964 and amended in 1971. The air pollution code contains a broad definition of "air contaminant" which is designed to ensure coverage of unknown as well as known pollutants: "Air contaminant means any particulate matter or any gas of any combination thereof in the open air, other than uncombined water or air."[52] An all-embracing clause prohibits any person from causing or permitting the emission of air contaminant which, by itself or in reaction with other air contaminants or solar energy, "causes or may cause" detriment to health and comfort or injury to property, business, or plant and animal life.[53] Specific emission standards, applying to all sources, are set down for cadmium, beryllium, mercury, and asbestos, while emission standards applying only to particular sorts of equipment (such as boilers and refuse and fuel burning equipment) are set down for other named pollutants (sulfur compounds, particulate matter, and nitrogen oxides).[54]

An interesting approach exemplified in the emission standards article of the air pollution code is the use of "environmental ratings" to determine permissible emission rates for particulate matter from "processes, and exhaust and ventilation systems."[55] Emissions from exhaust and ventilation systems are rated on a descending scale from A to D on the basis of the adverse effects of their contaminant discharges; A applies to systems producing the most serious adverse effects on receptors or the environment, D to those whose discharges are relatively innocuous. Each equipment operator is required to propose an environmental rating for himself based on emission data and "pertinent environmental factors." The administrator is free to reject and replace the proposed environmental rating with his own if the proposed rating is found unacceptable. Among the environmental factors on which information must be submitted, the following are worth noting:

(b) physical surroundings of emission sources . . .
(d) dispersion characteristics at or near source; (e) location of emission source relative to ground level and surrounding buildings, hills, and other features of the terrain; (f) current or anticipated ambient air quality in vicinity of source.[56]

The above provisions regulate emissions from stationary sources. The prevention program of the ordinance works through a system of installation permits and operating certificates as well as fuel standards and operator licensing provisions which need not concern us here. A permit is required[57] for the installation or alteration of "equipment," defined expansively as "any device capable of causing the emission of an air contaminant into the open air, or any stack, conduit, flue, duct, vent or similar device connected to or serving such device."[58] Equipment which is subject to the permit requirement for installation or alteration must still be granted an operating certificate before it can be put into operation.[59] Fuel burning and refuse burning equipment and "equipment used in a manufacturing process" must also receive an operating certificate.[60]

In order for the applicant to obtain a permit for installation under the air pollution code he must show "to the satisfaction of the administrator" that his equipment meets some generally phrased performance standards, the first two of which require that "(1) The equipment is designed and will be installed or altered to operate without causing a violation of the provisions of this code; and (2) The equipment incorporates advances in the art of air pollution control developed for the kind and amount of air contaminant emitted by the applicant's equipment. . . ."61

While the emission standards of New York City's Air Pollution Control Code are indisputably more comprehensive than those in the zoning ordinance and are thus better suited for air pollution abatement, the air pollution code is not as effective as a <u>preventive</u> tool. This is because the code does not allow the air pollution agency to enter the picture early enough to review and veto proposed industrial construction from the very start. Instead, the agency is restricted to the clumsy and indirect method of threatening to withhold the installation permit for the equipment. Although "installation" is defined as the "placement, assemblage or construction of equipment . . . at the premises where the equipment will be used, and includes all preparatory work at such premises,"62 in practice considerable work on the project can be accomplished before an application has to be made for the equipment installation permit. By that time, confronted with the sums already invested in plant construction, the air pollution authority may be reluctant to deny the permit.63

Reconciling Performance Standards with the
Air Pollution Code

It is self-evident that a separate air pollution ordinance will always be necessary, if only to cope with those pollution sources (the nonindustrial, the nonstationary, or the already established) that are not covered by performance zoning. But it is still not clear whether air pollution control should be entirely deleted from the zoning ordinance and made the exclusive province of the pollution code. Each approach has disadvantages, but these might be overcome by proper drafting.

Performance standards, we have seen, deal almost solely with industry. But there is no intrinsic reason why performance standards zoning cannot be extended to provide across-the-board coverage of residential and commercial uses, as indeed they have been in some ordinances. This would go a long way towards reducing both neighborhood and areawide pollution, for factories are not the only polluters.

Zoning ordinances, we have seen, deal only with particulate matter, smoke, and toxic matter. Again, there seems to be no intrinsic reason why this coverage cannot be expanded to include sulfur oxides and other major air contaminants.

Zoning ordinances generally apply only to new sources of pollution, but there is no reason why the zoning ordinance, along with the performance standards, could not include a provision similar to the amortization provisions more frequently found in zoning ordinances. Such a provision would set time limits for correcting the nonconforming characteristics of uses. As in other amortization tables, this provision should be carefully tailored to fit the particular circumstances, taking into account the frictions created by the nonconforming uses in the districts involved, the problems of making corrections, the circumstances of the community, and the sophistication of the courts of the state.[64]

Finally, zoning performance standards have as their starting point source controls that are geared to industry's ability to comply and are intended to protect adjacent districts. But there is no reason why the zoning ordinance cannot also incorporate predetermined ambient air quality standards to define the air environment aimed for. Puerto Rico has done this.

On the other hand, emission codes, which are strong on enforcement and abatement, are weak on prevention. Here, too, there is no real reason why the air pollution ordinance cannot be redrafted to give the air pollution agency the authority to screen, and veto if necessary, all new industrial construction while the latter is still in the planning stage. As we have seen, it is paradoxical but true that the air pollution agency is best able to monitor the installation of incinerators and boilers in individual plants after major development decisions have been made. At this point, however, it is difficult for the air pollution agency to refuse an installation permit. More control over industrial development could be exercised by air pollution agencies if they were permitted to review plans for industrial development before major construction is attempted.

What form the accommodation between the zoning ordinance and the air pollution code (and the respective institutional bodies) should take is not immediately evident, but it is clear that there must be some accommodation beyond the bare minimum of bringing their standards into compatibility. One approach is for the air pollution authority to concentrate on obtaining compliance from existing industries while the zoning agency concentrates on trying to avoid new problems.[65] This division of functions assigns prevention to the zoning ordinance and enforcement to the air pollution code. Another approach would delegate responsibilities for prevention to the air pollution agency. The latter would review all industrial plans for their "air quality impact," while the zoning agency would still evaluate proposed industrial development on other bases. Air pollution considerations, as advanced by the air pollution authorities, would thus form another set of "constraints" (in addition to the usual constraints, such as population growth and transportation network) with which the traditional planning process would have to cope. Planning agencies would provide additional intelligence concerning air pollution potential, since they alone possess information on such relevant factors as commuting habits and trends. Something of this sort of division of functions appears in one suggestion that "overlay" zones be established by the pollution agency to screen out uses undesirable because of their air pollution effects, while zoning bodies continue to locate specific industrial sites within nonrestricted areas.[66] Finally, we note parenthetically that even if the emission code becomes the exclusive means of air pollution control, performance standards could still have a role in the zoning ordinance when source controls more stringent than those provided in the air pollution code are called for.

Conclusions on Performance Standards

1. Performance standards zoning can be both narrower and broader than the direct control of air pollution by stationary sources. Performance standards do not usually cover all of the stationary sources that are covered by the air pollution code, and they may not cover all of the pollutants for which federal standards have been published. At the same time, performance standards in zoning may cover pollutants and noxious substances for which federal standards have not been issued.

2. Under some circumstances, performance standards appear to be a useful element in state air quality implementation plans. For example, performance standards can be used to control air pollution levels in parts of an air quality control region where national standards are generally met but where localized areas of excessive air pollution ("hot spots") still remain.

3. Problems of coordination between performance standard zoning and air pollution control can be troublesome. One problem is that performance standards zoning is usually enacted and applied by municipalities and counties, while air pollution is often the responsibility of a state or regional agency. Coordination of performance standard zoning and air pollution control by means of carefully written state legislation will be required in most jurisdictions.

SPACING CONTROLS IN ZONING ORDINANCES

It is sometimes argued that to control certain pollutants, sources of emission should be spread out in order to avoid localized high concentrations (hot spots) of air pollutants. The following section examines the question whether the zoning ordinance might be utilized to achieve this separation. The type of land use examined is the filling station since it is a source of reactive hydrocarbons that contribute to photochemical smog and is the subject of restrictive controls both by the land use planning agency and, in some cases, the air pollution control agency. An example of the latter is the attempt by the Bay Area Air Pollution Control District (San Francisco) in 1972 to impose a ban on the construction of all new filling stations when it found that oxidant levels had exceeded the air quality standard throughout most of the air quality control region.[67] The analysis concludes that the typical zoning regulations adopted by most municipalities are not sufficient to regulate the location of gasoline filling stations when air pollution control is the dominant purpose behind such regulation.

Two zoning problems relating to filling station construction are of interest. The first is the case law relating to the location of filling stations. The principal point to be made here is that the cases are presently ambivalent about the location of filling stations in relation to other uses. In particular, the presence of other filling stations in proximity to the filling station whose application is under consideration is sometimes favorable and sometimes unfavorable to a decision concerning the new location. The cases reflect this ambivalence even though the overconcentration of filling stations at any one point in the urban environment may have harmful effects on the quality of the air in the vicinity of those stations.

Another type of control to be discussed here permits the municipality to regulate the location of filling stations in relation to churches, schools, and other places of public assembly. Local regulations conventionally prevent the location of filling stations within a stated distance of such public and semipublic places of assembly on the ground that filling stations are hazardous uses and should not be located in proximity to large numbers of people. A zoning restriction of this type is too crude to be applied with any degree of success to the air pollution problem. However, it does provide a precedent for regulations limiting the location of filling stations on the grounds that the pollutants they discharge are health hazards.

A recent Maine case, Buck v. Kilgore[68] illustrates how a spacing requirement can also act as a total ban on all filling stations in a municipality. This case deserves brief notice here because it points out that even marginally restrictive regulations of filling stations may have an almost prohibitory effect because of the nature of the area in which they are applied. In the Maine case, an ordinance prohibiting all filling stations within 2,000 feet of places of public assembly had the effect of banning all filling stations in South Portland, the city that enacted the restriction. While commenting on this impact of the ordinance, the court did not consider it decisive. Instead, it held the ordinance unconstitutional on the ground that fire hazards from filling stations were not demonstrably greater than those from other businesses. As a result, there was no basis for establishing a relationship between the storage of gasoline in filling stations and the prevention of fire in places of public assembly.

Zoning Controls over the Location of Filling Stations

The Maine case also suggests that a preliminary review of the basis for regulating filling stations would be helpful before examining the law relating to their location in more detail. Zoning controls over filling stations have often been based on the hazards thought to be associated with such facilities, but filling station hazards have often been taken for granted. This approach may have been proper when early forms of this use presented obvious dangers or when the efficiency of precautionary measures had not been tested, proved, or subject to study for a significant period of time. Logic demanded that the storage of flammable liquids must always present a danger, and that a municipality could act in anticipation of such danger. Hence, the New York Court's statement in Tartasky v. Larkin:[69]

> The court takes judicial notice of the fact that no matter how great the precautions taken by the operators of such filling stations, gasoline is still flammable, combustible, explosive material, and that the burning or explosion of even one of these gasoline storage tanks could be catastrophic to the surrounding area.[70]

The modern filling station may make an anachronism of this judicial posture. The extent of the danger presented by filling stations is in dispute. As was pointed out in a recent report:[71]

> Use of improved equipment in transporting, storing, and pumping gasoline has all but eliminated these hazards [fire and explosion], as illustrated by a comparison of the standard insurance rates for selected activities in Ohio.

Type of use	Annual rate per $100
Single-family	$0.12
Doctor's office	$0.42
Restaurant	$1.047
Automobile salesroom	$1.515
Filling station	$0.35

183

Other studies show fewer fires in service stations than in other commercial facilities. The relative incidence of fires at restaurants is stated to be three times that of service stations, and the service station is purported to have a propensity to catch fire equal to that of a local food store.[72]

Traffic problems said to be created by filling stations may also be negligible. Stations have wide approaches, are set back from the sidewalk and have more than adequate lighting. This type of planning "results in driving and pedestrian safety of the highest order."[73] It is as difficult to estimate the traffic dangers posed by service stations as to estimate the danger of fire and explosion. Uses that generate large volumes of traffic are recognized as being particularly dangerous at places where traffic circulates poorly.[74] Bottlenecks are the usual result.

Since traffic and service stations are inseparable, a frequent conclusion is that the latter generates the former. However, filling stations may have been falsely branded. A filling station requires traffic sufficient to make business profitable, so it is equally plausible to say that traffic generates filling stations. Circumstantial evidence can be used to support either position. The steady residential customer supports many stations not in the mainstream of large thoroughfare competition; thus the service station attracts business in the form of traffic. Thoroughfare customers produce service station clusters; thus business attracts the service station.

Clearly, the traffic-generating effect of the filling station is more evident in residential areas where large volumes of traffic do not already exist. Courts are therefore not reluctant to cite traffic problems as a reason for excluding filling stations from residential areas. In nonresidential areas the high traffic volume camouflages any possible hazard a station may create. Streets are already notched with curb-cuts, especially if other stations have begun to cluster. Under these conditions, the additional danger of another station may either be negligible or not enough to surpass the saturation point. Service station clustering may be reason for excluding yet another station or for concluding that one more cannot hurt. This paradox is beyond judicial resolution. The potential traffic hazard of a service station is greater where volume is already high, but it is a less consistently available basis for exclusion.

One can predict judicial turmoil whenever hazards are used to justify control under the police power, but many cases have held that hazards justify control by zoning. Thus the Mississippi Court in Ballard v. Smith[75] held that it was reasonable for the city to prohibit gasoline stations in all but industrial zones:

[Filling] stations involve highly inflammable commodities
and affect the flow and hazards of traffic. The city

authorities may take these and other circumstances into consideration in determining proper zoning for filling stations.[76]

Judge Hall dissented:

So far as the fire hazard is concerned, if any there be, the present method of operating gasoline stations is such that there is substantially no fire hazard whatsoever and a check of the records of the city fire department in practically every city will show that there are very few calls of the fire department to gasoline filling stations.[77]

Most courts have also held that gasoline stations located in residential areas have a tendency to depreciate property values in those areas.[78] To some courts this is sufficient reason to prohibit stations in such areas, since property owners in residential areas purchased in reliance upon the residential zoning classification. Yet the fact that service stations would depreciate the surrounding property values is not necessarily conclusive on the question of whether to allow a station in a residential zone. The Supreme Court of Arkansas allowed a service station in a residential zone in Herring v. Stannus,[79] even though there was evidence that the value of surrounding property would depreciate. Other businesses nearby and heavy traffic within the residential zone caused the decrease of surrounding property values to be a nondeterminative factor.

Other courts recognize inherent unpleasantnesses. A New Jersey court, in Vine v. Board of Adjustment,[80] held that it was reasonable for a city to zone gasoline stations out of residential districts because of their peculiarly obnoxious fumes. In Kidder v. City Council of Brockton,[81] the Supreme Judicial Court of Massachusetts held that the city was not limited to the consideration of fire hazards when deciding whether a service station would be harmful to the public welfare. Other factors relating to the public interest were also relevant, such as traffic, noise, and odors. In fact, many courts allow control on the basis of traffic alone.

In Dickinson v. Plainfield,[82] the owner of a lot which already had pumps fronting on one street was denied permission to install additional pumps on the opposite side. The New Jersey Court upheld the Board of Adjustment's decision, asserting that it was clear that traffic congestion endangering motorists and pedestrians would result, and that the additional factor of other facilities in the immediate vicinity rendered the Board's action reasonable. The opinion expressed in the Dickinson case is typical.

On the other hand, a number of decisions have refused to bar service stations from proposed sites solely on the basis of alleged inherent risks to the public safety and welfare. In Sandenburgh v. Michigamme Oil Co.,[83] the Supreme Court of Michigan allowed a service station to locate in a residential neighborhood, holding that "It is well settled that a gasoline station is not a nuisance per se."[84] According to the court, whether or not the station would prove to be a nuisance at a later time would depend upon the particular circumstances and could not be answered before it began operations.

In Reheis v. City of Newark,[85] the Supreme Court of New Jersey held that the particular circumstances surrounding the proposed use determines whether or not a filling station is contrary to the public welfare. The court allowed gasoline stations to be erected in zones barring stations when the proposed site was on a major highway between two cities, when the number of stations in that area was not excessive, when the value of the residential property in the area would not be harmed, and when danger to schoolchildren was negligible.

When a field engineer testified for an oil company to the effect that filling stations are no greater fire hazards than grocery stores or any other commercial enterprises, the Supreme Court of Indiana (in Board of Zoning Appeals v. La Dow[86]) allowed a gas station to locate in a commercial zone, where stations were otherwise forbidden:

> The undisputed evidence . . . shows filling stations to have little if any effect on pedestrian and traffic safety, no appreciable effect on danger of loss by fire or injury to health.[87]

Additional problems arise when an application for yet another filling station is filed in an area where several stations have already been constructed. In some cases, like the North Carolina case of Horden v. Raleigh,[88] the courts have held that the fact that service stations had previously been allowed in an area was not controlling on whether additional stations would be permitted to locate there. But courts face a real dilemma in this situation. Since zoning decisions tend to be based on the character of uses already existing in the surrounding area, the presence of other filling stations may simply lead to further approvals. Eventually there may simply be too many filling stations within the district, and excessive congestion and pollution may be the result.

On the other hand, traffic and other hazards resulting from filling station overconcentration may be the basis for the exclusion of additional stations under the hazard theory. While exclusion of an additional station in this situation may be open to the objection that the zoning power to exclude has been improperly used to regulate competition,[89] municipalities that are careful to place their exclusionary decisions on other grounds will not run the risk of such criticism.

The relevant cases are divided on the question whether to allow another filling station in this type of situation. In State ex rel. City of Algoma v. Peterson,[90] the Supreme Court of Wisconsin reasoned that since the proposed additional station would not be a public nuisance, its construction permit should be granted. The court held that as there were a number of other stations in the immediate vicinity there was no real evidence that another station would be unsafe or unhealthy to the public. A related case involving the application of a state statute governing filling station locations is Executive Television Corp. v. Zoning Board of Appeals.[91] In that case the local board of zoning appeals had refused a permit for a gasoline filling station under a state statute authorizing the board to issue such permits. On the facts of the case, a permit could have been denied under the statute only if the station would be an undue peril to the safety of the public. The Supreme Court of Connecticut held that a permit for the construction of a gasoline station should have been granted. No places of public assembly were in the area, the site was on a busy street, and there was a large station across the street from the proposed site. In addition, there was no evidence that the proposed station would create any additional peril to the public.

The presence of other stations in the vicinity may even support the case for construction of another on property zoned for residential use. In State v. City of Bedford ex rel. Rosenthal,[92] the Court of Appeals of Ohio issued a writ of mandamus to compel the city to grant a construction permit. Although the site was zoned residential, there were prior acquisitions in the area for utility and highway purposes, the site was located at a busy intersection, and filling stations were already located on two corners of the intersection. These circumstances prompted the court to hold that the zoning power was being used to destroy the potential value of plaintiff's property without any showing of justification.

The site of a proposed station in Town of Homecroft v. Macbeth[93] was zoned residential although it was along a busy highway and there were other gas stations in the vicinity. The Indiana Supreme Court granted a variance to allow construction of the station, commenting that the usual reasons for not allowing service stations in residential districts were not controlling. The site fronted a busy highway. Fumes, dirt, and noise already bombarded surrounding residential lots. The proposed filling station could do no worse than this. "We are not dealing," said the court, "with a situation where an owner seeks a variance in a secluded and quiet section of a town."[94] In this case the proposed site was zoned for a use for which it was unreasonable, and under those circumstances a variance was granted.

On the other hand, a number of cases have held that the presence of other gasoline stations in the vicinity is not enough in itself to support a permit for another, since too many other factors come into play. For example, in McKinney v. City of Little Rock,[95] the plaintiff sought to build a gas station in a district zoned for two-family dwellings. The Supreme Court of Arkansas, in the face of evidence to the effect that there were a number of stores, factories, or filling stations in the immediate vicinity, sustained the city's refusal to grant a permit. The fact that there were other stations nearby, said the court, was irrelevant. They might be near but not in the residential zone in which plaintiff's property was located. A zoning line must be drawn somewhere, and those whose property is near the line but wish to be on the other side will always complain. But such is the price they must pay for living in a city that attempts to plan its growth in a systematic way.

Similarly, the Supreme Judicial Court of Massachusetts, in Kidder v. City Council of Brockton,[96] affirmed a denial of a service station permit even though the district was zoned to allow stations. The court pointed out, however, that the intersection in question was busy, that other stations were at the intersection, and that another would add to traffic congestion and thus endanger schoolchildren.

This review of the legal basis for zoning gasoline filling stations suggests that the rationale behind the zoning of filling stations may be changing. If supposed ground hazards allegedly traceable to filling stations do not really exist, the basis for municipal control over these stations by means of the zoning ordinance may be weakened. Exclusion of filling stations from residential areas may still be supportable in most instances, but controlling their location in industrial and even in commercial areas may be more difficult to accomplish. Even when an overconcentration of filling stations leads to traffic congestion and other undesirable effects the municipality may be powerless to prevent the construction of another. The municipality will be especially restricted if the court takes the view that the area is already committed to filling station use, so that the addition of yet another filling station is only marginal. The courts in zoning cases are very sensitive to the way in which an area of the municipality has previously developed. A considerable reorientation in zoning law thus appears to be necessary before existing zoning controls over filling stations can be useful in implementing air quality programs, especially in areas of the city in which a substantial amount of commercial and related filling station development has already occurred.

Spacing Controls over Filling Stations

Air quality control programs have been particularly sensitive to the interaction between air pollution sources and uses that may be affected by the pollution generated by these sources. Zoning regulations prohibiting filling stations from locating within a certain distance of places of public assembly, such as churches, initially appear to make sense as an air pollution control strategy. These regulations are not based on air quality factors, and the spacing formulas adopted may not incorporate standards considered necessary from the point of view of air quality control. Nevertheless, these ordinances do provide some judicial precedent favorable to the use of zoning regulations to implement air quality objectives.

The basis for spacing ordinances has often been the risk of explosion and fire, a risk that should not be taken in cases where a major catastrophe might result. Courts have also considered the increased danger to large numbers of pedestrians, especially to children when a school is involved. They have also considered the effect upon traffic when service stations are located where large numbers of automobiles are likely to converge, and the effect of noise and fumes upon religious services, classes, and the like. The hazards associated with the service stations are particularly influential upon a determination of constitutionality when a public assembly ordinance is invoked.

Hazards, despite their severity, may not justify unreasonable spacing. The prescribed distance within which stations cannot be constructed must be reasonably related to the increased danger associated with public assembly uses. In Cayce v. Hopkinsville,[97] danger to young pedestrians, possible disruption of services or classes, danger of fire or explosion, and traffic hazards were cited as reasons for upholding a Kentucky zoning ordinance barring service stations from within 100 feet of churches or schools. Similar dangers were cited in Suburban Tire and Battery Co. v. Mamaroneck[98] as justification for an ordinance requiring a 200-foot spacing and in Kramer v. Mayor and City Council of Baltimore[99] as justification for a 300-foot spacing. "It is readily conceivable," the court said in the Kramer case, "that the establishment of filling stations in proximity to institutions where large numbers of persons assemble may materially intensify traffic and fire dangers which in other sections might be attributable to such stations only to a negligible degree."[100]

Spacing ordinances have also been upheld when they require that filling stations be kept a specified distance from residences and apartment houses. Thus the ordinance challenged in Radick v. Zoning Board of Review[101] prohibited service stations within 100 feet of apartment districts or dwelling houses. The Supreme Court of Rhode Island gave the ordinance a practical interpretation. It held that the word "district" in the zoning ordinance did not refer to the zoning classification but to the actual use. Thus service stations within 100 feet of a zoning district zoned for apartments would be allowed, but filling stations within 100 feet of an actual residence or apartment would be prohibited.

Ordinances that prescribe a reasonable distance from recognized places of public assembly within which filling stations are prohibited are generally acceptable. We have noted above, however, that the validity of the assumption that hazards such as fire, explosion, danger to pedestrians, and undesirable traffic patterns accompany service stations has recently been under attack. Thus, while some courts uphold distance regulations on the basis that gasoline stations create a hazard to the public health, safety, and welfare, other courts have found that no such danger exists, at least in certain situations. They have therefore struck down the application of gasoline spacing ordinances in certain fact situations. The courts upholding spacing regulations consider gasoline stations to be dangerous per se, while other courts see nothing inherently dangerous in regard to gasoline stations, and look for other factors upon which to base a particular decision.

In Pal Sexto Corp. v. Larkin,[102] the New York Court found that gasoline stations are no greater risk to the safety of schoolchildren than are other kinds of retail establishments. In this case, the plaintiff sought to build a gas station about 600 feet from a school property. However, there was a gasoline station closer to the school than the plaintiff's proposed site. And, in the words of the court:

> Moreover, no facts appear in the record from which it appears that the presence of a gasoline station on the subject property would present a greater hazard to children than any of the permitted uses such as stores, restaurants, etc. Assuming that the children attending Mepham High School were children of tender years instead of adolescents, there is no proof that such children are exposed to particular danger in passing gasoline service stations.[103]

The New York trial court for Nassau County also ordered a permit to be granted for the construction of a gasoline station in Bar Harbour Shopping Center, Inc. v. Andrews,[104] where the plaintiff sought to build a gas station on a 30-acre shopping center site. The village board had denied the application on the grounds that it would constitute a traffic hazard near a high school. What seemed to be crucial to the court was the fact that there was a buffer between the school and the station site, so that the danger to schoolchildren from fire risk was minimized:

With respect to the fire hazard, the station will be separated from the school building by Merrick Road, which is a wide arterial highway, and by the school yard.[105]

For our purposes, the intervening factor of the buffer is important. The cases suggest that the courts may look closely at the fact situation in which a spacing ordinance is applied and may not be willing to accept a spacing restriction without additional factual analysis.

It should therefore be noted that some courts will look at each spacing case on its own particular facts, without approving or disapproving distance requirements per se. Some courts will not uphold the distance requirement if the purpose for the regulation is not applicable in that case. In Crone v. Town of Brighton,[106] plaintiffs sought to have a spacing ordinance declared unconstitutional as applied to their property so they could build a gasoline station on it. Under the ordinance, a gas station was not allowed in the commercial zone of the town, except where the Planning Board, with the approval of the Town Board, issued a temporary permit for no longer than five years. However, no gas station could have an entrance or exit within 300 feet of the entrance or exit of a school, playground, or church. In this case, the gate to a school was within 300 feet of the site of the proposed station. The court found, however, that the gate was only being used as an excuse by the Board to deny the permit for the station, and so the court granted the temporary permit:

> In view of Mr. Crone's uncontested warning that the members never used the rear door to pass to and from Monroe, the obvious improbability of nursery children being allowed to use the gate, the timing of the installation hard on the board's approval of the application, and the deadly silence on any need or use of the gate, it stands as a gesture to thwart the relief sought by a newly created technicality, and is clothed with no significance warranting the acceptance of its mere existence as proof of use.[107]

Effectiveness of Local Controls

This review of zoning regulations for filling stations suggests that the law of zoning as it has developed so far is not directly applicable to programs of air quality control that seek to place limitations on pollutants from gasoline filling station sources. Zoning regulations governing the location of filling stations are often responsive to the existing development in the area of a prospective filling station site. For this reason they may not place effective limits on the construction of new stations in areas where there is already an overconcentration of filling stations. Spacing requirements prohibiting the location of filling stations near churches and other places of public assembly may have some application in air pollution control programs. But spacing requirements may be arbitrary and not properly related to the control of air pollution hazards created by filling stations.

It would appear, therefore, that controls over filling station locations that are implemented as part of an air pollution control strategy may have to be based on more general health and safety factors not related to zoning regulations. Air pollution controls regulating filling station locations would then have to be based on the health dangers involved in leaving the release of pollutants from filling stations uncontrolled. There would be no difficulty in upholding the constitutionality of such regulations if the linkages between health hazards and filling station locations could be shown. Presumably, filling station controls imposed under the air quality regulations can be made to preempt any local zoning ordinance to the contrary. The impact of such preemption on local zoning regulation may still be quite disturbing, and the issue may need more careful attention than it has previously been given.

Another important issue concerns the priority to be given to filling station controls as compared with other types of air pollution regulations, such as improvements in technology and the control of other pollution sources. Developing a comprehensive air pollution control strategy, with control over the regulation of filling stations as one of its elements, may thus require regulatory systems at the metropolitan level so as to take the entire air quality region into account. Controls based on the air quality region could avoid some of the localized factors that have influenced many court decisions on the regulation of filling stations at the local level.

THE DESIGN OF URBAN STRUCTURES

A review of architectural literature reveals that project design criteria often do not include the project's impact on air quality. Environmental design has come to signify an aesthetic blending with the surrounding area rather than an empirical consideration of the effects of the project on environmental quality. One of the main goals of architecture is to provide people with a comfortable environment. However, many of the technical problems have become entirely the province of specialist engineers who often consider only one quantity—air temperature in heating and air conditioning or lumens in lighting, for example—and neglect the impact these considerations have on the total environment.[108] But in theory, the role of architecture has evolved to a point where it can integrate air quality considerations into design of buildings. According to E. Cermach and F. Chaudhry:

> Architecture has evolved from the art and science of designing and constructing buildings with primary reference to beauty and function of form into a complex effort to control the environment of a building system. This control is a part of the total design of a building system which attempts to establish and maintain an optimal environment for the well-being and constructive participation by the occupants. One of the most important elements of control is the concern about the quality of air supplied to closed spaces and the quality of air exhausted from such spaces. The quality of air depends on the characteristics of air flow around the building structures, which, in turn, are controlled by the meteorological conditions, the distinctive shapes and distributions of structures, and the distribution of air pollution sources.[109]

An important consideration for the architect concerned with designing an optimal environment is the indoor-outdoor pollutant concentration levels. Although the data available on indoor-outdoor concentration ratios lack substantiation and comprehensiveness, it is possible to make a few generalizations. It generally appears that indoor concentrations of gaseous pollutants are lower than outdoor concentrations in nonindustrial structures. There are exceptions to this, however, and more often than not it is best to assume that indoor concentrations of air pollutants are equal to or slightly less than outdoor concentrations. At best, unless outdoor concentrations are exceptionally high, there is usually less than a 50 percent difference between them. In some instances, indoor concentrations have registered higher than outdoor ones when the latter are fairly low.[110]

Three sets of factors determine the relative concentrations affecting building occupants: (1) those influencing the outdoor concentrations about the building; (2) those influencing the exchange of outdoor and indoor air; (3) the amounts and types of pollutants generated within the building.[111]

One goal of design solutions should be to improve the indoor concentration levels, since this is where people spend most of their time, especially those most sensitive to air pollution: the young, the sick, and the elderly. This does not mean that people would be sealed up in what are essentially controlled containers. The primary vehicle for improving indoor concentrations should be the improvement of outdoor concentrations. Thus, the following section examines the impact of present design strategies on air pollution generation and the effect such strategies can have in protecting receptors and dispensing pollutants.

Current Building Design

The architectural design of a building may increase the generation of air pollution by incorporating features that increase energy demands. Such features as sealed windows, air conditioning systems, central heating systems, the exhaust systems from central cooling and heating units, and the amount of lighting required to meet lighting standards all demand energy. Electricity is the principal energy source.

Production of electricity and its projected increase in use during the next fifteen years is significant in terms of air pollution generation. The use of fossil fuels in generating electricity supplied approximately 83 percent of the electric utility energy requirements in 1970. Although it is predicted that fossil fuels will supply 45.2 percent of the total electric utility energy requirements by 1985, with hydroelectric and nuclear fuels providing 7 percent and 39 percent respectively, it has been estimated that fossil fuel requirements will nevertheless increase 46 percent between 1970 and 1985.[112] The significance of these statistics lies in the fact that although fossil fuels will supply a lesser percentage of total energy supplied by 1985, barring severe energy conservation measures, there will still be an increase in the use of generators powered by fossil fuel and consequently an increase in air pollution.

Inevitably, tradeoffs occur between the use of air conditioning and increased energy demands, usually in favor of air conditioning. It is sometimes argued that sealed windows are designed to protect the occupants of a building from air pollution by placing them in a controlled environment cooled by air conditioning. However, most air conditioning systems merely alter the temperature of the air and do not enhance air quality because the present systems utilize inadequately filtered outdoor air.

A study done in Boston indicated that ozone concentrations were not generally affected by air conditioning and that sulfur dioxide concentrations were not affected unless air conditioning systems included water sprays on the cooling coils.[113] A study done in Hartford indicated that carbon monoxide levels inside an office building were exactly the same as those outside, and that this infiltration was facilitated by air conditioning.[114] Nitric oxide and light hydrocarbons are also difficult to remove.

Particulate concentrations may be reduced slightly by the roughing filters commonly used in air conditioners, but more efficient filters must be used to obtain significant reductions. Pollen is the only pollutant that is eliminated by air conditioning. Although they are not generally employed in air conditioning systems currently in use, air filtration and purification devices that could significantly reduce indoor concentrations of most pollutants are available but are relatively expensive.[115] A study of the electric air conditioning in New York State offers an alternative for reducing energy demands. It showed that large buildings requiring central air conditioning can be cooled more efficiently with gas air conditioning than with electric air conditioning.[116]

Exaggerated lighting standards also create an unnecessary demand for energy. Approximately one-fourth of all electric power goes into electric lighting. In new office buildings, which are built to meet the most recent minimum lighting standards promulgated by the lighting industry, lighting accounts for 50 to 60 percent of the total power requirements. Successive increases in the standards have provided the user with only marginal increases in visibility for a steadily increasing cost, since every footcandle sells more lamps and more electric power.[117]

Another trend in urban design is to put parking facilities underground, building multilevel parking garages and using available air rights over roadways for buildings. The exhaust from the concentration of automobiles within parking garages creates important air pollutant sources that increase concentrations both outside and inside surrounding buildings. The construction of buildings over roadways also increases the risk of exposure to higher concentration levels within the structure.[118]

The Effects of Building Design on Air Pollution Dispersal

The air quality outside a building is the most important determinant of the air quality inside the building. The level of pollution at any point among the buildings of a city is the sum of three contributing factors: (1) Background concentrations: background air pollutant concentrations generated by sources outside the city itself and carried by the wind into the city. (2) Overall urban pollution: the air pollution generated within the city itself, which influences the air quality of the entire city. (3) Local sources: sources in which the scale of the diffusing plume has not grown large with respect to the size of the roughness elements (for example, building height and shape) about which it is flowing. Local sources mainly influence the area immediately surrounding them. For a local source, the bulk transport and diffusion of its effluents are dominated by properties of the aerodynamics of the flow around nearby buildings or other obstacles.[119]

Presently, the most effective way to determine how pollutants are dispersed around buildings is to study the air flow around a scale model in a wind tunnel. Wind tunnel studies can be useful in examining a building complex where the turbulence field is dominated by building configuration and the effect of atmospheric stability is negligible. Equations have been developed to predict pollutant concentration fields around the surface of buildings as well as downwind from sources both internal and external to the buildings.

The general equation used to express the distribution of gas concentration in the flow field around a building is:[120]

$$C = KQ/AV$$

where:

C = Concentration
Q = Gas Release Rate
A = Maximum Frontal Projected Area of the Building
V = Wind Speed at Roof Level
K = Nondimensional Coefficient that is a Function of Space Coordinates

An example of a wind tunnel study and its usefulness in predicting concentrations around buildings, indoor concentrations, and the impact of receptors is provided by the air pollution control study made of the proposed Children's Hospital National Medical Center in Washington, D.C.[121] The study was made in order to consider the dispersion of exhausts from underground parking garages and from the hospital's contagious diseases laboratory. The model of the Children's Hospital consisted of the proposed building, the neighboring structures of the National Medical Center, the topography of the surrounding terrain, and an appropriate representation of the city block extending about a mile upwind from the hospital. Eighty pollutant tracer sampling taps, one-eighth of an inch in diameter, were placed at the proposed air conditioning intakes of the model.

The data revealed that underground parking area exhausts caused maximum concentrations at the north and southwest intakes and that the contagious diseases laboratory exhaust gave highest concentration at the intakes around the northeast corner. This information is useful because it identifies the critical locations of potentially high pollutant concentrations. On the basis of this study, the use of nonoperating windows on the north side at the critical points or relocation of some of the garage exhaust ports was recommended.[122]

Patterns of concentration within the building cavities derived in full-scale studies with tracer techniques have been reported to compare closely with those predicted by wind modeling.[123] However, at greater distances downwind and on larger scales, the current wind tunnel modeling technique has limitations which render it inadequate for evaluating diffusion under the complete range of atmospheric conditions required. Conditions such as the turning of wind with height and thermally driven circulation cannot be reproduced in wind tunnels at the present time.[124]

Wind tunnel tests have also shown that architectural shapes can have large effects on the climatology of structures. Eric Kahn [125] demonstrated the effects of building mass, height, depth, and length upon the size and shape of a downwind eddy, finding that the eddy, a low-pressure area, is key to microclimatology. The larger the eddy, the lower the volume of air flowing around a building and the smaller the eddy the higher the volume of air. In cold climates, building shapes and orientations that maximize eddy areas offer the greatest protection from the wind, while in hot climates configurations that give the smallest eddy area allow a maximum of cooling air to flow around and through the structures. Larger low-pressure areas could result in air stagnation and the build-up of air pollutants, while smaller eddy areas would be more conducive to the dispersion of pollutants. It was found that building height considerably increases eddy area and that many minor variations, such as the direction and pitch of roofs, result in very large changes in air flow.[126]

Winds are influenced by a building's size and shape, the geometry of streets, and the local topography. Higher winds at the base of a building are caused principally by the building's height and bulk. These winds maintain more suspended dirt in the air than would be aloft around lower and smaller buildings, but they also have the opposite effects of augmenting vertical mixing and dispersing air pollutants faster.[127] The wind speed at the base of a tall building is the product of two flow fields. The first is caused by the pressure distribution on the windward face of the building, which relates to the local wind pressures and increases with height. (The fact that wind pressure increases with height is due to the frictional drag effect of the ground and other obstacles, like low buildings, along the ground surface.) This pressure induces a vertical flow down to the face of the building from the stagnation point. Upon reaching the ground, the air flows into a vortex, causing high winds.

The second type of flow is caused by the pressure difference between the low pressures leeward and adjacent side faces and the high-pressure base of the windward side of the building. Flow between these areas around corners can cause very high local winds. The low wake pressure is dependent on the wind velocity at the top of the building, and the taller the building, the greater the velocity at the top. Therefore, the taller the building, the lower the wake pressure and the higher the velocities induced.[128]

Full-scale studies are the alternative to wind tunnel models, which are limited to the small scale. Full-scale studies monitor the effects of buildings on the overall pollution levels of a city, beyond the effects of individual building complexes. Buildings, on a larger scale, mainly affect the determination of the mixing layer into which pollutants are dispersing. The mixing layer is defined as that layer in contact with the ground which is in near-neutral static stability. It comes about because of the solar heating of the ground during the day and the subsequent convective motions induced in the lower layers of the atmosphere or because of the mechanical turbulence set up by the wind flow over rough surfaces. Over cities, a mixing layer can usually persist at night when temperatures are cooler, which gives rise to the "heat island phenomenon."[129] The heat island phenomenon does not permit rising hot air to be cooled according to its normal rate. As a result, the warmer air subsides and spreads over the lower layer of the atmosphere. In the absence of prevailing winds, the heat island can become stabilized and trap concentrations of pollutants.[130]

Siting Controls and Building Codes

Given the present state of knowledge, modifying urban form to reduce the impact of air pollution concentrations probably should be considered a matter of secondary priority simply because we are not sure what the large-scale effects are and do not know whether the costs of such modifications would be worth the effort. Clearly, more research is needed on this topic. One can, however, make recommendations on siting controls and revisions in building codes.

Most of the recommendations refer to energy use, which is related to the generation of air pollutants. For example, the siting of new office buildings rarely takes direction into account. Although critics often attack buildings on aesthetic grounds, architects are now finding that it may be economical as well as aesthetically desirable to orient a building away from the sun or to use different materials on the sunny south side than on the north.

It is asserted that with different design, materials, and mechanical systems, office buildings could be constructed to use 75 percent less energy than they do now.[131] Building codes, which are concerned primarily with assuring the safety and structural soundness of buildings, can be rewritten to enforce limited energy consumption. Such a project is currently being undertaken by the National Bureau of Standards in Washington, D.C., which is preparing a model energy-conserving building code. Among the items to be considered for such a code would be requirements that buildings contain minimum levels of insulation or meet "energy budget" limitations worked out using a formula that would take into account a building's size, use, location, and materials. Buildings that exceeded their assigned energy budget would be forced to pay a penalty.

NOTES

1. Sec. 111 (a) (1).
2. O'Harrow, "Performance Standards in Industrial Zoning," 1951 Planning 42.
3. Gillespie, "Industrial Zoning and Beyond: Compatibility Through Performance Standards," 46 J. Urban L. 723, 741-742 (1964), hereinafter cited as Gillespie.
4. New York City Zoning Resolution Sec. 41-11 (1961).
5. Id. Sec. 41-13.
6. (1) noise (2) smoke (3) odor (4) dust and dirt (5) noxious gases (6) glare and heat (7) fire (8) industrial wastes (9) transportation and traffic (10) aesthetics (11) psychological effects.
7. Adding (1) vibration, (2) electromagnetic interference, (3) radioactive emissions. American Society of Planning Officials (ASPO), Planning Advisory Service, Information Report No. 78 (Sept. 1955).
8. Marion County, Ind. Dwelling Districts Zoning Ordinance (1968), and Commercial Zoning Ordinance (legal draft, 1969).
9. Salzenstein, Industrial Performance Standards, Planning Advisory Service, Report No. 272 (1971), hereinafter cited as Salzenstein.
10. Proposed Comprehensive Amendment to the Chicago Zoning Ordinance, Sec. 10.3 (1955).
11. New York City Zoning Resolution, Sec. 42-00 (1961).
12. Salzenstein, 8.
13. New York City Zoning Resolution, Sec. 41-00 (1961).
14. Id. Sec. 42-231.
15. Id. Sec. 42-232.
16. Salzenstein, Appendix B, "Proposed Industrial Performance Standards, Auburn, New York."
17. New York City Zoning Resolution Sec. 42-232 (1961).
18. Id. Sec. 42-234.
19. Salzenstein, 21.
20. Id. at 22.
21. New York City Zoning Resolution Sec. 42-231 (1961).
22. Id. Sec. 42-233.
23. Id. Sec. 42-233.
24. Proposed Comprehensive Amendment to the Chicago Zoning Ordinance Sec. 10.7 (1955).

25. Schulze, "Performance Standards in Zoning," 10 J. Air Pollution Control Assn, 156, 159 (1960).

26. Salzenstein, 24. The formula is:

Let Q1, Q2 . . . Q_n represent the maximum emission rates of a pollutant, from all stacks and vents on a zoning lot. Then the maximum ground level concentration (C) of the air pollutant anywhere in the area of measurement is given by the Basic Dispersion Formula, as follows:

$$C = \sum_{i=1}^{n} \frac{0.037 \ Q_i}{V_i^{0.71} d_i^{1.29} h_i K_i}$$

where:

C = Maximum acceptable ground level concentration.

V_i = Stack gas velocity in feet per second.

d_i = Internal stack diameter in feet.

h_i = Stack height above grade in feet.

K_i = Correction factor for distance from stack to area of measurement.

27. Id. at 25.

28. Id.

29. New York City Zoning Resolution, Sec. 42-232 (1961).

30. Proposed Comprehensive Amendment to the Chicago Zoning Ordinance Sec. 10.7 (1955).

31. Some zoning ordinances (for example, in Chicago and New York) use "noxious matter" as synonymous with toxic matter. Others (for example, in Cook County) put it together with odorous matter. And still others (for example, in Auburn, New York) omit the term entirely.

32. New York City Zoning Resolution, Sec. 42-251 (1961).

33. Cook County Zoning Ordinance; in Voorhees, "A Guide for Reducing Air Pollution Through Urban Planning," prepared for the Office of Air Programs, U.S. Environmental Protection Agency, Appendix B (Dec. 1971), hereinafter cited as Voorhees.

34. Salzenstein, Appendix B

35. Id. Sec. 24-60.

36. Schulze, supra note 25, at 160.

37. National Association of County Officials Foundation, Air Pollution Control: Community Action Guide for Public Officials, Report No. 3 (1966); also, Voorhees; Salzenstein; Schulze, supra note 25.

38. New York City Zoning Resolution Sec. 41-00 (d) (1961).

39. Salzenstein, 9.

40. Cook County Zoning Ordinance, in Voorhees, Appendix B.

41. Voorhees, 22.

42. Breivogel, "Air Pollution Potential Advisory Service for Industrial Zoning Cases," 11 J. Air Pollution Control Assn. 334 (1961).

43. As candidly conceded by an administrator in the New York City Planning Commission who said, in a telephone interview (July 1972), that it was not known whether performance standards in the zoning ordinance could work in air pollution, since they had never been enforced. Apparently the Buildings Dept. is in charge of enforcement.

44. New York City Admin. Code ch. 47 Sec. 1403.2 - 3.11 (Supp. 1971), hereinafter cited as N.Y.C. Admin. Code.

45. Wash. Rev. Code Ann. Sec. 70.94.230 (Supp. 1971).

46. Marion County, Ind. Industrial Zoning Ordinance Sec. 2.06C (1963) in Gillespie 747.

47. Presently the Department of Air Resources within EPA.

48. New York City Zoning Resolution Sec. 42.20 (1961).

49. Id. Sec. 42-232.

50. Id. Sec. 42-233(e).

51. Id. Sec. 42-252.

52. New York City Admin. Code Sec. 1403.2 - 1.03(c).

53. Id. Sec. 1403.2-9.01.

54. Id. article 9: Emission Standards.

55. Id. Sec. 1403.2-9.23.

56. Id. Table 1, Sec. 1403.2-9.23.

57. Id. Sec. 1403.2-5.01.

58. Id. Sec. 1403.2-1.03(x).

59. Id. Sec. 1403.2-5.05(a).

60. Id. Sec. 1403.2-5.05(b).

61. Id. Sec. 1403.2-5.11(a).

62. Id. Sec. 1403.2-1.03(cc).

63. The author is indebted to Mr. Keegan, Legal Counsel, New York City Department of Air Resources, for this observation (telephone interview, July 1972).

64. Salzenstein, 13.

65. Voorhees, 22.

66. Id. at 23; also Breivogel, supra note 42.

67. News Release, Bay Area Air Pollution Control District, Oct. 27, 1972. The ban was lifted after ten weeks. Marin County

Independent Journal, Jan. 4, 1973, at 1. Subsequent regulations require vapor recovery controls on stations.

68. Buck v. Kilgore,___ Me.___, 298 A 2d 107 (1972).

69. 13 Misc. 2d 648, 177 N.Y.S.2d 252 (Sup. Ct. 1958).

70. Id. at 253.

71. American Society of Planning Officials, Planning Advisory Service, Information Rep. No. 140 (1960).

72. Mosher, "Proximity Regulation of the Modern Service Station," 17 Syracuse L. Rev. 1, 5 (1965).

73. Mosher, supra note 6, at 6.

74. Fonoroff, "Controlling Traffic Through Zoning," 21 Syracuse L. Rev. 857, 861.

75. 234 Miss. 531, 107 So.2d 580 (1958).

76. Id. at 587.

77. Id. at 592.

78. Romano v. Village of Ridgewood, 14 N.J. Misc. 301,184 Atl. 411 (1936).

79. 169 Ark. 244, 275 S.W. 321 (1925).

80. 136 N.J.L. 416, 56 A.2d 122 (1947).

81. 329 Mass. 288, 107 N.E.2d 774 (1952).

82. 122 N.J.L. 63, 4 A.2d 91 (1939).

83. 249 Mich. 372, 228 N.W. 707 (1930).

84. Id. at 708.

85. 117 N.J.L. 593, 190 Atl. 777 (1937).

86. 238 Ind. 673, 153 N.E.2d 599 (1958).

87. Id. at 601. See also Kairis v. Board of Appeal of Cambridge, 337 Mass. 528, 150 N.E.2d 278 (1958).

88. 192 N.C. 395, S.E. 151 (1926).

89. Mandelker, Control of Competition as a Proper Purpose in Zoning, 14 Zoning Digest 33 (1962).

90. 239 Wis. 599, 2 N.W. 2d 253 (1942).

91. 138 Conn. 452, 85A.2d 904 (1952).

92. 74 Ohio L. Abs. 425, 134 N.E.2d 727 (Ohio App. 1956).

93. 238 Ind. 57, 148 N.E.2d 563 (1958).

94. Id. at 569.

95. 201 Ark. 618, 146 S.W.2d 167 (1941).

96. 329 Mass. 288, 107 N.E.2d 774 (1952).

97. 217 Ky. 135, 289 S.W. 223 (1926).

98. 104 N.Y.S.2d 850 (Sup. Ct. 1951), aff'd, 279 App. Div. 1084, 113 N.Y.S.2d 449 (1952), aff'd, 304 N.Y. 971, 110 N.E.2d 894 (1953).

99. 166 Md. 324, 171 Atl. 70 (1934).

100. Id. at 74.

101. 84 R.I. 472, 125A.2d 105 (1956).

102. 195 N.Y.S.2d 190 (Sup. Ct. 1959).

103. Id. at 192.

104. 23 Misc. 2d 894, 196 N.Y.S.2d 856 (Sup. Ct. 1959).

105. Id. at 870.

106. 19 Misc. 2d 1023, 119 N.Y.S. 2d 877 (1952).

107. Id. at 898.

108. Thomas Markus, "Climatology and Architecture," 128 Architectural Rev. 452 (Dec. 1960)

109. E. Cermach and F. Chaudhry, "Urban and Architectural Planning for Air Pollution Control" (June 1972), prepared for presentation at the 65th annual meeting of the Air Pollution Control Association, hereinafter cited as Cermach and Chaudhry.

110. Ferris Benson et al, "Indoor-Outdoor Air Pollution Relationships: A Literature Review" (1972) (AP-112) 5-8, hereinafter cited as Benson.

111. R. A. McCormick, Air Pollution in the Locality of Buildings 522 (1971), hereinafter cited as McCormick.

112. Thomas Browne, Impact of Energy Conservation on Energy Demands 14 (1972), hereinafter cited as Browne.

113. Benson, 40-2.

114. Id.

115. Id.

116. Browne, 4.

117. "Lighting: The Eyes Have Had It," Environmental Action (October 28, 1972), at 13.

118. McCormick, 522.

119. McCormick, 516.

120. McCormick, 517.

121. Cermach and Chaudhry, 11.

122. Id.

123. McCormick, 518.

124. Id.

125. Eric Kahn, "Air Flow Around Buildings," 107 Architectural Forum 167 (September 1967).

126. Id. at 167-8.

127. D. Dornbush and Co., Intensive Commercial and High Rise Development Impact Study, San Francisco, California, V, 14 (1972).

128. Id. at 14-5.

129. McCormick, 518.

130. McCormick, 519.

131. New York Times, Dec. 6, 1973, at 49. Stein concludes that in the special case of the modern commercial skyscrapers, savings of about 50 percent of operating power requirements could be achieved by proper design (use of windows that open, efficient heating and air conditioning, reduction in excessive illumination). See Richard Stein, "Architecture and Energy," paper presented at AAAS Annual Meeting, Philadelphia, Dec. 29, 1971. See also Eric

Hirst and John Moyers, "Efficiency of Energy Use in the United States," <u>Science</u> 1299-1304 (March 30, 1973); G.A. Lincoln, "Energy Conservation, <u>Science</u> 155-162 (April 13, 1973); Charles Berg, "Energy Conservation through Effective Utilization," <u>Science</u> 128-138.(July 13, 1973).

7

THE GENERATION
OF EMISSIONS

A GENERAL FRAMEWORK

The development of a particular configuration of land uses and transportation networks for a metropolitan region has implications beyond the basic issues of aesthetics and economic efficiency. In particular, the urban spatial structure of a region will affect the total amount of air pollutants emitted as well as the distribution of these emissions over the defined area. In this chapter, a conceptual framework to examine the extent and distribution of pollutant emissions will be developed. This framework will then be fleshed out with a basic set of generation equations and specific examples. Finally, the problems associated with the estimation of the emissions will be discussed. The dispersion of these pollutants into the atmosphere will be examined in Chapter 8.

Basically, the two variables of primary importance in studies of emission generation are the nature and extent of the different activities within the region and the pollution-generating capacities of each of the activities. For example, an acre of land located on the fringe of a metropolitan area might contain a number of residences, a small shopping center, roads, and vacant land. Each of these land use categories would have a different pollution-generating capacity. Residences emit sulfur oxides and the other pollutants associated with the heating of interior space, but they do so only during winter months when home heating systems are in use. A shopping center will also have space-heating requirements during the colder period of the year. Because shopping centers are traffic generators, the contiguous parking lots will serve as areas from which automobile-related pollutants—particularly carbon monoxide, hydrocarbons, and nitrogen oxides—will be generated. Vacant land, on the other hand, will emit a small amount of pollutants. For example, dust blown about from a field is considered as a pollutant contributing to the level of particulates in the ambient air.

The first task, then, in estimating emissions from a defined area is the identification of the kinds of activities conducted in that area. This identification process requires both a land use classification system for the urban planner and a system by which one can make accurate estimates of pollutants generated. It will be assumed that the traditional land use classification system employed by urban planners is a suitable basis for estimating emissions. Thus, the categories of residential, commercial, institutional, and industrial land uses can form the basic core of a methodology for estimating emissions.

The second task in determining the extent and distribution of emissions from an area is to estimate the intensity of development for the particular land use category under investigation. An acre containing a single-family residence, for example, has a different pollution-generating capacity from an acre containing a twenty-unit apartment complex. Different petrochemical plants generate different amounts of pollutants, depending on daily output.

The third task in estimating emissions is to determine the amount of pollutants emitted by a particular activity type with a specified intensity of utilization. A twenty-unit apartment complex located on one acre will emit a specific amount of sulfur oxides and other pollutants during the winter. Estimates of the amounts of these pollutants can be made. In general, it can be said that:

$$EM = ACT * EMACT \tag{7.1}$$

where:

EM   = Amount of a pollutant emitted by an activity, such as a residence, shopping center, or industry, in a defined spatial zone or a particular time period.
ACT   = Number of units of the activity in the zone.
EMACT = The amount of emissions per unit of activity per time period.

Immediately, it must be realized that this basic equation can be expanded in a number of ways to fit particular needs. Different researchers have examined alternative methods of developing emission estimates.[1] We cannot attempt to encompass the entire spectrum of techniques and methodology for the emissions estimation process, but we will discuss the emissions estimation procedures for different categories of land use and transportation activities. In particular, we will examine industrial, residential, commercial, institutional, and transportation sources. The problem of estimating the current emissions from already existing land use and transportation categories is not the same problem as projecting future emissions from spatial configurations. Thus, before examining techniques for estimating future emissions, it is important to examine current emission inventory practices.

CURRENT EMISSION INVENTORY PROCEDURES

Present emission inventory practice divides stationary emission sources into two categories, point sources and area sources, and into two kinds of emissions, space-heating and process emissions. This classification scheme may be represented by a four-celled chart.

Each cell of the chart represents a different problem in information development. It is usually most convenient to begin by identifying a reasonable number of individual point sources and to determine the emissions to be expected from each of these sources. The most straightforward way to obtain this information is to request it; however, individuals responsible for a particular source may not know the nature of the emission in detail, or they may have reason to distort the actual figures. Therefore, while point source information is often obtained from individuals responsible for the source, it is sometimes estimated on the basis of other data which are easier to obtain or thought to be more reliable. For example, fuel-use data are often used as a basis for estimating emissions resulting from space heating (Cell A). If the amount of fuel consumed for space-heating purposes is known, and the effectiveness of the emission control devices can be determined, emissions can be accurately estimated upon the basis

Type of Emission

		Space-heating	Process
Type of Source	Point	A	B
	Area	C	D

Space-heating   Process

of published information relating various fuel types to pollutants generated.[2]

Process emissions from a point source (Cell B) present a more complex problem. A given process may be characterized by several kinds of emission. The amount of fuel required for the process to function will indicate the nature and the amount of some portion of the pollutant emitted, but it is also necessary to determine what other emissions may result from the process. The usual practice is to determine, through examination of an individual process, the quantity of each kind of pollutant per unit of processed input or output, and then to determine total process emissions on the basis of total process input or output. For example, the amount of pollutants generated by an incinerator would be measured in terms of the amount of input, which in this case is garbage. On the other hand, the amount of pollutants generated by a steel plant would be related to the amount of output manufactured, which is in tons of steel. Published material is available that indicates the emissions to be expected from various industrial processes in a number of industries.[3]

In current practice, area sources are those emitters remaining after the large point sources have been investigated individually. Since their large numbers and relatively small sizes make the development of specific information about each of these area sources an impractical proposition, procedures have been developed to consider these sources as a group. Again, space heating (Cell C) is the easier case. In residential neighborhoods, most homes have similar heating facilities. At most, two or three different kinds of fuels will be used within a particular locale. Information on fuel use, whether the fuel is oil, gas, or electricity, is usually available; this data can be translated directly into the amount of pollutants emitted for the particular residential area being examined. In nonresidential areas containing a mixture of commercial and small industrial sources this information on fuel use cannot be applied directly, since industries generate both space-heating and process emissions. Information on the amount of floor area is sometimes available and can be used to determine average space-heating requirements for a variety of establishments in an area.

Process emission sources for an area (Cell D) are the most difficult to determine, especially in areas that are heterogeneous with respect to the type of processes present. In order to estimate process emissions with any accuracy, it is necessary to establish which kinds of emissions are most prevalent in the area. Further, it is important to determine the extent to which process emissions from area sources are present, both in terms of the number of facilities in the area and the nature of the average emissions for each of the facilities.

ESTIMATING CURRENT AND FUTURE EMISSIONS

In an existing metropolitan area, future air pollutant emissions generated by a particular land use and transportation system are a tautological product of both current development and changes in urban structure up to a certain point in the future. Both redevelopment and new configurations on vacant land in the metropolitan region will shape the shifts in urban structure. These changes in structure, however, will be integrated with an already existing base. It makes sense, then, to begin an analysis of future emission generation by examining both current emission inventories and planned emission control strategies directed at existing sources. The planner can determine the availability of emission inventory data from local, state, and federal air pollution control officials.

If there are relatively few structural changes in the region between current emission estimates and the chosen point in the future, then one can be reasonably certain that current air quality monitoring and emission data will be an approximation of future air quality. However, it becomes increasingly important to develop an adequate land use and transportation forecasting mechanism as the change component becomes an increasingly significant element in the shaping of future metropolitan structure.

The Guidance System Approach

The public sector has traditionally utilized such devices as zoning, subdivision regulations, building permits, and the provision of various services (such as water and sewers) to directly influence land use patterns. It is also obvious that the public sector indirectly influences land development through such devices as the location of highways and transit lines. The general framework encompassing this set of direct and indirect instruments for shaping the structure of a metropolitan region can be called an "urban development guidance system."[4]

In order to estimate future emissions, a guidance system approach must be capable of developing a reasonable approximation of what future land use patterns will be in the region. In the final analysis, a map of future development must be generated from the information available to the planner. The structuring of such a map of expected development is an entirely feasible product of the land use planning process. The long-range comprehensive plan for a community is an example of such a map. The translation of the comprehensive plan into a zoning classification scheme can operate, in conjunction with other governmental controls, such as subdivision regulations, to direct development.

Environmental Research and Technology, Inc., utilized the long-range development plan for the Hackensack Meadowlands area of New Jersey as a basis for calculating future emissions.[5] The plan was transformed into a zoning classification scheme which contained various land categories—industrial, commercial, institutional, and residential. The use of the guidance system concept for projecting future emissions is only viable where a governmental or private decision-making body has reasonable control over the land allocation process within the area of interest. Most of the Hackensack Meadowlands region is under the jurisdiction of a relatively strong commission which can control, to some degree, the land development process. New towns, such as Columbia, Maryland, planned and constructed by a private organization are also candidates for a guidance system approach, since a map of proposed development has a reasonable probability of success.

In order to use the development map as a basis for estimating emissions, three assumptions must be made. First, it must be assumed that relatively coarse land use categories (often all industry is divided into only two categories, light and heavy) can capture the differences in the pollution-generating capacities of the complete spectrum of land uses within the particular region being examined. Argonne National Laboratory concluded that there are many instances in which the land use categories utilized by the development map were not useful in the prediction of emissions because the categories were too broadly defined.[6]

The second assumption is that the map of future development is a meaningful indicator of what will actually occur in an area. As has been discussed, this assumption holds when there are direct controls on location decisions. It is less clear that the guidance system approach would work in many communities where there are a complex set of public and private forces operating in the determination of land use patterns. As a first approximation, the guidance system may be a reasonable approach, provided it is realized that the estimated future emissions may be in error because actual development may not be in accordance with the proposed development scheme.

The final assumption is that there is total development of each of the land use categories within the overall scheme. It is obvious that a 500-acre industrial park with only 50 acres developed as a light manufacturing facility cannot be said to generate pollutants at the estimated emission rate for the entire area. Ideally, the planner would have to determine the development rates for the various land areas in the community in order to correctly predict the amount of pollutants that will be generated at some particular time in the future.

Mathematical Extrapolations

The problem with the guidance system concept, which relies heavily on direct and indirect governmental controls, lies in the historical role of the marketplace in the allocation of land. Through zoning variances and other devices, a long-range development plan for a community may be altered to such a degree that emission estimates based on the plan are useless. An even greater problem is that the general development plan is often so coarsely specified that accurate emission estimates are difficult to develop.

In order to accommodate the influence of the marketplace and to refine emission estimates, mathematical models have become a viable alternative. The simplest approach is to utilize a single-equation mathematical model that "grows" an activity variable over time. One basic equation of such a growth model is:

$$V_n = V_1(1 + GR)^{n-1} \qquad (7.2)$$

where:

V_n = A magnitude of a variable—for example, employment or population—for a facility or land use area in time period n.

V_1 = The magnitude of a variable for a facility or land use area during the initial time period.

GR = The growth rate.

This application of the compound growth formula, as described by Alan S. Cohen, is directed towards projecting such variables as employment or population.[7] These measures of future activity can then be coupled with estimates of emissions per employee or household to yield future emissions for the facility or land use area. Thus, estimates of growth in employment in an industrial sector can be developed, and the corollary emissions generated can be ascertained. Also, the population growth of a residential area can be forecast and emissions estimated.

The formula cited above, utilized in air quality studies, is only one of a more extensive set of potential equations for estimating variables that can be fed into an emissions generation framework. For example, there is a set of widely utilized linear and nonlinear population projection techniques which can operate as a basis for estimating future growth.[8] Also, a number of techniques have been developed to examine alternative ways of projecting industrial employment by different classifications.[9] The use of various single-equation estimators can form the basis for estimating future emissions from stationary sources, such as industries or residences.

Of course, there are several problems involved in the use of such single-equation estimates of a future activity. First, there is the difficult task of projecting future activity, particularly employment, at a detailed enough level so that emissions can be estimated accurately. Work has been done on projecting employment at the two-digit and four-digit Standard Industrial Classification (SIC) code levels.[10] However, as will be discussed below, even the four-digit level may not be useful in accurately determining emissions.

The second problem centers on the inability of single-equation estimators to encompass the interdependencies that exist between elements in the metropolitan system. Employment growth is coupled with shifts in population concentrations and land use patterns. Recognition of the linkages has led to the development of complex models which deal with these interdependencies in urban systems.

Such complex models of urban development have as their output a projected configuration of land use patterns and transportation system utilization which can feed directly into emission generation and dispersion analysis. Figure 7.1 is a broad sketch incorporating different models in order to project land use categories, vehicle miles occurring on the transportation system, the emissions generated, and the dispersion of these emissions into the atmosphere.[11]

The various models outlined in the system already exist and are discussed by researchers in the relevant disciplines.[12] In succeeding sections, analytic techniques for estimating emissions generated and dispersed will be discussed and critically evaluated. Any system of models developed to evaluate the future impact of alternative land use and transportation schemes must: (1) take into account the nature and extent of the interaction between land use and transportation; (2) develop reasonable estimates of expected emissions without significant error; (3) use an appropriate pollutant-dispersion model and; (4) develop a set of politically acceptable and technically competent evaluation components. It will become abundantly clear as the presentation proceeds that although the system of linked models displayed in Figure 7.1 can be developed in time with the appropriate resources, it is less clear whether the resources will ever be available to construct such a complex model set that can be used at the agency level.[13]

The succeeding discussion will attempt to exposit and critique an analytic framework for determining emissions from either present or future urban configurations. In estimating future emissions, it will be assumed that either a guidance system approach has produced a plan that will be reasonably approximated in future years or that a set of models in conjunction with limited planning controls has projected a reasonable facsimile of future structure. The framework that follows is generally applicable for either estimating present or projecting future emissions.

212

Figure 7-1

A System of Models Relating Land Use

and Transportation to Air Quality

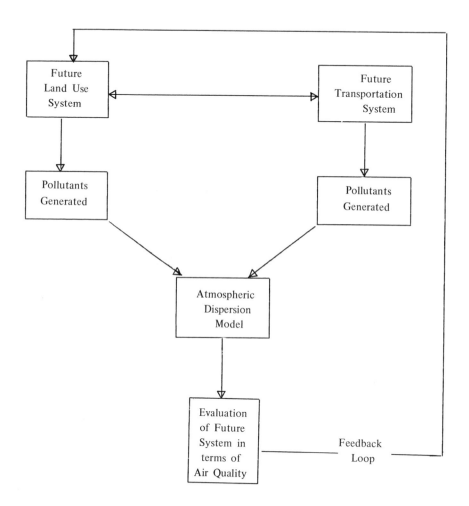

INDUSTRIAL EMISSIONS

Combustion and Process Components

Industrial emissions can be separated into combustion and process-loss components. The combustion element can be further divided into heating required for interior space (space heating) and heating necessary for industrial processes (process heating). A distinction must be made between the relatively constant level of emissions generated by process heating and the highly variable level of those generated by space heating. In Figure 7.2 this variation can be seen over the period of a year.[14]

Process-loss emissions result directly from the production of a good by an industry. For example, aluminum ore reduction produces particulates and fluorides from the chambers in which the aluminum is produced from bauxite. Also, there are evaporation losses from the organic solvents in dry-cleaning or surface-covering operations

Figure 7-2

Process and Space-Heating Emissions over the Year

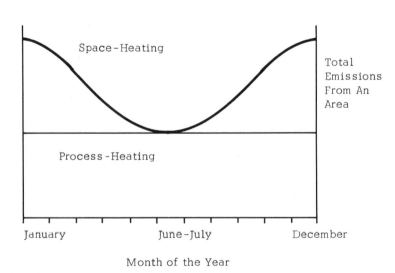

Month of the Year

and from the volatile components in petroleum products. Filling an automobile gasoline tank, for example, generates approximately twelve pounds of hydrocarbons for every 1,000 gallons pumped.[15]

It has been argued that reasonable estimates of future emissions can be obtained when the space-heating and process-heating components of combustion are combined.[16] One might even argue that it may be preferable to ignore process-loss emissions in certain situations. Basically, the planner lacks the ability to accurately predict what particular type of industry will locate in a given place. The industrial location literature has simply not provided him with detailed techniques for locating specific industries.[17] Without a detailed projection of what particular industry will locate in a particular area it is extremely difficult to estimate, even crudely, the pollutants that will be emitted, since pollutants generated by the process-loss component of production vary widely by industry. Even analysis of process-loss emissions on a highly detailed four-digit SIC classification level, assuming projection ability at this degree of detail, may not always be satisfactory.[18] For example, the manufacture of nitric acid and phosphoric acid are both coded SIC 2819. However, while nitrogen oxides are emitted during nitric acid processing, particulates and fluorides are emitted during phosphoric acid production.

The planner, then, either needs to have an accurate base upon which to estimate process-loss emissions or he must attempt to incorporate the pollutants generated by process losses in another way. One viable procedure is to adjust the combustion process figures for industrial uses in order to account for process-loss emissions. To the degree that process-loss pollutants are the same as those encompassed by the analysis of combustion-emission generation, this can be done. For example, particulates and hydrocarbons are examined in combustion-emissions analysis; hence, processes that produce these pollutants are encompassed by a combustion-specific model of industrial emissions. On the other hand, fluorides or chlorine are not considered in the combustion analysis equation and thus would not be estimated by a combustion-based model.

To illustrate further how one might proceed in estimating emissions from industrial sources, two basic techniques will be discussed. The first is based on combustion, and the second is directed towards analyzing production output. Examination of these two models is useful in presenting alternative ways of generating emissions without using emission inventory data. The models each contain a set of structural variables which can be estimated from generally available data. The models for projecting industrial emissions are both derived from the general equation cited earlier, which stated that the number of units of a particular type of land use activity and the amount of emissions per unit activity jointly determine the emissions generated by a land use category.

Fuel Input

The generalized model of industrial emissions presented here focuses solely on combustion-based pollutants, relegating process-loss emissions to a secondary role. Emissions per unit area are considered to be a function of emissions per unit of heat consumed and the amount of heat required.
The general equation to perform this calculation is:

$$EM = EMHT * HEAT \tag{7.3}$$

where:

EM = Emissions by weight for a defined unit area of a particular industrial class for a defined time period.
EMHT = Emissions by weight per unit of heat.
HEAT = The total amount of heat required for a facility of a particular industrial class over some defined time period.

Also, the emissions generated by a unit of heat is a function of three variables: (1) emissions generated by a unit of fuel, (2) the amount of heat generated by a unit of fuel, and (3) the proportion of the different kinds of fuels used.
The equation stating this relation is:

$$EMHT = \sum_i p_i (E_i * H_i^{-1}) \tag{7.4}$$

where:

p_i = The proportion of the total amount of fuel supplied by fuel i.
E_i = The amount of emissions of a specific pollutant generated by a unit of fuel i.
H_i = The amount of heat produced by a unit of fuel where the gross heat production is modified by the combustion efficiency of the heating mechanism.

For example, to calculate the amount of hydrocarbons emitted yearly by a one-acre industrial site, one must make certain assumptions about the type and size of the industry and about the emission data utilized. Using the equations above, the units of heat required yearly for a unit area—in this case one acre—can be calculated. Assuming that an industrial structure will cover approximately 40 percent of the site with a floor area ratio of 1.0 and that space-heating demand is 27.5 British thermal units (BTU) per square foot per hour, then one acre (43,560 square feet) of industrial land yields the following BTU per acre per hour:[19]

216

BTU/acre/hour = 27.5 * 1.0 * .40 * 43,560 = 479,160

Two classes of industry can be analyzed, light and heavy. Heavy industry is assumed to operate continuously throughout the year or for a total of 8,760 hours. Hence:

BTU/acre/year = 479,160 * 8,760 = 4.2 x 10^9

At this point, our earlier discussion about space-heating and process combustion emissions becomes important. Basically, the strategy is to estimate space-heating requirements and then to add on a proportional amount to the estimate to cover the process-heating component. For example, since it has been estimated that roughly only 10 percent of total combustion needs are for space heating in heavy industry, then total heat requirements are ten times the amount required for space heating alone.[20] Thus, the total amount of heat required per acre of heavy industry on a yearly basis would be the following:[21]

$$\text{HEAT} = 4.2 \times 10^{10} \text{ BTU/acre/year}$$

The calculation of the amount of emissions per unit heat requires information about the proportions of different fuels used and the emissions and heat generated by these fuels. It will be assumed in this example that heavy industry uses residual oil 75 percent of the time and natural gas the rest of the time. Equation 7.4 will be used to develop estimates of emissions per unit of heat. The following values for calculating residual oil emissions per unit of heat can be determined:

p_1 = .75
E_1 = 24 pounds SO_2 per 1,000 gallons[22]
H_1 = 84,286 net BTU per gallon[23]

For natural gas the following values will be used:

p_2 = .25
E_2 = .6 pounds per 10^6 cubic feet[24]
H_2 = 788 BTU per cubic foot[25]

Thus, substitution in equation 7.4 yields the following value for emissions generated per unit of heat:

$$\text{EMHT} = 2.1 \times 10^{-7} \text{ pounds } SO_2 \text{ per BTU}$$

Further substitution of the emissions generated by each unit of heat and the amount of heat required per acre of heavy industry in Equation 7.3 yields the following estimates of total emissions of sulfur dioxide per acre:

$$EM = (4.2 \times 10^{10}) * (2.1 \times 10^{-7})$$
$$EM = 8,800 \text{ pounds } SO_2 \text{ per acre per year}$$

The technique just outlined moves from heat consumption data and emission factors to an estimate of the amount of pollutants generated by a land use category. The specific example focused on heavy industry where assumptions had to be made about the amount of square footage contained in a structure located on an acre of land. Table 7.1 shows the amount of pollutants generated by different land use categories.[26] The values, developed by Environmental Research and Technology, Inc., are estimates for 1990 based on certain assumptions about fuel utilization, emission controls, and physical characteristics of the structures located on the land. Most important, the values are generated by a technique similar to the one developed above to estimate heavy industrial emissions of sulfur oxides on an areal basis. Note that the 8,800 pounds of sulfur dioxide estimated in the analysis above is greater than the 5,400 pounds listed in Table 7.1 for the heavy manufacturing land use, reflecting differences in the numeric values utilized.

A note of caution is important. The figures in Table 7.1 are specific to the Hackensack Meadowlands project for which they were developed. They are illustrative only and should not be used in other applications without a careful assessment of how the values might vary. In particular, the kind of fuel utilized in an area is a critical determinant of emissions generated.

Production Output Analysis

The distinction between combustion and process emissions can be viewed somewhat differently when one examines production outputs rather than heat inputs. In the heat-based technique, the focus was on fuel emissions as a function of both process heating and space heating. The space-heating requirements were calculated initially and then process-heating requirements added on in a simple multiplicative operation. Process emissions per se could not be directly handled in the heat-based analysis.

In production output analysis, a relationship is established between the process emissions and the amount of output generated by an industry. Utilizing available research findings, the analyst can estimate emissions, provided that outputs can be ascertained.[27]

TABLE 7.1

Pollutant Emissions by Land Use Category and Transportation Activity

Land Use Category	Pollutant Emissions* (lb/year/acre)				
	TSP	SO2	CO	HC	NOx
Residential					
10 Dwelling units/acre	25	1	35	12	7
20 Dwelling units/acre	180	120	4	54	85
30 Dwelling units/acre	180	120	4	54	85
50 Dwelling units/acre	250	160	5	75	120
80 Dwelling units/acre	200	140	4	63	100
Commercial & Industrial					
Commercial	60	45	1	12	95
Manufacturing					
Light	1,100	1,100	10	140	850
Heavy	5,400	5,400	60	900	5,400
Research	2	15	1	5	35
Distribution	60	45	1	12	95
Open Space	0	0	0	0	0
Other	Emission Factors				
Highway (lb/10^6 vehicle-miles)	700	400	11,000	1,000	1,500
Parking lots (lb/10^3 hrs. idling)		4	12	3	1

*The pollutants in the table are: total suspended particulates (TSP), sulfur dioxide (SO_2), carbon monoxide (CO), hydrocarbons (HC), and oxides of nitrogen (NO_x).

Source: Byron H. Willis and James R. Mahoney, "Planning For Air Quality," paper presented at annual meetings of American Insitute of Planners, Boston, Mass., November 1972.

The basic equation for estimating emissions from an industrial source is:

$$EM = (OUTPUT * EMOUT) + EMSPCE \qquad (7.5)$$

where

EM   = The emissions of a particular pollutant generated by both process and process-heating activities as well as by space-heating needs from an industrial facility over some time period.

OUTPUT = The estimated output of the facility over some time period.

EMOUT   = The amount of emissions of a pollutant generated by a unit of output.

EMSPCE = The emissions generated from the space-heating needs of the facility over a defined time period.

The emissions generated by space heating can be developed from a combustion-based analysis like the one outlined in the preceding section. The emissions generated for a unit of output is developed from an equation similar to Equation 7.4, the one utilized earlier in estimating emissions per unit of heat. In order to use Equation 7.5, it must be assumed that the process and process-heating emissions can be separated from the strictly space-heating requirements. Even more, the role of control technology in reducing emissions must be understood and the necessary data available.

For example, hydrofluoric acid manufacture produces fluorides and particulates as emissions. One ton of manufactured acid will produce 50 pounds of fluorides if the process has no emission controls and only 0.2 pounds per ton when controlled. Hence, knowledge of the number of tons produced during some defined time period will allow the estimation of the amount of fluorides emitted under different control levels.

There are several problems in the output analysis approach. The first of these refers to the assumption just made about the separation of process and space-heating components. The emission factors contained in the Compilation of Air Pollutant Emission Factors put out by the Environmental Protection Agency do not differentiate sufficiently between combustion-based and process-based emissions. For example, the manufacture of brick involves both process-heating emissions from the drying and firing of bricks in ovens and process emissions from the brick itself. Process-heating emissions vary according to the kind of fuel used in the heating of the ovens. Gas-fire ovens emit 0.6 pounds of nitrogen dioxides per ton of bricks manufactured, while oil-fired furnaces emit 1.3 pounds. In the heating of the bricks, the clay will give off process emissions of 0.8 pounds of fluorides per ton of bricks.[28]

The analyst, then, is faced with a difficult estimation task. The earlier distinction between combustion emissions, including both space-heating and process-heating components, and process emissions breaks down in this production output framework. If one could be certain to include both process and process-heating emissions in a production output analysis, one could cover the space-heating component either by utilizing the heat-based strategy outlined earlier or by monitoring the fuel records. The process-heating component derived from fuel record examination would only be utilized in the emission estimates if it were determined that they were not included as a component of the emission factors.

Beyond this initial problem with production output analysis, there is the further one with the usefulness of the technique to the urban planner. The problems inherent in forecasting industrial development at a detailed enough level for accurate assessment of emissions has already been discussed. Consider, however, the difficulty in estimating process and space-heating emissions across the full set of industries found in any metropolitan area.

Equation 7.5 describes the emissions generated by a single facility. To fully describe the emissions generated by a defined area, the entire set of polluting industries would have to be examined. In determining the present level of emissions, industrial sources can be treated as individual point sources and the output of Equation 7.5 directly fed into the atmospheric dispersion model. The planner can seldom be so specific about the location of future industrial facilities. Hence, the planner requires areal approximations of potential emissions akin to those found in Table 7.1.

A strategy for projecting emissions for defined areas can be sketched out. First, current industrial development is studied and emission rates generated either through direct stack monitoring or through a version of the production output analysis outlined above. Then the fuel input analysis technique is utilized for potential industrial development, where emissions are estimated on an areal basis. This strategy can provide an initial approximation of emissions for some specified point in the future.

With continuing research it may be possible to use an aggregative form of production output analysis to refine the approximations generated by a combustion-based analytic framework. In particular, it seems likely that more refined estimates of industrial emissions on an areal basis can be developed than those outlined in Table 7.1. Location theoretic considerations, including agglomeration effects, dictate that particular kinds of localities have differing propensities for the development of specific kinds of industries or groups of industries.[29] The examination of existing industries coupled with knowledge of the locational behavior of firms can act as a base to improve future approximations of emissions from a defined area.

221

RESIDENTIAL EMISSIONS

Residential land use is considered as an area source and is treated in a dispersion model as if the defined area were emitting at a constant rate across its surface. The basic residential emission model is an extrapolation of the earlier generalized equation. The residential model is as follows:

$$EM = 1.1 \; (EMHT * HTDU * DUAREA) \tag{7.6}$$

where:

EM   = Emissions of a pollutant for a defined time period for an area of residential land at a specified number of dwelling units per area.

EMHT   = Emissions of a pollutant per unit of heat.

HTDU   = Amount of heat required for a dwelling unit for some defined time period.

DUAREA = The number of dwelling units per unit area.

The equation is a straightforward multiplicative function. The factor of 1.1 above increases the figure for space-heating emissions by 10 percent to encompass process-heating emissions for cooking and other household activities.

The amount of heat required for a dwelling unit over a certain time period can be ascertained in a number of different ways. First, current data available from fuel records and engineering data can be used to establish a fixed value of heat for dwelling units of a particular class. For example, estimates have been made of the total yearly requirements for heat of a typical single-family unit. The value calculated is 70×10^6 BTUs.[30]

Other researchers have estimated an hourly requirement for a single-family unit at 18,750 BTUs.[31] These basic figures, modified by variations in room size and by the degree-day differences, provide a basic framework for estimating the amount of heat required for a dwelling unit.

A more general approach is the following:

$$HTDU = S * Q * T \tag{7.7}$$

where:

S = The average amount of square footage in a dwelling unit.

Q = The amount of heat required per square foot of the dwelling unit for some defined time period.

T = An adjustment factor to take into account the differences between temperature in the region of study and temperatures in the region where the measurements of heat required per square foot of dwelling unit space were developed. On a yearly basis, the ratio can be conceived of in terms of annual degree days.

One can calculate the amount of sulfur dioxide emissions generated by an acre of a residential area containing 10 single-family dwelling units. This density approximates an older suburb where lots are 3,000 to 4,000 square feet. It will be assumed that these residences average 1,200 square feet, or six rooms, and that the feet per square foot values are directly applicable without adjustment to the region in which the dwelling units are located. This implies the following values:

$$S = 1,200 \text{ square feet}$$
$$Q = 113 \times 10^3 \text{ BTU per square foot yearly}[32]$$
$$T = 1$$

and therefore:

$$HTDU = 135.6 \times 10^6 \text{ BTU per dwelling unit}$$

Also, since it will be assumed in this example that half of the total BTUs are produced by distillate oil and half by natural gas, then for particulate emissions:

$$E_1 = 10 \text{ pounds of particulates per 1,000 gallons of oil}[33]$$
$$H_1 = 84,286 \text{ net BTU per gallon}[34]$$
$$p_1 = .50$$

For natural gas:

$$E_2 = 19 \text{ pounds of particulates per } 10^6 \text{ cubic feet}[35]$$
$$H_2 = 788 \text{ net BTU per cubic foot}[36]$$
$$p_2 = .50$$

Equation 7.4 will be used to determine the amount of emissions of particulates per BTU averaged over the proportional mixture of fuel types used. Hence:

$$EMHT = 7.1 \times 10^{-8} \text{ pounds of particulates per BTU for ten dwelling units per acre}$$

When estimating yearly emissions, the general equation (7.6) becomes:

223

$$EM = 1.1 \ (7.1 \times 10^{-8}) * (135.6 \times 10^6) * 10$$
$$EM = 106 \text{ pounds of particulates per acre per year}$$

A recalculation of this emission estimate, using only natural gas as a fuel, indicates that emissions dropped to 36 pounds per year of particulates. Table 7.1 includes emissions from a residential land use category of 10 dwelling units per acre. According to Table 7.1, this land use category will generate 25 pounds of particulates per year, where natural gas is assumed to be used exclusively. The 25 pounds figure approximates the estimate of 36 pounds of particulates per year from natural gas heating derived above.

COMMERCIAL AND INSTITUTIONAL EMISSIONS

Commercial and institutional emissions estimates are a straight extrapolation from the earlier discussions. The basic formula is:

$$EM = EMHT * HTFT * FT \tag{7.8}$$

where:

EM   = Emissions of a pollutant for a defined time period for an acre of commercial or institutional land use.
EMHT = Emission of a pollutant per unit of heat.
HTFT = Amount of heat required per square foot of commercial or institutional space for some defined time period.
FT   = The amount of square footage.

Once again, the emissions of a pollutant per unit of heat is a joint function of the proportion of different fuels used, the emissions per unit of fuel, and the heat generated by a unit of fuel, as outlined in Equation 7.4. Given an estimate of the square footage of interior space and the amount of heat required per square foot for the time period in question, then emissions of a pollutant can be estimated. The time period to be used must be clearly specified. Of course, the yearly estimate of pollutants generated by a land use category includes both winter and summer seasons; since space-heating requirements are usually confined to winter, any yearly estimate of emissions will, of necessity, average both winter and summer use. An hourly estimate of BTUs needed per square foot must take into account the hours during the year when space-heating is required. In Equation 7.8 the amount of heat required per square foot of commercial or institutional space for the period of a year is an average combining both winter and summer needs.

224

On a yearly basis, the equation for estimating the amount of heat required for a square foot of space can be written thus:

$$HTFT = HTFTU * T \qquad (7.9)$$

where:

HTFTU = Heat required per square foot unadjusted for the differences between the region in which the heat requirements were determined and the region for which the initial estimates are being generated.

T = Adjustment factor, which on a yearly basis can be conceived of in terms of annual degree days.

For example, one can calculate the amount of particulates emitted by a commercial facility of 10,000 square feet located on 1 acre of land. It will be assumed that the yearly amount of heat required unadjusted for degree-day differences between regions is 48,750 BTUs per square foot.[37]

Assuming that there is no adjustment required for temperature differences between regions, the following substitutions can be made:

$$T = 1$$
$$HTFT = 48,750$$

It follows, then, that for a commercial facility using only distillate oil, the emissions per unit of heat can be calculated using Equation 7.3:

E_1 = 15 pounds of particulates per 1,000 gallons of oil[38]
H_1 = 84,286 BTUs per gallon[39]
P_1 = 1.0

Thus:

$$EMHT = 17.8 \times 10^{-8} \text{ pounds particulates per BTU}$$

If, for example, it was assumed that a 10,000 square foot facility would be constructed on 1 acre, then the emissions of particulates from this acre of land is:

$$EM = (17.8 \times 10^{-8}) * 48,750 * 10,000$$
$$EM = 87 \text{ pounds particulates}$$

Obviously, such an analysis of emissions from commercial or institutional land uses assumes knowledge of heating requirements

225

and the size of the various facilities. The analyst would necessarily
have to have reasonable estimates of future developments in order
to accurately assess the emission generation potential. Hence, the
estimation of the heating requirements of schools would have to be
cognizant of the response of educational planners to the community's
needs for classroom space. It becomes immediately obvious that one
cannot separate the land use planning process from air quality considerations. Indeed, the planners' inputs in terms of community needs
are essential to the development of emission estimates.

TRANSPORTATION EMISSIONS

The technique for estimating emissions from automobiles, trucks,
and buses focuses directly on the best single measure of travel activity,
vehicle miles occurring over a defined length of roadway for a specific
time period. Since vehicles traveling at different speeds have different
emission rates, ideally one would like to know the vehicle miles
traveled over a length of roadway and the various speeds as well as
the mix of idling, acceleration, deceleration, and cruising.[40] Since
transportation sources emit pollutants continuously over a finite
stretch of roadway of relatively small width, they are generally termed
line sources. The basic equation for estimating the emissions generated by a known volume of traffic for a length of roadway is:

$$EMLT = VHMI * EMSP \qquad (7.10)$$

where:

EMLT = Total emissions generated over a defined length of roadway
for some time.
VHMI = The vehicle-miles traveled over the length of roadway at an
average speed.
EMSP = The amount of emissions per vehicle-mile at the average
speed designated.

This basic equation assumes one average speed for the finite
length of roadway and presumes that the emission factor used takes
into account a mixture of automobiles, trucks, and buses traveling
the roadway. Table 7.2 lists illustrative emissions factors for cars,
gasoline-powered trucks, and diesel trucks and buses for 1976 and
1990 at different speeds. The differences between 1976 and 1990
reflect the influence of current federal emission standards on new
vehicles mandated for the years up to 1976.[41]

226

TABLE 7.2

Motor Vehicle Emission Factors, 1976 and 1990
(grams per vehicle mile)

	1976		
Speed	Carbon Monoxide	Hydrocarbon	Nitrogen Oxides (NO_2)
15 mph			
Cars	80.32	8.80	4.52
Trucks	131.00	18.50	6.33
Diesels	12.39	1.75	27.74
25 mph			
Cars	49.19	6.96	4.52
Trucks	81.40	13.79	6.33
Diesels	12.39	1.75	27.44
50 mph			
Cars	29.40	5.28	4.52
Trucks	38.10	11.34	6.33
Diesels	12.39	1.75	27.44
All speeds	1990		
Cars	5.00	0.454	0.688
Trucks	6.70	0.907	0.998
Diesels	3.62	0.399	0.770

Source: Environmental Research and Technology, Inc., Environmental Impact Statement, Governor Alfred E. Driscoll Expressway, prepared for the New Jersey Turnpike Authority, September 1972.

For example, 100,000 vehicles traveling over the period of a day on an expressway at an average speed of 50 miles per hour will contain a mixture of cars, trucks, and buses. The following general equation can be used to calculate an average emission rate:

$$\text{EMSP} = \sum_i (p_i * \text{EMSP}_i) \qquad (7.11)$$

where:

p_i = The percentage of total vehicle-miles attributed to the kind of vehicle

EMSP_i = The emission factor of the ith kind of vehicle at a specified average speed.

Assuming that there are 94 percent cars, 3 percent gasoline trucks, and 3 percent diesel trucks and buses traveling at an average speed of 50 MPH, one can calculate daily carbon monoxide emissions for 1976:

$$EMSP = .94(29.40) + .03(38.10) + .03(12.39)$$
$$EMSP = 29.15 \text{ grams per vehicle mile}$$

The total daily emissions in 1976 for a mile of expressway with an average speed of 50 miles per hour is:

$$EMLT = 100,000 * 29.15 = 2.9 \times 10^6 \text{ grams}$$

Depending on the exact problem, the equations above can be enriched on a number of different levels. For example, to determine the total emissions generated over an area, the emissions from each of the lengths of roadway in the area can be summed. Or the equations can be made more realistic by including the changes that take place in emission rates as vehicles move through the different stages of the traffic cycle. Whatever the detail or scale of the study, the importance of the transportation sector in generating emissions cannot be underestimated.

PLANNING IMPLICATIONS

The planner interested in estimating future emissions from a region is faced with a number of problems. Not only must he be able to generate the necessary information but he must also be assured that the data and models utilized are relatively free of error, not overly expensive, and relevant to the problems at hand. What follows is an examination of the current state of the art and suggestions for appropriate strategies.

Following on the earlier discussions, it should become apparent that the planner must be able to appropriately specify what future land use and transportation patterns are likely to occur; this task is one of the primary responsibilities of the urban planner. He can rely on air pollution control specialists to provide emission data and the potential level of pollutant control, but he must still estimate the nature and extent of the land use structures and transportation systems which will act as a base to the emissions generation phase. Two issues become important at this point: the scale of the study, and the use to which the analyses will be put in the context of validity and measurement questions.

The Scale of the Study

The methodology examined earlier is generally applicable to a study area of any size. However, the scale of the investigation does affect the treatment of the different variables in terms of the level of detail required and the anticipated impact on the environment. At one extreme, there is the focus on regional air quality. In this case, the concentration is on the long-term average air quality in a region and on the pollutants generated by a web of land use structures and travel patterns. The Environmental Research and Technology study of the Hackensack Meadowlands development in northern New Jersey examined both land use and transportation systems for their effects upon air quality.[42] Other investigators have examined regional subsystems. J. A. Kurtzweg and D. W. Weig studied the transportation systems in the Seattle area,[43] while researchers at the Argonne National Laboratory have examined the future growth of the industrial sector in St. Louis.[44] The planner interested in focusing on the air quality problem on a regional scale has a basic reference set of already existing studies.

Of primary importance to the planner is the land use and transportation system which forms the basis of emissions generation. Unfortunately, in the studies to date, this is exactly the area that has not been emphasized. Examination of these studies indicates the relative primitiveness with which the dynamics of urban spatial structure have been treated. Little of the extensive work in urban development models, specifically designed to forecast future land use patterns and transportation system requirements, has been utilized in air quality investigations. The earlier discussion of complex models of urban structure is, at this point, only a harbinger of the research that can be expected in future years.

In all of this discussion of regional air quality an emphasis has been placed upon forecasting expected future states. It is suggested here, and emphasized by other investigators, that the urban planner should not take on the task of attempting to alleviate short-term air quality problems.[45] This is the primary responsibility of the air pollution control agency. Rather, the planner will need to carefully assess the variety of direct and indirect controls that potentially can shape land use and transportation configurations in the long run. The viability of the long-range development plan for the region may be a critical determinant in the ability of the planner to estimate future air quality. If the plan is incapable of being implemented, then air quality projections based on the plan may be in serious error. As previously suggested, some combination of public policy directives and the modeling of market dynamics may have to be undertaken in order to reasonably approximate future emissions.

The degree of accuracy of the emissions projection is less important for the regional case than for the examination of local conditions. The proposed location of a particular land use or transportation structure and the localized effects of the emissions generated is a very different problem from the study of long-term regional air quality. On the one hand, the analysis of the effects on air quality of a single source is simpler than the examination of an entire region. A single source will emit an identifiable amount of pollutants. Reasonable approximations of the amount of emissions to be found at some distance from the source can be estimated through the use of an atmospheric dispersion model. For localized effects, the techniques outlined earlier for estimating emissions are applicable. In particular, the emission factors discussed with regard to process emissions are useful in estimating pollutants generated by an industrial source. Also, the generalized equations for transportation sources can be used quite readily for a single line source, such as a stretch of proposed expressway.

On the other hand, since one is dealing with only a single source and examining its localized effects, the questions of model validity and of measurement error are of overriding importance. The inaccurate estimation of pollutant concentrations from a single source, such as a new industrial plant or highway, can have grave consequences for the health and well-being of local residents. In a regional situation, the same inaccuracy in the estimation of pollutant concentrations from any single source will not dramatically affect regional air quality. It must be noted, however, that the question of error in measurement and in models must be examined for both the local and the regional case.

Utility and Imperfect Data

The proper utilization of a procedure for determining the nature and sources of emissions on the local or regional levels depends on an understanding of data limitations. In the following chapter a detailed analysis will be undertaken of the error propagation potential inherent in models that predict the dispersion of pollutants. For our purposes here, it is more important to examine the kinds of errors that can occur in the estimation of emissions generation and the ways in which the data utilized can be improved.

There are a number of potential sources of error in estimating present and future emissions from the different sources found in a region. Present emission estimates are at best rough approximations of what exactly is going into the air at any given time. There are three basic sources of error in the determination of present emission levels. These are: (1) incorrectly locating the source in space; (2) underestimating the total amount of pollutant emitted over an area because sources are missed; (3) incorrectly estimating the amount of pollutant emitted over some defined period of time.

A source location may be incorrect if the grid coordinates describing the location are erroneous. The model for calculating the dispersion of pollutants across a region requires a locational fix on the emitting sources. Thus, incorrect source location will affect the calculation of concentrations expected to occur at a given receptor point. A second kind of error occurs when sources are missed and the emissions generated are thus systematically underestimated.[46] One can easily conceive of situations where an industrial process is missed or residences not enumerated. There is a systematic bias in this type of error. While sources may easily be overlooked, they are seldom created where none exist.

These two types of error can be minimized through appropriate data-handling procedures. Error-checking routines, common in the social science research literature, are easily adapted to the collection of emissions-generation data.[47] However, the third type of error cited above is a more difficult case. The estimation of the amount of pollutants emitted by a source is a major measurement problem. The virtual impossibility of actually measuring even a major portion of the sources through field visits means that estimation procedures must be employed. The equations described earlier, which estimate the amount of pollutants emitted by a particular kind of source through the use of emission factors, are examples of such estimation methods.

Emission factors are developed through a sampling of sources. From this sample one can develop an anticipated expected value of the amount of pollutant emitted by a unit of production output or heat input. These factors are averages, and since they are based on sample data, contain sampling error. Fortunately, the data used to develop emission factors are continually improving. At the present time, however, emission factor data are barely adequate for the tasks assigned to them. The most recent comprehensive document on emission factors, the Compilation of Air Pollutant Emission Factors, includes a rating of the quality of the emission factors contained, based on the amount of sampling and analysis undertaken. The highest ratings have been given to the data and analysis used in the development of emission factors for such activities as coal and fuel oil combustion and iron and steel mills. Unfortunately, the overall rating of other emission factors is not as satisfactory.[48]

Granting that industrial processes about which a great deal is known are often major polluters, it is still true that in selected areas agglomeration effects and resource constraints are such that industrial processes about which little is known may be significant contributors to air quality degradation. The continued development of more accurate factors is critical to the increased reliability of source emissions estimates.

An important problem with the current status of emission factor data is that the sampling procedures utilized are not fully described nor are estimates of the deviations in data observations about the estimated average values supplied. Assuming that sampling procedures are used in the collection of emission factors from a series of sources in order to develop an average value, information about the statistical variance and sample size of the data would be useful. In particular, given certain statistical assumptions, particularly normality, the analyst could place confidence intervals about the estimates of an emission factor. A range of values could be developed within which any particular source would be expected some defined proportion of the time.

When one realizes that the estimation of a particular source may be in error by some percentage and that there are a multiple number of sources within any defined area, the error potential of the emissions estimation procedure can be seen even on a purely quali- tative level. Assuming that the errors in emissions generated by different sources in some area are randomly distributed, the error attached to the total estimate of a pollutant from all sources is effectively dampened. An acre containing residences, a small grocery store, and streets will emit a defined amount of nitrogen oxides. The amount of nitrogen dioxides emitted by residences and commercial activities might be overestimated in the model while automobile emissions might be underestimated. In this case, there would be an effective reduction in the amount of total error generated when resi- dences, grocery stores, and streets are combined. In point of fact, this kind of additive model does not produce a larger percentage error in the total than can be found for each of the component variables. However, a larger numeric error value can be expected. The error propagation potential of various models is discussed in detail in the next chapter.

Thus far, our discussion of errors in emission-generation estimates has focused on the present. Two of the potential errors in emission estimates, underestimation and mislocation of sources, are controllable through careful enumeration of sources and continual checks to ensure data integrity. The other kind of error, inaccurate estimates of the amount of pollutants emitted, is not so easily handled. There is an obvious need to continually refine the emission factor data. However, the inability to check on emission factors by means other than examination of the processes themselves is a serious dilemma. Since generated pollutants are immediately dispersed into the atmosphere, it is difficult to differentiate errors in the emission

232

generation models from errors found in the dispersion analysis. The errors that occur in the estimates of the pollutant concentrations calculated to exist at a receptor point in the region are a function of both the emissions-generation and dispersion models.

Beyond the concern with the kinds of errors attributable to estimates of emissions from present land use and transportation configurations, there is the further concern with future land use and transportation structures and their effect on air quality. Not only must the planner face the problem of developing reasonable emission estimates from an already existing regional structure, but his necessary concern with the future dynamics of land use and transportation systems also requires that he be able to generate reasonable estimates of how the region will appear some years hence. The kinds of estimation techniques described earlier, including urban development models and a guidance system framework focusing on legal and administrative tools for shaping land use, are important elements in approaching this task.

The planner should realize that there are techniques available for developing reasonable estimates of future emissions. However, the question remains: Can a study of future air quality in a region be undertaken within the resource constraints of many agencies? Before answering, it will be necessary for us to move to a discussion of another part of the land use and air quality interface—dispersion analysis.

NOTES

1. In particular, the work done by Argonne National Laboratory, Air Pollution-Land Use Planning Project, and Environmental Research and Technology, Hackensack Meadowlands Air Pollution Study, are two recent attempts to examine the land use planning and air quality management interface. Specific documents arising from these research efforts will be cited where appropriate.

2. See Office of Air Programs, U.S. Environmental Protection Agency, "Compilation of Air Pollutant Emission Factors" (Publication No. AP-42 1972), hereinafter cited as Compilation of Air Pollutant Emission Factors.

3. See Guntis Ozolins and Raymond Smith, "A Rapid Survey Technique for Estimating Community Air Pollution Emissions" (U.S. Public Health Service Publication No. 999-AP-29 1966), hereinafter cited as Ozolins and Smith. See also Compilation of Air Pollutant Emission Factors.

4. The seminal piece is by Stuart Chapin, Jr., "Taking Stock of Techniques for Shaping Urban Growth," 29 J. Amer. Inst. of Planners

76-87 (No. 23 May 1963). See also David Heeter, "Toward a More Effective Land Use Guidance System: A Summary and Analysis of Five Major Reports," Planning Advisory Service, Amer. Soc. of Planning Officials (No. 250 1969).

5. See the multivolume research investigation by Environmental Research and Technology, Inc. on the Hackensack Meadowlands Development Plans.

6. Allan S. Kennedy et al., "Air Pollution-Land Use Planning Project Phase I-Final Report" 15-8 (Publication No. ANL/ES-7 1971).

7. Alan S. Cohen, "The Use of Three Growth Models to Evaluate the Future Effectiveness of Air Pollution Control Regulations," a paper presented at the annual meeting of the Air Pollution Control Association (June 1972), or Alan S. Cohen et al., "Growth Analysis Report for the Illinois Implementation Planning Program" (Publication No. IIPP-7 1972).

8. See F. Stuart Chapin, Jr., Urban Land Use Planning (1965), and Donald A. Krueckeberg and Arthur Silvers, Urban Planning Analysis: Methods and Models (forthcoming).

9. See, in particular, Michael Greenberg, "A Test of Alternative Models for Projecting County Industrial Employment at the 2,3, 4-Digit Standard Industrial Code Levels," Regional and Urban Economics 397-417 (February 1972), hereinafter cited as Greenberg. See also Edward L. Ullman et al., The Economic Base of American Cities (1971), on the extrapolation and minimum base requirements; and Charles Tiebout," The Community Economic Base Study" (Paper No. 16 1962), on economic base studies.

10. Greenberg.

11. Figure 1 and an extension of this discussion can be found in Richard K. Brail, "Modelling the Interface Between Land Use, Transportation and Air Pollution," in The Relationship of Land Use and Transportation Planning to Air Quality Management (G. Hagevik ed. 1972), hereinafter cited as Brail.

12. For an excellent discussion of urban development models, see H. James Brown et al., Empirical Models of Urban Land Use: Suggestions on Research Objectives and Organization (1972). For an example of an extensive effort in urban modeling, see Jobs, People and Land: Bay Area Simulations Study (1968). Transportation planning methodology is discussed in Roger Creighton, Urban Transportation Planning (1970), and W. R. Blunden, The Land Use/Transport System (1971). For a general discussion of the models required and their relation both to each other and other elements in the regional system, see Brail.

13. The urban planning research literature contains pieces that exhibit both the euphoria and the despair with which complex simulation models have been viewed. One need only read Britton Harris,

"Quantitative Models of Urban Development: Their Role in Metro-politan Policy Making," in Issues in Urban Economics (H. Perloff and L. Wingo eds. 1968), and more recently William Goldner, "The Lowry Model Heritage," 37 J. Amer. Inst. of Planners 100-10 (No. 2 March 1971), on the optimistic side. For comparison, see Richard Bolan, "New Rules for Judging Analytical Techniques in Urban Planning," in Analytical Techniques (1969), and particularly, Douglass B. Lee, Jr., "Requiem for Large-Scale Models," 39 J. Amer. Inst. of Planners 163-78 (No. 3 May 1973).

14. Figure 7.2 is extrapolated from Ozolins and Smith, 9.

15. Compilation of Air Pollutant Emission Factors, 4-5.

16. John C. Goodrich, "Task 1—Emission Projection Methodology and Its Application to the Hackensack Meadowlands Development Plans, Part 1: Emissions Projection Methodology" (Document No. P-244-1 (1972), hereinafter cited as Goodrich.

17. See Greenberg and see Jobs, People and Land: Bay Area Simulation Study, for attempts at using detailed industrial codes in projections.

18. Goodrich, Task 1 Part 1.

19. These figures are drawn from Goodrich, Task 1 Part 2.

20. Goodrich, Task 1 Part 1.

21. An important variable in the determination of the amount of heat required for a particular facility is the number of degree days occurring over the year. On any given day the number of degree days is determined by subtracting the mean temperature of the day from 65 degrees. Thus, an average temperature on a winter day of 30 degrees would mean a total of 35 degree days. See Ozolins and Smith for a further discussion; and see the succeeding section on residential emissions for an analysis of how to introduce degree-day estimates into the heat requirements needed for a facility.

22. Compilation of Air Pollutant Emission Factors, 1-7.

23. Assumes 150,000 BTUs per gallon gross thermal value and a 60 percent efficient heating system. See Compilation of Air Pollutant Emission Factors, A-6, for thermal equivalents, and Ozolins and Smith for the suggested efficiency of different heating systems.

24. Compilation of Air Pollutant Emission Factors, 1-9.

25. Assumes 1,050 BTUs per cubic foot gross heating value and a 75 percent efficient heating system, supra note 24.

26. See the five-task research document on the Hackensack Meadowlands by Environmental Research and Technology, Inc., or Byron H. Willis and James R. Mahoney, "Planning for Air Quality," a paper presented at the annual meeting of the Amer. Inst. of Planners (November 1972).

27. In particular, see Compilation of Air Pollutant Emission Factors.

28. Compilation of Air Pollutant Emission Factors, 8-3,4.

29. For an example of where basic locational factors were utilized in an applied simulation model to locate groups of industrial classes, see Jobs, People and Land: Bay Area Simulation Study.

30. Ozolins and Smith, 43.

31. Goodrich, Task 1 Part 1 106-7.

32. Extrapolated from the value used by Goodrich, Task 1 Part 2. The estimate has been changed from an hourly to a yearly value.

33. Compilation of Air Pollutant Emission Factors, 1-7.

34. Derived in the same manner as shown in note 23 supra, except that the gross heating value of distillate oil is 140,476 BTUs per gallon.

35. Compilation of Air Pollutant Emission Factors, 1-9.

36. Supra note 25.

37. This 48,750 BTUs per square foot figure is extrapolated from an average hourly estimate of 16.25 BTUs per square foot used by Goodrich, Task 1 Part 2 107-8. It is assumed that commercial facilities operate 3,000 hours a year.

38. Compilation of Air Pollutant Emission Factors, 1-7.

39. Supra note 34.

40. See J. A. Kurtzweg and D. W. Weig, "Determining Air Pollution Emissions from Transportation Systems," a paper presented at the Association for Computing Machinery meetings (October 1969), for one interesting example of a methodological framework; hereinafter cited as Kurtzweg and Weig.

41. See Fed. Reg. July 7, 1971.

42. See the five-task report by Environmental Research and Technology, Inc., on the Hackensack Meadowlands.

43. Kurtzweg and Weig.

44. A. S. Cohen, L. J. Hoover, and J. E. Norco, "The Impact of Economic Growth on Air Quality in the St. Louis Region," a paper presented at the Amer. Inst. of Chemical Engineers meetings (May 1972).

45. See Willis and Mahoney, "Planning for Air Quality," a paper presented at the annual meeting of the Amer. Inst. of Planners (November 1972).

46. Glenn R. Hilst, "Sensitivities of Air Quality Prediction to Errors and Uncertainties," Proceedings of Symposium on Multiple-Source Urban Diffusion Models (Arthur C. Stern ed. 1970).

47. For example, simple error checks such as are described in Charles H. Backstrom and Gerald D. Hursh, Survey Research (1963), are often useful. Also, simple computer programs that check for consistencies in the data can be developed. For example, a program can be written to check if the grid coordinates specified in the data set that identify polluting sources spatially are within appropriate

numerical limits and seem reasonable in the context of the land use patterns. Is an industrial establishment located in the center of a residential area, or is that an error? For some uses, computer mapping procedures are especially valuable.

48. The ratings are on a five-point scale. If "5" is designated to mean excellent data and "1" to mean poor data, with "3" as an average, then the overall rating is not impressive. Examining 63 industrial processes and combustion activities from six SIC two-digit codes the overall average is 3.2, slightly above the numeric designation for average. Clearly, the rather subjective nature of the rating system, as discussed in the Compilation of Air Pollutant Emission Factors 1-2, can only contribute to the belief that better measurement is important. The sources of this analysis are Compilation of Air Pollutant Emission Factors, and H. C. Wohlers et al., "A Rapid Emission Survey Procedure for Industrial Air Pollutants," 19 J. Air Pollution Control Assn. 309-14 (No. 15 1969).

CHAPTER

8

THE DISPERSION
OF POLLUTANTS

The pollutants generated by a land use and transportation configuration are dispersed into the atmosphere and carried to the receptor
population through meteorological influences. Dispersion models which
predict pollutant concentrations resulting from a defined set of sources
are available to the urban planner and policy maker. This chapter is
directed toward: (1) explaining meteorological variables that affect
the transport and diffusion of pollutants, (2) developing an understanding
of applied dispersion models, and (3) discussing the validity and
measurement problems that circumscribe model utilization and create
the need to examine alternative strategies. The critical question
centers on the appropriate role of dispersion modeling, given resource
constraints and the nature of available data, in the context of a legal
and administrative framework for managing air quality.

METEOROLOGY AND DISPERSION

A detailed examination of the complex process of pollutant dispersion is beyond the scope of this presentation. Researchers in the field
of micrometeorology have developed analytic descriptions of the dispersion process.[1] The currently popular applied modeling approach
to the atmospheric dispersion process utilizes the Gaussian distribution
equation, discussed in the next section. The discussion of meteorological variables affecting dispersion will be confined to elements
recognizable in the Gaussian-based equation. Fortunately, an understanding of these model-based meteorological variables can act as a
suitable foundation for an understanding of the dispersion process.
Some of the meteorological variables that affect the dispersion
of a pollutant from a generating source are: (1) wind direction, (2)

wind speed, and (3) atmospheric stability and turbulence. Wind direction is a basic variable affecting pollutant dispersion. If the mean wind direction measured occurs at the height at which the pollutant is released, the pollutant will disperse in the direction of the observed wind. Wind speed also affects the dispersion of a pollutant; a wind traveling at twice a certain speed past an emitting source will only carry half the mass of the pollutant downwind for any fixed period of time. For example, if a source such as a smokestack emits a pollutant continuously at 20 grams per second and the wind is traveling at one meter per second, then each meter of plume downwind contains 20 grams of the pollutant. With a 5 meter per second wind, however, each meter of plume only contains 4 grams. To put this more generally, pollutant concentration is inversely proportional to wind speed.

The third variable cited, atmospheric stability and turbulence, is in reality a descriptive term encompassing a complex set of micrometeorological forces. Both vertical and horizontal movements of air operate as a function of a host of variables; the confluence of these motions at some point in time is called atmospheric turbulence.

Mechanical turbulence refers to those motions of the atmosphere resulting from the roughness of the surface over which the air passes. Generally, the greater the amount of roughness the greater the mechanical turbulence. In turn, the greater the turbulence the greater the dispersion of the pollutant. It has been suggested that one of the objectives of the planner interested in shaping urban structure to minimize air pollution effects is to increase wind turbulence.[2] Increasing the roughness of urban structure might mean, for example, the utilization of uneven roof lines. It is argued that uneven roof lines would cause a complex structure of eddy currents. Uneven roof lines, "rougher" than roof lines all the same height, would cause greater mechanical turbulence.

Unfortunately, it has also been suggested that uneven city roof lines do more than increase turbulence. They also create more frictional drag on the flowing air than do even roof lines.[3] This increased drag reduces wind speed, which in turn has the effect of reducing turbulence. Thus, with the joint effects of increased turbulence and increased frictional drag, it may well be that uneven roof lines are no better or worse than even roof lines. This illustration points out that roughness of surface per se is no guarantee of increased turbulence. The frictional properties of air must also be considered. The illustration also indicates some of the complexity involved in examining urban micrometeorological conditions.

Thermal turbulence relates to the level of atmospheric stability. Solar radiation heats the earth's surface during the day. Depending on the time of year and wind conditions, vertical motions in the air will occur. If, as occurs on clear summer days, a parcel of warm air at the earth's surface rises because the parcel is warmer than the environmental air surrounding it, strong vertical motions take place. In this situation, the air is said to be unstable, and thermal turbulence occurs. At night, however, the earth gives off heat. Without solar radiation to replace the lost heat, the air at the earth's surface cools, resulting in a stable atmospheric condition. There is little thermal-induced turbulence and much stability in this situation.

The role of wind speed and wind direction in the dispersion process are easily understood. However, the relationship between turbulence and stability, and the complex forces that influence them, are not so easily comprehended. F. Pasquill developed a set of stability categories for different atmospheric conditions, and a study of these categories can aid in illuminating these complex relationships.[4] In Table 8.1, six stability categories, from stable to very stable, are related to two variables that are prime determinants of the stability class of the surface ground layer. The most unstable conditions, where strong vertical motions of the air occur, are found during daylight hours on bright summer days with low wind speeds. Correspondingly, the most stable conditions exist on cloudy nights with very low wind speeds.

Atmospheric stability, then, is a function of wind speed and the amount of solar radiation present. In turn, atmospheric stability affects the mixing height, which refers to the distance from the ground within which pollutants are confined. Figure 8.1 is a graphic presentation of the "box" model.[5] Conceptually simple, the box model highlights the important fact that pollutants cannot migrate upward for an infinite distance. A temperature inversion occurs when cool air at the surface is trapped below warmer air above and cannot rise. While mixing height will be quite high under unstable conditions, stable night-time conditions can produce a low mixing height, thus confining pollutants to a small volume of air above a city.[6]

MODELING ATMOSPHERIC DISPERSION

A set of techniques have been developed to calculate the amount of pollutant dispersed by various sources to any given receptor point. Our purpose here is not to examine this complex area in detail. Rather, the focus will be on a particular dispersion model most widely used at present for policy and programing purposes. This model is based on the Gaussian diffusion equation. The term "Gaussian" is applied to the model because of the assumption that a pollutant mass emitted from an elevated source will distribute itself according to the normal, or "bell-shaped," distribution in the vertical and horizontal directions about the mean wind direction. As can be seen in Figure 8.2, a stack

TABLE 8.1

Stability Classes

| Surface wind speed at 10m (m/sec) | Day Incoming Solar Radiation | | | Night | |
	Strong	Moderate	Slight	Thinly overcast or 4/8 low cloud	3/8 cloud
2	A	A-B	B		
2-3	A-B	B	C	E	F
3-5	B	B-C	C	D	E
5-6	C	C-D	D	D	D
6	C	D	D	D	D

Note: A: very unstable; B: moderately unstable; C: weakly unstable; D: neutral (should be assumed for overcast conditions during day or night); E: weakly stable; F: stable.

Source. L. T. Fan and Y. Horie, "Review of Atmospheric Dispersion and Urban Air Pollution Models," CRC Critical Reviews in Environmental Control 434 (October 1971).

emitting a gaseous pollutant, such as sulphur dioxide, will affect an area downwind of some considerable size.

The basic equation for a single continuously emitting elevated source, where concentrations will be estimated at ground level, is:[7]

$$C = \frac{Q}{\pi \mu \sigma_y \sigma_z} \exp - \frac{H^2}{2\sigma_z^2} - \frac{y^2}{2\sigma_y^2} \qquad (8.1)$$

where:

C = Concentration of pollutant in weight per volume.
Q = Quantity emitted by the source per time period.
μ = Mean wind speed in a specific direction area in a time period.
H = The effective height of the emission at the source.
y = The perpendicular distance from the centerline of the downwind plume spread to the receptor.
σ_z, σ_y = The dispersion of the pollutant in vertical and horizontal directions at the distance downwind between the source and the receptor.

Figure 8-1

"Box" Diffusion Model

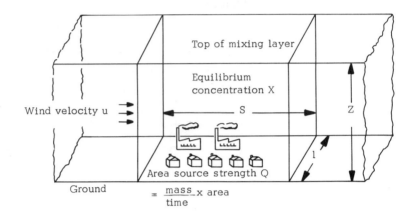

Top of mixing layer

Equilibrium concentration X

Wind velocity u

S

Z

Area source strength Q

Ground

$= \frac{mass}{time} \times area$

SOURCE: Robert J. Bibbero, Systems Approach Toward Nationwide
Air Pollution Control, Mathematical Models 8 IEEE Spectrum
48 (No. 12 December 1971).

Basically, a concentration of a pollutant, in terms of a specific amount of a gas or aerosol (particles less than about 20 microns in diameter) per unit volume, at a point directly downwind is a function of: (1) quantity emitted, (2) wind speed, (3) the effective height of emission, and (4) the dispersion of the pollutant in vertical and horizontal directions. The essential elements of the transport and diffusion process discussed earlier, wind speed and atmospheric stability, are embodied in Equation 8.1. Examining these four variables in greater detail will allow a deeper understanding of the Gaussian-based equation.

The quantity of a pollutant emitted during some time period must be properly estimated. In Chapter 7 there was an extended discussion of the potential errors attached to emissions-generation analysis from land use and transportation system configurations. In the multiple-source dispersion models used to calculate air quality on a regional level, there is the likelihood of a systematic underestimation of pollutants generated as well as random measurement error.[8] It will also be recalled that there are three basic types of pollutant sources—point, line, and area. The necessary dispersion equations for all three types of sources are readily available.[9]

The typical regional multiple-source dispersion model will include procedures to separate sources into point, line, and area sources. For example, the Martin-Tikvart multiple-source dispersion

Figure 8-2

Gaussian Diffusion from a Point Source

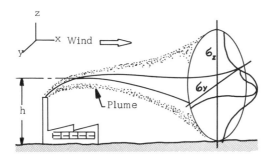

SOURCE: Robert J. Bibbero, Systems Approach Toward Nationwide
Air Pollution Control, Mathematical Models, 8 IEEE Spectrum
49 (No. 12 December 1971).

model treats all sources generating more than 100 tons of total pollutants as point sources.[10] Relatively low-level emitters, such as residential and commercial areas, are treated as area sources, where emissions are assumed to be generated at a constant rate across the surface of the defined parcel. Finally, highways are treated as line sources, where emissions are generated as a function of both a time period and a length of the line segment. For example, the number of grams of carbon monoxide generated by cars, trucks, and buses per second per meter of roadway length would be a typical output from a line source model.

To utilize the appropriate type of dispersion model—point, line, or area—the emissions data collected will have to meet the criteria required by each of the models. For example, in order to calculate the total number of pounds of sulphur dioxide emitted yearly by a defined area, it would not be sufficient to know how many pounds of sulphur dioxide are emitted yearly by a single-family oil-heated residence; one would have to introduce the emissions per residence into an equation that also includes the number of residences within the defined area. This example, of course, relates back to the chapter on emissions generation. Estimates of the quantities of the pollutants emitted must be of sufficient quality and must be specified in the appropriate manner. One can easily see that the amount of pollutants emitted will affect the quality of air downwind. In point of fact, with everything else held constant in Equation 8.1, twice the quantity emitted will produce twice the concentration at the receptor point downwind.

The second variable affecting the concentration at a receptor point is wind speed in a particular direction averaged over some period. The relationships between wind speeds and concentrations are not straightforward. The wind speed variable is built directly into the denominator of the Gaussian equation, implying an inverse correlation between wind speed and concentration levels. However, wind speed is also a variable in the smoke rise equations which relate to the effective height of the emission. If the source is at ground level, the calculations do not include the exponential calculation involving the effective height variable. In this case, concentration at a receptor point downwind is inversely proportional to wind speed, as was suggested in an earlier section on meteorology. Examples of ground-level emitting sources are burning dumps and highways.

There are two other variables that are important in the calculation of pollutant concentrations using the Gaussian dispersion equation. These variables are the effective height of the emission at the source and the dispersion of the pollutant in the vertical and horizontal directions. The effective height of the emission for an elevated source is not the height of the stack itself. Equations, such as the one developed by Holland, can be used to calculate the rise of the plume above the stack.[11] The dispersion of pollutants in the vertical and horizontal directions has been analyzed, so if atmospheric stability can be classified, the dispersions can be easily calculated.[12]

The Gaussian equation contains many of the variables that affect the transport and diffusion of pollutants in the atmosphere. Models based on the Gaussian framework are currently the most popular in the field of air quality management.[13] The continuing hints in the literature that the Gaussian model will be replaced by a better model have not yet been accompanied by widely used operational models of a better, non-Gaussian variety.[14] Since the focus is on operational modeling as it relates to urban planning and programming there is a justifiable need to concentrate on the Gaussian-based models. The next section pursues the question of the ability of dispersion models to predict pollutant concentrations accurately focusing on the Gaussian-based dispersion model, although the methodology utilized and the general conclusions can be extended to the full spectrum of complex models of atmospheric dispersion.

VALIDITY AND MEASUREMENT PROBLEMS

The extent to which a dispersion model will be utilized in an urban planning context depends largely upon how well the model can operate as a basis for decision making. Since resources expended to develop the data base and to operate the model will be justified in terms of results, the validity of the model and the measurement of the data utilized become critical issues. Questions can be asked about the accuracy and relevance of dispersion models when used in planning for improvement or maintenance of air quality. An attempt to answer these questions will form the basis of the discussion that follows.

A planner only needs to purchase the level of accuracy in the model that is necessary for the use to which the model will be put. For example, to know that a model may be accurate within a factor of two is unimportant in itself.[15] However, if the Gaussian dispersion-model estimates of a proposed highway extension are used to indicate whether or not the additional carbon monoxide concentrations, when summed with existing background concentrations, will or will not exceed the federal standards of 15 parts per million for an 8-hour average at a receptor near the roadway, the question of accuracy becomes more relevant. If the background level is 4 parts per million and the estimated addition from the highway is 9 parts per million, then the total is 13 parts per million within the 8-hour standard. If, however, the model underestimated by a factor of two and the addition was actually 18 parts per million, then the background level plus the additional monoxide concentration would total 22 parts per million. This is well over the federal standard for an 8-hour average.

This hypothetical example about the accuracy of dispersion models in determining violations of federal air quality standards can be further illuminated by empirical studies in the area. Generally, the amount of variation explained in the correlation of observed to calculated annual values of sulfur dioxides and particulates ranges from between 30 percent and 90 percent.[16] On a different level, recent work has indicated that data from monitoring stations may not reflect the actual concentrations breathed by urban populations. Wayne Ott and Rolf Eliassen found that carbon monoxide concentrations on downtown sidewalks were anywhere from 1.4 to 3.0 times higher than concentrations measured at a downtown monitoring station.[17] Thus, while data from monitoring stations may indicate that a particular location meets air quality standards, it may indeed be the case that the population is breathing air that is in violation of federal regulations.

Types of Error

Errors in the outputs from dispersion modeling are a joint function of the quality of both the data and the model. Basically, there are two general kinds of error that can be involved in the data collection process—sampling error and nonsampling error. Whenever data are collected on only a portion of all potential objects in some universe, there is the possibility that the sample drawn is not representative. Sampling error, then, occurs because of the variability inherent in the selection of a group from a larger universe; the sample mean of some variable will not always be equal to the universe mean of that variable. Probability theory, however, allows us to make certain statements about the nature and distribution of repeated sample values about a universe parameter.

Nonsampling errors occur because of imperfections in the process of gathering and handling data. Measurements are only accurate to a specific level. Whether one samples a fraction of a universe or calculates a parameter using all the elements in the universe, nonsampling error will still exist. Unfortunately, it is not easy to separate sampling error from nonsampling error in the typical situation where sample surveys are taken. As was already discussed in Chapter 7, quantities emitted from the stacks of plants of a particular industrial class are sampled and averaged. The emission factors generated are then extrapolated to the entire class. Does one attribute any divergence between quantities emitted by two different stacks of the same industrial class to sample variability or to measurement error or to both?

The discussion of error becomes more complex when one realizes that there are two types of sampling errors—random and systematic. The random errors are those encompassed by the process of statistical inference, where it is assumed that samples will exhibit characteristics that can be handled through the use of the appropriate statistical distribution. For example, repeated samples taken of the quantities of pollutants emitted by a number of stacks randomly selected and representative of a particular industry and manufacturing process can be expected to distribute themselves in some known form about the mean of the entire universe of stacks for that industry and manufacturing process. Through the utilization of appropriate statistical procedures, the necessary conceptual and methodological tools can be brought to bear on this problem of random errors. The use of statistical techniques, however, does require that measurements be made of both central tendency (usually, the mean) and dispersion (for example, the standard deviation). Unfortunately, as was suggested in Chapter 7, much air quality management data is not presented with both estimates of the mean and standard deviation.

Systematic errors, on the other hand, occur when there are biases in sample selection. These biases will virtually ensure that the sample is not representative of the universe from which the sample was drawn. As already suggested, emissions inventories are systematically biased and underestimate emissions in the real world because some emitting sources inevitably will be missed.[18] While random errors can be handled through the use of the appropriate statistical technique, systematic errors are not so easily overcome. Only careful and continuous monitoring of sampling procedures can reduce the effect of systematic errors on air quality management data.

Both sampling and nonsampling errors will be designated as measurement error in this study. Thus, any error associated with the generation of air quality data, whether the error be a function of the sample, the measurement instrument, or the data handling process, will be considered as a measurement error. In mathematical terms, measurement error will be incorporated in our analysis by placing an interval about the point estimate of the variable under examination. For example, a stack emitting 25 tons of sulfur dioxide a year would be said to really be emitting 25 (±5) tons yearly.[19] By broadening the definition of measurement error, a distinction can be made between errors associated with the data (measurement errors) and errors related to the model into which the data are placed (specification errors). Hence, specification errors do not refer to the collection and manipulation process itself. Rather, specification errors refer to the quality of the model in which the data will be utilized. A model is not properly specified if significant explanatory variables have been either omitted or not placed into the equations in the appropriate way. For example, a model of industrial location might be improperly specified if a variable describing the access to the raw materials required for production were not included somewhere in the model equations. Improper specification might also occur if the access variable was included but placed in an equation as straight numeric values rather than in its more appropriate logarithmic form.

Operationally, specification error is only determined by the running of the model with empirical data. The properly specified model is one that will explain a significant amount of variation in real world data. For purposes here, a significant amount of variation, conceived in terms of the coefficient of determination (R^2), is 80 or 90 percent.[20] As suggested earlier, values of 30 to 90 percent explained variation have been calculated for atmospheric dispersion models. Thus, while some empirical validations of dispersion models approach the 80 or 90 percent criterion suggested here, other validations have produced explanatory powers far below the criterion level.

There are two reasons why models of complex phenomena, such as the atmospheric dispersion process, seldom yield explanatory

247

power at the 80 or 90 percent level. First, the researcher often has great difficulty in developing a properly specified model that can handle the richness and complexity of real world systems. Second, measurement error in the data collection and analysis phase will contribute to the problem of correctly estimating real world data. For example, a researcher developing a dispersion model that estimates the pollutant concentrations at a receptor point has to deal with both appropriate specification of complex meteorological phenomena and measurements error in input variables. If certain of the input variables are systematically biased, the task of the researcher in developing an adequate model is made more difficult.

Error Propagation: Single Sources

The continual development of atmospheric dispersion models will probably mean a corollary reduction in specification error. The development of the instantaneous puff Gaussian dispersion model for short-term pollutant concentration estimates is a logical outgrowth of earlier work and an example of how research can reduce specification error in a basic model framework.[21] However, there is the continuing problem with measurement error. Assuming a model is perfectly specified, where the model is an exact predictor of the real world values taken by some variable, then measurement error in the input variable will produce error in the output variable.

There is a well-known error propagation formula for a single-equation model relating a dependent, or output, variable to a set of independent, or input, variables:

$$y = f(x_1, x_2, x_3, \ldots, x_n)$$

Of course, models are seldom perfectly specified and thus measurement error is only part of the total error potential in model calculations. The measurement error propagation formula is of the following form:

$$e_y^2 = \sum_i \sum_j f_{x_i} f_{x_j} e_{x_i} e_{x_j} r_{i_j} \tag{8.2}$$

where:

e_y^2 = The square of the error associated with the output variable y.

f_{x_i}, f_{x_j} = The partial derivative of the function with respect to x_i, x_j.

e_{xi}, e_{xj} = The errors associated with the x_i, x_j parameters.

r_{ij} = The simple produce-moment correlation coefficient.

This model is based on the notation of William Alonso, but as presented here it is not the Alonso model.[22] The correlation coefficient in the equation is utilized as an indicator of the amount of linear correlation between independent variables. As such, the use of the equation should be limited to linear equations, but Alonso claims that the equation contains a degree of robustness that makes it useful in the analysis of any single-equation model.

One can see that where there is no correlation between the independent variables:

$$r_{ij} = 0 \text{ for } i \neq j$$

and:

$$r_{ij} = 1.0 \text{ for } i = j$$

then Equation 8.2 reduces to:

$$e_y^2 = \sum_i f_{xi}^2 \, e_{xi}^2 \tag{8.3}$$

Utilizing Equations 8.2 and 8.3, a simple example can indicate the magnitude of error generated in the output of a single-source Gaussian-equation dispersion model from preordained estimates of measurement error in the input variables. Suppose a burning dump emits oxides of nitrogen, and we want an estimate of the ground-level concentrations three kilometers directly downwind.[23] This is a particularly simple example, with no elevated source and the receptor at ground level directly in the center of the wind vector. The dispersion equation, then, is simply:

$$C = \frac{Q}{\pi \, \sigma_y \sigma_z \, \mu} \tag{8.4}$$

The following values and associated errors are placed in the equation:

Q = 3 (±.3) grams per second
σ_y = 190 (±19) meters
σ_z = 65 (±6.5) meters
μ = 7 (±.7) meters per second

Through substitution in the dispersion equation, we get the following:

$$C = \frac{3}{\pi \, (190) \, (65) \, (7)}$$

Then the point estimate of the amount of oxides of nitrogen found 3 kilometers downwind is

$$C = 1.1 \times 10^{-5} \text{ grams per cubic meter}$$

The errors attached to the four variables in the equation are each ten percent of the point estimates in the example. These errors may be thought of as standard deviations about the variable mean. In the long run, assuming that the measurements taken of a variable are normally distributed, two-thirds of the measurements will be located within the interval defined by the error estimate. Hence, in repeatedly sampling the quantity of oxides of nitrogen emitted by the burning dump one would expect to find a mean value of 3 grams per second, with two-thirds of the measured quantities between 2.7 and 3.3 grams per second.

In the case of single sources, the error propagation equation (8.2) will be utilized because of the correlation between independent variables. More specifically, there is a very strong positive correlation ($r = .998$) between the horizontal and the vertical dispersion estimates.[24] It is assumed that the other variables are not correlated.[25] Taking the appropriate partial derivatives with respect to each of the parameters and utilizing ten percent error values for each of four independent variables, and substituting into the following equation,

$$e_c^2 = \sum_i^4 \sum_j^4 f_{x_i} f_{x_j} e_{x_i} e_{x_j} r_{ij}$$

where

$$\frac{r_{ij} = 1.0 \text{ for } i = j}{r_{\sigma_y, \sigma_z} = r_{\sigma_z, \sigma_y} = .998}$$

and all other correlation coefficients are zero, we get:

$$e_c^2 = .71 \times 10^{-11}$$

$$e_c = .27 \times 10^{-5}$$

Recalling that

$$C = 1.1 \times 10^{-5}$$

then the percentage of error in the output is:

$$\frac{e_c}{C} = \frac{.27 \times 10^{-5}}{1.1 \times 10^{-5}} = .24$$

Roughly, then, 10 percent error estimates about the central values of the four independent variables of the single-equation model generate 24 percent error in the output variable, the concentration of pollutants downwind.

Consider the case where errors are on the order of 50 percent of the values in the dump-burning example. Then, using the same formula,

$$e_c = 1.3 \times 10^{-5}$$

Here it can be seen that the error associated with the output variable is larger than the output itself. Hence

$$\frac{e_c}{C} = \frac{1.3 \times 10^{-5}}{1.1 \times 10^{-5}} = 1.21$$

There is about 120 percent error in the measure of pollutant concentrations if each input variable has an error attached of 50 percent. Thus, standard deviations half the size of the mean value of the independent variable will generate a standard deviation in the output larger than the expected value itself.

In choosing a relatively simple case, we have ignored certain complexities; measurement error is an even more serious problem than has been shown here. For the typical single-source calculation, exponential elements must be included to account for an elevated source and to permit calculations for receptors not directly downwind. These added variables will increase the potential amount of error in the output exactly because each variable will itself contribute some amount of error.

Error Propagation: Multiple Sources

As contrasted with the single-source models that calculate the dispersion of pollutants from only one source, multiple-source dispersion models estimate pollutant concentrations from a series of point, line, and area sources. The error propagation potential of multiple-source models is best examined through an example. The problem is to determine the concentration of nitrogen oxides that will result at a receptor point from all significant point sources in a region. Assuming that there are only three sources, the error associated with the estimate of concentration can be determined.

The calculation of concentrations at the receptor point basically followed the logical structure of multiple-source dispersion models. Additivity of the concentration levels at the receptor contributed by each of the sources is assumed. Furthermore, it is assumed that the background level of oxides of nitrogen is negligible. It follows, then, that

$$C_T = C_A + C_B + C_C \qquad (8.5)$$

where:

C_T = Concentration from all sources at a receptor point.

C_A, C_B, C_C = Concentrations contributed respectively by sources A, B, and C at receptor point.

The burning dump will be designated as Source A. We will use the same amount of absolute error occurring in the calculation of the concentration of oxides of nitrogen from the dump when the input variables were assumed to each have 10 percent measurement error. Hence, our source concentrations are:

$$C_A = 1.1 \ (\pm .27) \times 10^{-5} \text{ grams per cubic meter } (gm^{-3})$$
$$C_B = 3.0 \ (\pm .27) \times 10^{-5} \text{ gm}^{-3}$$
$$C_C = 4.0 \ (\pm .27) \times 10^{-5} \text{ gm}^{-3}$$

Assuming that:

$$r_{ij} = 0 \quad \text{for } i \neq j$$

then Equation 8.3 will be used:

$$e_y^2 = \sum_i f_{x_i}^2 \ e_{x_i}^2$$

The partial derivatives of Equation 8.5 are all unity. Hence the error propagation formula (Equation 8.3) becomes

252

$$e^2_{C_T} = [(.27)^2 + (.27)^2 + (.27)^2] \times 10^{-5}$$

$$e_{C_T} = .47 \times 10^{-5} \text{ gm}$$

From Equation 8.5, the total concentration at the receptor point from the sources A, B, and C can be calculated:

$$C_T = 8.1 \times 10^{-5} \text{ gm}^{-3}$$

The calculation of the percent error in the output from three sources,

$$\frac{e_{C_T}}{C_T} = \frac{.47 \times 10^{-5}}{8.1 \times 10^{-5}} = .06$$

shows the relative benignness, to use Alonso's language, with which the error propagation formula treats additive equations. The relatively small measurement errors in the input variables, 10 percent for the burning dump source and less than 10 percent for the other two unspecified sources, has produced a relatively small error in the output variable. Note, however, that the absolute magnitude of error for total concentration does increase. We shall see the implications of this increase in an analysis of larger values of measurement error.

When the input variables have measurement errors of 50 percent of the central values, then it will be recalled that the absolute amount of error in the concentrations of oxides of nitrogen was 1.3×10^{-5} grams per cubic meter. Utilizing this amount of error about each of the three sources of oxides of nitrogen, then

$$e^2_{C_T} = [(1.3)^2 + (1.3)^2 + (1.3)^2] \times 10^{-5}$$

$$e_{C_T} = 2.4 \times 10^{-5} \text{ gm}^{-3}$$

Hence, the estimate of nitrogen oxide concentrations at the receptor point is:

$$C_T = 8.1 \, (\pm 2.4) \times 10^{-5} \text{ gm}^{-3})$$

Assuming that this concentration is a yearly average, how does it relate to national ambient air quality standards? The federal primary standard for nitrogen dioxide for an annual average (arithmetic mean) is 100 micrograms per cubic meter—this is equivalent to 0.05 parts per million.[26] Rewriting the federal standard for comparability, we get:

$$\text{federal standard} = 10 \times 10^{-5} \text{ gm}^{-3}$$

The estimate of concentrations at the receptor point from the three sources,

$$C_T = 8.1 \times 10^{-5} \text{ gm}^{-3}$$

does not exceed the federal standard.

However, if the error estimate about the expected concentration level at the receptor is a standard deviation and we assume normality of error distribution about the central value, then there is a 21 percent chance that the federal standard is being exceeded.[27] Basically, there is one chance in five that the federal standard is being exceeded, even though the concentration at the receptor point is below the federal standard. Granting that this is an artificial example, it is entirely plausible that one could attach the error value of $1.3 \times 10 \text{ gm}^{-3}$ to each of the three sources. Given the error propagation formula and a calculated concentration of $8.1 \times \text{gm}^{-3}$, the potential of exceeding the federal standard is one chance in five.

The Implications of Measurement Error

This analysis of measurement error propagation has a number of implications. The planner or air pollution specialist must recognize the problem of measurement error in dispersion calculations. This means that the quality of the data utilized in dispersion equations must be of sufficient caliber to generate estimates of concentrations at a receptor point that do not have error intervals so large as to make the expected central values relatively meaningless. As was shown, federal air quality standards may be exceeded even when comparisons of the expected value with the standard seem to indicate no violation.

In estimating current emissions, an initial step in improving decision making would be the publication of emission factors with sample size and estimates of variance about expected values included. This beginning step could be followed by the development of a more comprehensive set of emission factors which would be useful to the planner who is accustomed to dealing with land use categories. Thus, the development of emission factors directly keyed to residential, commercial, and institutional square-footage estimates would be an aid to the land use planner.

In projecting future emissions from a land use and transportation system, the question of measurement error becomes even more critical. Not only do emission factors require estimates of variance, but the likelihood of the expected future land use and transportation system configuration must also be estimated. Obviously, the estimates of measurement error for quantities of pollutants emitted from expected future land use and transportation configurations would be quite large. This suggests that simple models of dispersion may be better suited to projecting future emissions than more complex versions.

Alonso has noted, and it has been reaffirmed here, that additive models are superior to multiplicative models in terms of dampening error about output estimates.[28] The single-source and multiple-source examples presented earlier point out the advantages of additive models. Alonso has also suggested, and it has been emphasized here, that simple models with relatively few variables are often preferable to complex models with many variables when there is the potential for significant measurement error. Basically, every additive variable entered into a model will increase the potential for error in the output estimates.

The model-builder, then, faces a different balancing task. While increasing model complexity by using more variables may increase error in the output variable, it is also true that the more complex model may better represent the real world phenomena under study. Thus, a more complex model may have less specification error. In the final analysis, the quality of the data must be balanced off against the quality of the model. In some situations, the benefits gained in using a more complex model outweigh the error propagation potential of utilizing additional variables. For example, a mathematically more complex dispersion model for estimating pollutant concentrations on a short-term basis (daily periods or less), the "instantaneous puff" Gaussian model, has been shown to predict better than the "steady-state" version.[29] On the other hand, it has been argued that one can construct a very simple area source dispersion model that is comparable in prediction ability to the area source version of the Gaussian equation.[30]

The modeler is faced with balancing out the effects of specification and measurement error. If two models appear to do an equal job of predicting the output variable, then the simpler model should be chosen to reduce measurement error. This obvious tenet is only true, however, if the validity of the models has been checked across a set of situations. It is totally inappropriate to claim that a model explains 75 percent of total variation in the data on the basis of only one case study. That 75 percent figure is a function of both measurement and specification error. Rather, a group of studies should be done before a decision about the validity of the model is reached. Through repeated sampling of the data by performing many validation experiments, the randomness of parameter values resulting from measurement error is dampened. This dampening ensures that the model's specification error can be evaluated more successfully.

In conclusion, it should be obvious by this point that there is an important link between the quality of the emissions generation data available and the appropriate complexity of the dispersion equations utilized to estimate air quality. The urban planner, faced with the difficult task of estimating future land use patterns and transportation system developments as a base to emissions estimates, must be particularly sensitive to the problems incurred by utilizing imperfect data. In the concluding section of this chapter, we will develop a set of guidelines for the urban planner who must place quantitative estimates of future air quality within the appropriate legal and administrative framework.

STRATEGIES FOR PROJECTING AIR QUALITY

An Alternative to Dispersion Modeling

To this date, dispersion modeling has not received universal acceptance as a means of estimating future air quality. A well-known alternative to dispersion modeling is the "rollback" technique. A rollback strategy involves the use of a proportional model that calculates the degree of improvement needed in current or projected air quality over a region so that federal air quality standards are not exceeded.[31] The proportional model equation is:

$$P = \frac{A - C}{A - B} \times 100 \qquad (8.6)$$

where:

P = Percent reduction in pollutant concentration required to meet air quality standard for a pollutant.

A = Existing or projected air quality as measured or estimated for the location (usually a monitoring station) in the region with the highest concentration.

B = Background concentration of the pollutant.

C = The federal standard for the pollutant.

The simplicity of the analytic structure of the proportional model is evident. Aggregate current or future emissions are rolled back on a percentage basis across the entire region without regard for long-term average meteorological conditions.

An example taken from the Connecticut Air Quality Implementation Plan shows how the proportional model can be used.[32] In the Eastern Connecticut Interstate Air Quality Control Region, the Putnam monitoring station has the highest annual suspended particulate concentration— 85 micrograms per cubic meter (annual geometric mean). Assuming that the annual geometric mean of 36 micrograms per cubic meter represents the background level as measured at Mansfield and that the federal primary standard is 75 micrograms per cubic meter, then the proportional model would be calculated as follows:

$$P = \frac{85 - 75}{85 - 36} \times 100 = 20.4 \text{ percent}$$

Thus, particulate concentrations would have to be rolled back by 20.4 percent. In 1969 it was estimated that 13,702 tons of suspended particulates were emitted in the region. It was estimated that by 1975 emissions would be reduced through control measures to 4,115 tons. By 1975, then, there would be a 70 percent reduction in particulate concentrations, and this would far exceed the required rollback of 20.4 percent.

The underlying assumption of the proportional model is that a percentage rollback from the maximum concentration in a region to the federal standard requires only that the needed percentage reduction occur for all sources in the region. Obviously, cutting back of stationary and mobile source emissions will improve air quality, given relatively fixed meteorological conditions over the long run. However, depending on the location of the sources that are reduced, air quality at the maximum concentration monitoring station may or may not be improved enough to meet federal standards. In the Connecticut example, there are no assurances that a rollback strategy dictating a 20 percent reduction in total regional emissions would mean a 20 percent reduction at the Putnam monitoring station. If all the source reductions take place downwind of the monitoring station, Putnam may still record concentrations exceeding the federal standards. In the example, of course, it was estimated that a 70 percent reduction would be effectuated for particulates by 1975. It could be easily assumed that an actual 70 percent reduction, when 20 percent is mandated, would probably guarantee that Putnam would meet the standards. However, without some estimate of the atmospheric dispersion of pollutants resulting from source location and meteorological conditions, any conclusions would be somewhat speculative.

In spite of the inherent inability of the proportional model to deal analytically with meteorological conditions, it has received a good deal of attention in air quality implementation plans of different states.[33] The reasons for this utilization are obvious. The proportional model does not require the monitoring data, meteorological information, or economic and human resources required for the atmospheric dispersion models. The field-level engineer and planner often has a good sense of the usefulness of a methodology.[34] Resistance to more complex methodologies can often be based on more than just a preference for the status quo. In choosing between dispersion modeling and proportional modeling, data availability and a resource base are crucial considerations.

This is not to say that dispersion modeling has not been used in state implementation plans. Dispersion modeling has been used by several states for the Set I pollutants (sulfur oxides and particulates). Both Connecticut and Illinois, for example, use the Air Quality Display Model (AQDM) which is based on the Gaussian diffusion equation.[35] The reason the use of dispersion modeling has been confined to the Set I pollutants has to do with data availability. While monitoring has been carried on extensively for the Set I pollutants, this is not generally the case for the Set II pollutants (carbon monoxide, photochemical oxidants, hydrocarbons, and nitrogen dioxide).

While Connecticut and Illinois, for example, utilized dispersion modeling satisfactorily, Maryland had a different experience. Attempts at using the AQDM model in the Baltimore region were not satisfactory.[36] The correlations between the observed and expected pollutant concentrations were low.

Guidelines for Utilization of Techniques

General Observations

In summarizing the discussions, we can make four general observations. First, the time frame upon which the study should focus must be clearly specified. It has been generally assumed that urban planners will focus on long-term (yearly or seasonal) averages. At the same time, certain federal primary or secondary standards may be couched in hourly averages and have to be translated into long-term averages. Ralf I. Larson has developed a potentially useful model for converting concentration levels from one averaging period to another.[37]

Second, the resource question must be squarely faced. Assuming that the planner has already available a plan or set of alternative plans that he would like evaluated in terms of air quality, then the resources will be directed towards the generation, dispersion, and evaluation phase. Since the AQDM is widely available as a computer package, this or a similar dispersion model can be used. The main resource sink, then, will be the estimation of future emissions from land use data and available current emission inventories. Depending on resource availability, it may be that while estimates of aggregate emissions for the region can be calculated, the allocation of these emissions to areal grids within the region may not be feasible. In this case, proportional modeling suggests itself as a necessary alternative to dispersion modeling.

Third, the problems concerning measurement and validity must not be overlooked. Projecting future land use and transportation system development is a difficult task, and air quality estimates based on these projections are potentially error-prone. This implies that a systems approach, involving continual feedback of changes in urban structure, should form a basic part of the planning process.[38]

Geocoding of current and expected land uses in the region should be an integral component of such a systems approach. By continually updating a computerized land use file and running air quality models, monitoring station data can be compared with estimated pollutant concentrations from the models. Continual evaluation of the generation and dispersion models in this manner, when coupled with continually updated land use data, should do much to dampen the error potential in the models and data utilized.[39]

Finally, the legal and administrative framework within which air quality management is undertaken must be cognizant of the potential and problems of estimating future pollutant concentrations. This means that any system of controls directed at improving or maintaining air quality must take into account the relationships between the different land uses and how a particular urban configuration jointly emits pollutants. For example, stationary source control, such as through a permit system, does not really tell the planner the expected quality of the air.[40] Only when the emissions generated by the source are added to the emissions from other existing sources, and dispersion patterns taken into account, is one able to estimate concentrations at selected receptor points.

Consider, also, the situation of estimating future emissions. A reasonably accurate development plan for a region will enable the planner to ascertain where future pollutant concentrations could occur. The appropriate legal and administrative machinery can be established to prevent the development of these pollution "hot spots." Coordination between the estimation of future air quality from land use and

transportation systems and the legal and administrative mechanisms
to ensure compliance with federal mandates is a necessary step in
systemizing an approach to the air quality problem.

Specific Analytic Alternatives

Depending on available resources, the study of the impact on air
quality of a source or set of sources can be done on a number of levels.
For the single-source situation, where the localized impact of a particular source, such as a new industry, power plant, or highway, is being
examined, there are two basic analytic alternatives. First, one can
calculate the amount of emissions to be generated. If regional air
quality, as measured at monitoring stations, is already in violation of
federal standards, then there would be grounds for denying permission
for construction of a new source. However, a simple estimation of
emissions generated would not allow one to determine the contribution
of the source to existing concentrations as measured at selected
receptor points. The second alternative would be, of course, to both
generate and disperse the pollutants.[41] It seems particularly important to use a dispersion model when analyzing localized concentrations.

For the multiple-source case, where the focus is on regional air
quality, three alternative approaches appear reasonable. First, a
simple trend extrapolation can be performed. Population, employment,
and vehicle-mile estimates can be extrapolated into the future in terms
of percentage change. These percentage changes in pollution parameters can then be modified by the projected influence of pollution
abatement technology. Current estimates of air quality, as measured
by monitoring stations, can then be extrapolated into future years as
a function of the pollution surrogates, such as population and technology.

A second approach would be to use the proportional model outlined earlier. For this alternative, aggregate future emissions would
have to be estimated for the region, combining current inventory data
with estimates of future land use and transportation development. Since
emissions would not have to be estimated on a regional basis, considerable savings in resources could be expected over the full-blown
generation and dispersion approach.

The third approach, then, is to estimate future emissions on
a subregional basis and disperse the pollutants using seasonal or
annual average meteorological data. This approach utilizes the most
resources of the three alternatives. However, it is the most power-
ful in aiding the planner. In particular, the air quality impact of
specific projects can be analyzed in the context of existing and proposed
land use configurations. If the problems concerning validity and
measurement are squarely faced, the planner can utilize the results

of generation and dispersion analysis as approximations of what could happen in future years in terms of air quality. Viewed as an approximating device, generation and dispersion analysis could form the basis for the development of a legal and administrative framework for managing air quality.

PUTTING THE STRATEGIES TO WORK

The strategies suggested above have received only limited application. One attempt, utilizing the multiple-source proportional model, was carried out in Middlesex County, New Jersey.[42] An industrialized, rapidly growing county in the center of the state, Middlesex has a present population of approximately 600,000. In very much of a pilot study, it was concluded that none of the secondary air quality standards would be met in the year 2000 under either the County's "trend plan" or its alternative plan. Although the study would have to be redone on a more comprehensive scale before the analysis could become the basis for governmental policy, it is not hard to imagine that the tentative conclusions will be replicated in other rapidly growing parts of the country. The following chapter looks at some of the first attempts to come to grips with this problem.

NOTES

1. See, in particular, the classic text by O. G. Sutton, Micrometeorology (1953).
2. Thomas R. McCurdy, "Vehicular Emissions and the Location of Highways in Urban Areas" (master's dissertation Pennsylvania State U., Regional Planning Program 1969).
3. Peter Rydell and Gretchen Schwarz, "Air Pollution and Urban Form: A Review of Current Literature," 34 J. Amer. Inst. of Planners 115-20 (No. 2 March 1968).
4. See F. Pasquill, Atmospheric Diffusion (1962).
5. For further discussion, see Robert J. Bibbero, "Systems Approach Toward Nationwide Air Pollution Control: Mathematical Models," 8 IEEE Spectrum 47-58 (No. 12 December 1971).
6. For a further discussion of mixing heights, see George C. Holzworth, Mixing Heights, Wind Speeds, and Potential for Urban Air Pollution Throughout the Contiguous United States, particularly 3-7 (1972).
7. A basic reference outlining the Gaussian model is D. Bruce Turner, Workbook of Atmospheric Dispersion Estimates (revised 1970), hereinafter cited as Turner.

8. An excellent synopsis of the development of the multiple-source dispersion model can be found in Arthur C. Stern, ed., Proceedings of Symposium on Multiple-Source Urban Diffusion Models (AP-42 1970), hereinafter cited as Stern.

9. See Turner, 39-41, for an introduction to area and line source pollutant calculations.

10. D. O. Martin, "An Urban Diffusion Model for Estimating Long-Term Average Values of Air Quality," 21 J. Air Pollution Control Assn. 16-9 (No. 1 January 1971).

11. See Turner, 31-34.

12. See, for example, Turner for an introduction to the concept of atmospheric stability classes and their relationship to vertical and horizontal dispersion of pollutants.

13. The most widely used model of atmospheric dispersion is based on the structure developed by D. O. Martin, supra note 10. The Air Quality Display Model (AQDM) developed by Martin is a computerized version of the Gaussian-based model. This model predicts long-term average air quality from multiple sources located within the study area.

14. See L. T. Fan and Y. Horie, "Review of Atmospheric Dispersion and Urban Pollution Models," CRC Critical Reviews in Environmental Control 431-57 (October 1971), for an excellent review of specific analytic solutions to the generalized equation for diffusion. Much of the current work centers on modeling the reactive processes which occur between pollutants.

15. Turner, 7-10.

16. See Martin, for example, where the coefficient of determination was improved from 36 percent to 71 percent by removing 5 of the 40 data points relating predicted to observed sulfur dioxide concentrations. Unpublished work from the U.S. Environmental Protection Agency indicates that this 30 to 90 percent range in explained variation, relating predicted to observed pollutant concentrations at receptor points, usually monitoring stations, is reasonable.

17. Wayne Ott and Rolf Eliassen, "An Urban Survey Technique for Measuring the Spatial Variation of Carbon Monoxide Concentrations in Cities," a paper presented at the annual meetings of the Air Pollution Control Assn. (June 1972).

18. See Glenn Hilst, "Sensitivities of Air Quality Prediction to Input Errors and Uncertainties," in Stern, 8-5.

19. The placing of a numeric interval about a point estimate is not a standard practice in air quality management literature.

20. See any standard statistical text for a discussion of the coefficient of determination. Two basic well-known reference works are Frederick E. Croxton, Dudley J. Cowden, and Sidney Klein, Applied General Statistics (1967), and Hubert M. Blalock, Jr., Social

Statistics (1972). It should be noted that there is no one value of R^2 that can be deemed as the breakpoint between the significant and the nonsignificant amounts of variation explained. In the physical sciences, high R^2 values approaching 100 percent are common, while in the social sciences, values of 20 or 30 percent are often cited as important. Note also that the use of the term "significant" in the discussion here is not meant to be confused with the more formal term "statistical significance" found in inferential statistics.

21. See D. M. Rote, J. W. Gudenas, and L. A. Conley, Studies of the Argonne Integrated-Puff Model (Publication No. ANL/ES-9 1971), hereinafter cited as Rote.

22. William Alonso, "Predicting Best with Imperfect Data," 34 J. Amer. Inst. of Planners 248-55 (No. 4 1968), hereinafter cited as Alonso. Note, however, that as presented, the Alonso model is incorrect. In the case where $r_{ij} \neq 0$, the model as displayed in the Alonso paper double-counts the contribution to error when $i = j$. In other words,

$$f_{x_i} f_{x_j} e_i e_j r_{ii}$$

is squared twice, rather than the correct situation where the equation is only squared once. For comparison, see the presentation in E. B. Wilson, Jr., An Introduction to Scientific Research 272-4 (1952).

23. This example is drawn from Turner, ch 7.

24. As an illustration of the intercorrelation between the horizontal and vertical dispersion variables, a correlation analysis was run using estimates of dispersion from Figures 3-2 and 3-3 in Turner, at 8, 9. For stability class D and a sample of 10 observations taken from 0.1 kilometer to 1 kilometer by tenths, $r = .998$.

25. It is readily apparent that there is no correlation between quantity emitted and the other variables in the equation. Also, for any particular stability class, there is no correlation between wind speed and either vertical or horizontal dispersion coefficients.

26. 36 Fed. Reg. 6680 (1971).

27. Using the formula for the calculation of a Z-score,

$$Z = \frac{x - \bar{x}}{s} = \frac{10 - 8.1}{2.4} = .79$$

then there is a 21 percent chance that the value of 10 is exceeded, assuming 8.1 as the mean of the distribution.

28. Alonso, 250-4.

29. See Rote for a comparison of the integrated-puff model and steady-state Gaussian-based dispersion models.

30. See the very interesting paper by Stephen R. Hanna, "A Simple Method of Calculating Dispersion from Urban Area Sources," 21 J. Air Pollution Control Assn. 774-7 (No. 12 December 1971).

31. The proportional model is described in the 36 Fed. Reg. 15490 (1971).

32. Department of Environmental Protection, State of Conn., Air Quality Implementation Plan 150-3, 283.

33. See, for example, the implementation plans of the state of Maryland, including the Plan for Implementation of the Ambient Air Quality Standards of the Metropolitan Baltimore Intrastate Air Quality Control Region (1972).

34. For a devastating critique of the model-building enterprise from the viewpoint of the consumer, see Richard Bolan, "New Rules for Judging Analytical Techniques in Urban Planning," in Analytical Techniques 75-89 (1970).

35. The Connecticut use of the dispersion model is discussed in the implementation plan by the Department of Environmental Protection, State of Conn., particularly 79-110. The Illinois use of the dispersion model is found in 1 State of Illinois Air Pollution Control Implementation Plan, particularly Section 4.2. The Air Quality Display Model is discussed in National Air Pollution Control Administration, Air Quality Display Model (AQDM) (1969).

36. Plan for Implementation of the Ambient Air Quality Standards of the Metropolitan Baltimore Intrastate Air Quality Control Region 174-7.

37. Ralph I. Larson, A Mathematical Model for Relating Air Quality Measurements to Air Quality Standards (1971).

38. An interesting recent attempt at systematizing feedback processes is George Chadwick, A Systems View of Planning (1971). See also, J. Brian McLoughlin, Urban and Regional Planning: A Systems Approach (1969).

39. The computerized package developed by Environmental Research and Technology, Inc. for use in air quality analysis of alternative land use and transportation system configurations operates on a geocoded file of emitting sources. See the multivolume research effort on the Hackensack Meadowlands of New Jersey (ERT Document No. P-244).

40. Note, however, that the emission from a stationary source can be modeled and the concentrations resulting examined to determine air quality violations. A general reference work in permit processing is Arnold Stein, Guide to Engineering Permit Processing, U.S. Environmental Protection Agency (APTD-1164 1972).

41. See Turner as a basic reference work for the single-source case.

42. "The Relationship Between Land Use and Air Pollution in Middlesex County, New Jersey" (Rutgers U., Dept. of Urban Planning and Policy Development 1973).

9

**AIR QUALITY
MANAGEMENT
IN CALIFORNIA**

California probably has the worst air pollution problem of any state in the United States. Much attention has been given to programs to deal with California's air pollution problem, and a review of California's experience can provide useful lessons for the rest of the country.[1] In 1972 the state air pollution control agency, the California Air Resources Board (ARB), was told by its technical advisory committee that major changes in air pollution control plans were necessary if the state was to achieve and maintain pollution levels that are acceptable from the standpoint of health. The committee stated:

> Some or all of the following actions will be necessary if
> the air quality of the South Coast Basin (Los Angeles area)
> is to meet the proposed air quality standards: Limit the
> number and use of automobiles, trucks and aircraft per-
> mitted in the basin and substitute alternate modes of
> emission-free transportation; reduce emissions from
> these sources to levels below those now proposed; remove
> or make essentially emission-free all industries and
> fossil-fuel power plants in the basin; develop a com-
> prehensive, nonpolluting urban transport system; limit
> population growth by sharply restricting subdivision
> and residential expansion in the basin; limit commercial
> and industrial growth to zero-emission facilities and
> restrict emissions from commercial, agricultural,
> domestic and recreational sources.[2]

Although ARB has not accepted the position that all of these limitations are necessary, it is moving forward with a policy that markedly changes the approach to air quality management in the state. This approach, commonly called emission allocation, is the focus of most of this chapter. We will also examine the tentative movements of the Bay Area Air Pollution Control District in San Francisco towards an official policy on land use planning.

GOVERNMENTAL STRUCTURE

In California, ARB has the responsibility for controlling motor vehicle emissions, coordinating any statewide air pollution control effort, and overseeing the activities of the local air pollution control districts. ARB establishes emission standards and test procedures for new and used vehicles and promulgates statewide ambient air quality standards which include pollutants that are not covered by the national standards. Among other duties, ARB also advises and assists the local districts with their pollution control plans and enforcement activities. Technical assistance, personnel, and equipment are provided to those districts that lack the competence for evaluating specific sources for compliance with state or local regulations. It also reviews and can revise basinwide implementation plans and local rules and regulations prepared by the districts. If a district fails to take what the state considers to be reasonable enforcement action, ARB can take such action.

California enabling legislation resulted in the formation of local air pollution control districts in about half of the state by 1969 and in the rest of the state by 1973. The law provides that such districts can be county, multicounty, or regional districts, and it created "Basinwide Coordinating Councils" for any of the 11 air basins that include two or more districts. These councils, comprised of representatives of the local districts in the basin, perform planning and coordinating functions mainly related to the basinwide implementation plan. Thus in California there are a number of basinwide implementation plans in addition to the statewide general implementation plan prepared by ARB. Legal authority to carry out the basinwide plan remains with the local districts.

Unlike the air pollution control programs in many other states, the districts have the primary responsibility for the control of emissions from stationary sources. The districts control these emissions through the adoption of rules and regulations governing stationary source emissions, control new sources through the permit system, and inspect existing sources periodically to determine rule violations and equipment changes that would affect air pollution emissions. The districts also monitor air quality, issue and prosecute citations for rule violations, and hold hearings on citations, permit denials, and variances.

Not to be neglected in this structure is the role of the federal government, particularly the Environmental Protection Agency (EPA). As has been noted in Chapter 2, EPA's influence over state and local air pollution control programs has increased as a result of the 1970 Amendments to the Clean Air Act. In California, EPA directly controls sources within federal jurisdiction, establishes and implements national policies that would assist in reducing air pollution, develops control technologies, recommends control strategies, and sets national emission and air quality standards applicable in the state.

EPA can also promulgate state control strategies if it feels that the ones developed by California are not adequate. EPA has used this authority in the case of the transportation control strategies, which have resulted in the expression of a great deal of animosity towards EPA by some air pollution control officials in the state. Reductions in gasoline consumption and the institution of parking fees—two strategies advocated by EPA for reducing the use of automobiles in California air basins with severe air pollution problems—have not been well received by California elected officials. Aside from the obvious impact such measures would have on the automobile-oriented California way of life, one can argue that at least part of this negative reaction is due to the feeling in the state that California has led the nation in air pollution control and does not need the federal government to tell it how to run air pollution control programs.

THE STATE IMPLEMENTATION PLAN

It is fair to conclude that innovative approaches to air quality management, directly or indirectly resulting from the Clean Air Act, evolve in a form of learning process whereby management procedures are proposed internally within air pollution control agencies, in interagency committee, or by other informal means of communication, are discussed in public hearings, and are adopted. In some cases EPA might suggest guidelines or procedures and approve or reject regulations that are adopted by the states. Also, it is not uncommon to find an independent consultant assisting EPA, or in some cases assisting a state agency, in developing guidelines. After some time the procedure might be revised on the basis of experience gained in application.

It is too early to tell whether this model will be followed completely in the process of introducing land use controls as a part of air quality management on a nationwide scale, but California seems to be following the basic elements. Starting with only minimal interest in land use planning, ARB has arrived at a position of advocating land use controls as a means of maintaining air quality standards.

An early version of the State General Plan of the Implementation Plan for Achieving and Maintaining the National Ambient Air Quality Standards in the State of California suggests the earlier attitude.[3] The Plan suggests that land use controls are a "long term solution" with "control at the local government level."[4] "Green belts" and "self-contained communities" are mentioned as helpful programs that are "probably best based on land use decisions at the most local level."[5] But the Plan also states that "the consideration of air quality as a factor in land use planning must be made on a regional basis."[6]

A later version of the General Plan still calls for "basic land use planning at the local level"[7] and land use planning for air pollution control on the air basin level, but it goes on to state that the "carrying capacity" of air basins needs to be studied and that it may be necessary to "limit and regulate" growth patterns, the location of power plants and industries, develop a coordinated transportation system, and encourage the preservation of open space.[8] An even later draft version of the General Plan states that "the Air Resources Board will endeavor to obtain legislation in 1972 which will require (1) city and county general plans to include an air quality element, and (2) review of that element at the state level."[9] The final version concludes that:

> Present state law does not specifically direct planning agencies to include air pollution in the land use planning process. Legislation will be needed if local planning agencies are required to develop land use plans which include measures to prevent, minimize and reduce air pollution. The State will adopt criteria for local agencies to follow and will need authority to review the local plans. Coupled with the stringent measures that will be taken to control air pollution from existing sources, these land use policies further will add to the State's capability for attaining and maintaining satisfactory air quality in the metropolitan areas and to preventing air pollution from becoming a problem in areas where there is a potential but not yet a problem."[10]

These excerpts suggest ARB's seemingly contradictory attitude that air pollution is a regional problem but that land use control is a local prerogative; this is a fairly common attitude among air pollution control personnel. Since they are for the most part engineers and scientists, they have little insight into the nature of land use planning and are naturally somewhat unwilling to disturb what they interpret to be the status quo in a field that is outside their professional competence. Thus we find that in January 1973 the California legislature enacted Senate Bill 981 (SB 981), which charged ARB with preparing a report to the legislature on proposed guidelines for focusing local land use planning on the abatement of air pollution, and specified that the report be completed by July 1, 1973.

This approach had some logic since it was very much in keeping with the way the state has dealt with land use planning during the last decade. Under state mandate California cities and counties are required to develop a long-range general plan composed of seven mandatory elements. Land use, circulation, housing, and open space elements were to be adopted by June 30, 1973; and seismic safety, noise, safety, and scenic highway elements were due in late 1974. Since, as in other parts of the country, local zoning ordinances and subdivision regulations in California often have little relation to adopted general plans, the legislature in 1972 enacted Assembly Bill 1725 requiring zoning ordinances "to be consistent" with the local general plan by July 1, 1973. In addition, no tentative or final subdivision map can be approved by a city or county unless it conforms to the local general plan. Thus, the general plan is an important document in the land use planning process in California and is therefore a seemingly convenient place to introduce air quality considerations. As we will soon find, however, this has not entirely proved to be the case.

STATE LAND USE PLANNING IN CALIFORNIA

In 1970, the California legislature enacted legislation establishing an Office of Planning and Research in the Governor's Office. The Office is to advise the governor and the legislature on matters concerning land use policy and is charged with the task of preparing a statewide plan and implementation program for the protection of the state's land and water resources. In cooperation with various state agencies the Office of Planning and Research has completed a three-phase study of land use planning in the state. Phase one identified areas with land use problems or potential land use problems. Phase two involved the projection of development trends through the analysis of population growth and migration patterns. Phase three, completed in 1973, examined alternative population and land use policies and their social, environmental, and economic implications. In essence, scenarios were developed of various possible development patterns. The next step is for the Office to make proposals with respect to population growth, transportation policy, urbanization, and the location of polluting industries in the state. Partly because of budget and staff limitations, this planning effort cannot be viewed as the basis for a comprehensive state planning effort.[11] Indeed, the various state agencies with functional responsibilities have made and are continuing to make important decisions affecting land use although there is no comprehensive state planning process. This is, of course, common in the United States, but most likely this state of affairs cannot continue in California because of the increasingly pervasive set of state environmental regulations affecting land use.

One such regulation is the requirement contained in the California Environmental Quality Act (EQA), passed by the legislature in September 1970 and patterned after the National Environmental Policy Act.[12] The EQA requires all state agencies to prepare environmental reports on their own projects and on federal projects on which state agencies comment. The requirements of the EQA were made applicable to local governments by an amendment approved by the governor in 1972.[13]

The scope of this requirement was also expanded in 1972 as a result of the "Friends of Mammoth" decision. Mammoth Lakes are a group of lakes in sparsely populated Mono County on the Nevada border. The lakes were the site of a proposed condominium project which many local residents thought would overload sewage and water supply facilities. Despite their opposition, the Mono County Planning Commission approved the project and the County Board of Supervisors upheld the decision.

The citizens who opposed the project formed an association called "The Friends of Mammoth" and sought a Writ of Mandamus to invalidate the use permit granted to the developers. The citizens group argued that the permit was invalid because the EQA's requirement for an environmental impact report (EIR) had not been met, and that the EQA should apply not only to projects sponsored by government agencies but also to private projects requiring governmental approval. The Court of Appeals and the Superior Court both denied the writ, and the case was taken to the California Supreme Court in the Summer of 1972. In its decision the court stated:

> In this instance our task has been considerably simplified because the Legislature has expressly set forth its intent in sections 21000 and 21001 of the act. These two provisions captioned, "Legislative Intent" and "Additional Legislative Intent" contain no less than 14 references to the concern of the Legislature with the current deterioration of the environment . . . an analytical reading of these sections leads to the ineluctable conclusion that the Legislature intended to include within the panoply of the act's provisions, private activities for which a permit, lease or other entitlement is necessary.[14]

With this decision almost all development in the state fell under the environmental impact report requirement, while prior to this time public works projects received the most attention. With the decision, the court threw the construction industry into turmoil, and local government found itself unprepared for a deluge of EIRs. To bring some order to this confusion, the State Resources Agency hastily developed guidelines for the preparation and processing of EIRs. The guidelines, issued in February 1973, summarize the EQA and cover the two topics of primary concern to local government—the contents and processing of EIRs.[15] While clearly specifying the decisions and tasks that are to be included in the processing of EIRs, the guidelines allow considerable flexibility for local governments to devise procedures suited to their own needs. The result has been a proliferation of new job titles, special committees, and, in some cases, inconsistent procedures in county and municipal government. EIRs, of course, are required in addition to such other requirements as sewer permits, grading permits, subdivision permits, business license tax permits measured by number of dwelling units built, occupancy permits, and any other special purpose permits.[16]

Ad hoc regulation of land use in the absence of a comprehensive state plan can, of course, continue as it has in the past.[17] But one sees in the state an increasing concern with establishing a baseline for making decisions on environmental management issues that maintains the tradition of local control but at the same time increases the involvement of the state in land use decisions. The example that best demonstrates this trend is the emission allocation procedures proposed by the Air Resources Board.

EMISSION ALLOCATION

With the passage of Senate Bill 981 the staff of ARB began to address itself to the question of how air pollution control could be introduced into local planning activities. It was initially thought that the air pollution control element and the general plan should be submitted to air pollution control districts that had a regional jurisdiction or to basinwide coordinating councils and should be amended and adopted by July 1, 1975. The councils and districts were to evaluate the element and the plan for their air pollution potential by January 1, 1975, and the city and county zoning was to be consistent with the adopted air pollution control element by October 1, 1975.[18] Discussion within ARB produced three possible procedures for focusing land use planning on the abatement of air pollution. The first procedure would be for the air pollution control district in a given region to provide county and city planners with a qualitative report concerning the possibility of achieving and maintaining federal and state air quality standards.

A descriptive bulletin was to be issued by the ARB for use by city and county planners in order to provide information on the following points: (1) the primary and secondary effects on ambient air quality of major commercial and residential developments; (2) the secondary effects of proposed freeways and mass transit corridors; (3) the effects on ambient air quality of other elements in the general plan.[19]

EPA's reports on air pollution control and urban planning were to provide the basis for this bulletin. On the basis of this information the planners would develop or modify their city or county general plan and include a statement that they had considered air quality in the land use and circulation elements of the plan, and in any other element that might seem relevant.

The second procedure was a quantitative approach in which planning projections of emissions would be made using currently available techniques and utilizing allowable emissions from the state's implementation plan as desirable basinwide goals. Emission goals on a local level would be determined by the county air pollution control district in conjunction with the basinwide council. There would be no attempt to evaluate localized air quality and there would not be a mandatory requirement for revision of the general plans within the air basin. The procedure would be advisory only. ARB would provide planners with readily usable emission factors for ten-year and twenty-year periods.

Both the first and second procedures would make the planner aware of the emissions entailed by different plans for local areas. The second procedure would allow the state government to consider restrictions on the allocation of state funds utilized for development projects to air basins that exhibited poor long-term relationships between projected and allowable emissions.

The third procedure discussed would have been a quantitative system in which ARB would develop an air quality model or a variety of models applicable to different air basins. Emission allocations would be assigned to the cities and counties within each air basin by the basinwide coordinating councils. Planners could plan within these emission allocations using emission factors. A map of "distributed emissions" would be produced and plugged into a model that would determine basinwide air quality concentrations. If the concentrations were predicted to be in excess of those mandated by federal and state standards, a change in the emission allocation and consequently in the planning process would be mandated. This approach would attempt to set up a system that would provide for measurement of plans against emission goals, modification of plans to meet goals, and a "fair" method of resolving problems generated by the intercity and inter-regional transport of pollutants.[20]

In summary, the three alternative procedures were not viewed as mutually exclusive, but as stages of development and sophistication. The first procedure was purely qualitative, mandating consideration of air quality criteria in the preparation of the general plan. The second procedure was quantitative, allocating emissions in an advisory capacity only, but with some possible sanctions in terms of state funding. The third procedure was quantitative, based on the development of a modeling technology that could measure emissions and predict air quality and that, by implication, would give the basinwide coordinating councils the authority to allocate emissions.

During the course of this discussion ARB requested that an urban planning consulting firm prepare proposed guidelines for the preparation of an air pollution control element in general plans as required by SB 981. The report was to be prepared in collaboration with ARB. According to a March 1973 discussion paper prepared by the consultant, the primary purposes of the proposed air pollution control element were to educate the planner and the public to the air quality effects of the general plan, to provide data to the local air pollution control district and the basinwide coordinating council, and to establish procedures and controls in land use planning and development to assess and limit future emissions by regulating proposed development projects.[21]

According to the consultant, the proposed components of the air pollution control element were: (1) a description of existing air quality standards applicable to the city or county and a comparison of the city or county's air quality with air quality standards; (2) mapping of emissions of air pollutants generated by existing land uses; (3) mapping of projected emissions to be discharged by potential sources of air pollutants proposed by the general plan; (4) a listing of air pollution control orders in effect; (5) emission performance standards for incorporation into the zoning ordinance; (6) criteria for estimating emissions of air pollutants from proposed developments.[22]

It is interesting to note the consultant's emphasis on mapping data. Planners traditionally gather data on maps, but it is difficult to see how air pollution data could be gathered and analyzed in this fashion. In any case, subsequent work by the consultant does not mention a mapping technique.

The final study, completed in July 1973, reached the conclusion that a local air pollution control element could not meet the requirements of SB 981, although the study emphasized that general plans can serve as important instruments to help maintain air quality standards.[23] The study examined the relationships between land use and transportation planning on the local and regional level and concluded that local planning has traditionally neglected air quality considerations in the land use and circulation elements of general plans, but that local planners are realizing the need to guide growth through land use and transportation planning in order to meet air quality standards. Los Angeles, Marin County, San Diego, and the San Francisco Bay Area were mentioned as having devoted some attention to the relationship between land use and transportation planning and air pollution. In San Diego and San Francisco an air basin approach was used as the basis for study.

The study emphasizes that although air pollution is a regional problem, regional planning is mainly advisory in nature, particularly when carried out by councils of government which only have the A-95 review power, and that local plans have generally been "upheld" over regional plans in cases where they conflict. Regional plans seldom do much more than mention air pollution. The one exception was found in the San Francisco Bay Area, where the Metropolitan Transportation Commission, the agency responsible for the preparation of a regional transportation plan, provisionally adopted the following two policies in 1973:

> 1. All transportation program designs and plans shall be coordinated in cooperation with regulatory agencies to achieve present and future air and water quality standards.
> 2. Transportation program designs and plans shall include estimates of air polluting emissions, so that these plans can be evaluated by air quality standards.[24]

The study suggests that similar policies may be adopted by the new State Department of Transportation.

The consultant points out that there are over two thousand special districts not subject to the control of city councils and not fully integrated into the system of county and city governments in California. These districts can make decisions without consulting cities and counties and can have significant effects on growth. For example, if a district can sell a bond issue to finance utilities which will make land in their jurisdiction more developable, then population growth becomes necessary to pay off the bonds. The special districts do not consider the air quality impacts of growth except for the preparation of an impact report. Once the utilities are installed, a county has no choice but to approve the development unless it wants to bankrupt the district. The California legislature has passed the Knox-Nisbet Act creating local agency formation commissions to approve or disapprove proposals for the formation of special districts and to regulate the powers of special districts, but the commissions have not fully exercised their authority.

The consultant's report also examined the utility of the California Environmental Quality Act and found that reports prepared under the Act are mainly informational documents that discuss air quality in qualitative terms. Air quality impacts cannot be evaluated in these reports because the reports concentrate on incremental impacts of particular projects without considering the cumulative effects of several projects or being required to consider air quality standards.[25]

The study emphasizes the problems of introducing an air pollution control element at the local level. The first problem is that photochemical oxidant is an areawide pollutant, and no model is presently available to relate emissions to air quality concentrations. The second is that the impact of local land use on local air quality cannot be determined by a local agency because local agencies cannot determine background concentrations from other portions of the air basin. Third, it is beyond the abilities of local planning agencies to evaluate the impact of local land use on air quality for the rest of the same air basin without operational basinwide models. Fourth, the impact of local land use plans on traffic volumes cannot be evaluated without regional multimodel traffic models which are the responsibility of a regional transportation agency. And fifth, local efforts cannot improve air quality without comparable efforts on basinwide scale.[26]

Besides these five technical problems, the study found three administrative problems that would limit the value of a local air pollution control element. First, at present no effective machinery exists to resolve interjurisdictional conflicts. Second, an inadequate relationship among local general plan air pollution control elements, the regional transportation plan, and transportation projects could result in violations of air quality standards. Third, where there is insufficient coordination between local planning agencies and local agency formation commissions, there may not be adequate analysis of the air quality impacts of proposed incorporations, annexations, special district formations, or extension of special district areas.[27]

The study therefore proposes an alternative procedure that would utilize existing plans, air quality standards, and emission inventories to integrate air quality considerations into the land use and transportation planning process. The California Implementation Plan has set allowable emissions for each air basin, and an emission inventory was compiled for each basin in 1970 and is updated every two years. Six steps are proposed:

1. Compile detailed inventories of air polluting emissions in planning subareas of air basins. Planning subareas will have to be chosen to conform as far as possible to the boundaries of political subdivisions, census tracts, and existing planning sectors. The present inventories for counties and air basins are too general for detailed air quality planning.

2. Designate maximum allowable emissions for each planning subarea based on an analysis of present air quality and the environmental capacity of the atmosphere. Maximum allowable emissions can be calculated by two alternative methods—a proportional method and a validated air quality model.

3. Project planning subarea emissions likely to be generated by sources indicated in land use and transportation plans for designated future time periods (for example, 1985 and 1995), and compare these emissions with allowable limits.

4. Evaluate and revise land use and transportation plans so that prescribed emission limits would not be exceeded.

5. Adopt and implement land use and transportation plans that will meet air quality goals.

6. Monitor public and private development through a refined environmental impact assessment process in which directly or indirectly projected emissions by projects are accounted for in environmental impact reports.[28]

These six steps are designed to overcome the technical and administrative limitations of the local air pollution control element; the procedure is called "emission allocation." The application of such a procedure will require changes in the governmental framework. The choice is between strengthening the councils of government or utilizing single-purpose basinwide agencies. Under the first proposal, councils of government would be strengthened to include the six-step process in their comprehensive planning programs. Implementation would be carried out jointly with the basinwide coordinating councils, who would compile a planning subarea emissions inventory and set planning subarea emission limits. The regional land use and transportation plan would be revised so that projected emissions would not exceed the allowable emission limits. Cities and counties would be required to make their plans conform with the regional plan. Prior to construction, individual projects with significant air pollution potential would be subject to review in the air quality section of a revised environmental impact report and to a permit review by the air pollution control district.[29]

Under the second proposal, a single-purpose basinwide agency would be established to set planning subarea emissions limits and to evaluate the impact on air quality of local general plans and the regional transportation plan. The basinwide coordinating councils could be authorized to function as the air basinwide agency. Cities and counties would cooperate with the agency in the preparation of the emissions inventory and would project emissions from proposed general plans. The regional transportation agency would be responsible for estimating future emissions from its proposed transportation plan. These emissions projections would be submitted to the basinwide air pollution agency for evaluation. If necessary, local planning agencies or the regional transportation agency would be required to revise their plans to meet emission limits. Responsibility for enforcement of emission limits would rest with the air pollution control districts. The impact of new projects would be monitored through the revised environmental impact assessment report.[30]

The consultant's report concludes that proposal to strengthen councils of governments would have a number of advantages. Some of the councils have large technical staffs experienced in land use and transportation planning and who have prepared numerous regional plans. Except in the San Francisco Bay Region, the councils are responsible for preparing the state-mandated regional transportation plan. They conduct the A-95 review process and act as a clearing-house for environmental impact statements.

However, it is pointed out that the councils of governments are voluntary organizations and their functions are only advisory. Except for their veto power over federal grants, councils of governments are not empowered to implement plans or policies. Legislative efforts to vest governmental powers in multipurpose regional agencies have consistently been defeated in California. It is noted that councils of governments are not directly accountable to the public, and their policies sometimes reflect local perspectives or tend to be based on compromises between local views. The regional plans prepared by councils of governments also typically lack the detail necessary to project emissions. Except for those of the San Francisco Bay Area and San Diego County, the councils of governments' jurisdictional boundaries do not conform with air basins.[31]

The study therefore favors the utilization of a single-purpose air basinwide agency on the grounds that it would offer the following advantages. Most important, the agency would possess the statutory powers necessary to implement its programs. Its boundaries would coincide exactly with those of the air basins throughout the state. By concentrating its efforts on air quality and the relationship of air quality to land use and transportation planning, a basinwide agency could achieve the objective of meeting air quality goals significantly earlier than the councils of government, with their multiplicity of planning responsibilities. It is argued that as a resource center to evaluate land use and transportation plans only for their impact on air quality, the single-purpose air basinwide agency would probably be more efficient, as well as more effective, provided that it kept the councils of governments continuously advised of its activities and decisions.[32]

To implement the first proposal, statutory authority to implement and enforce regional plans would have to be given to councils of government. The report states that if regional planning is to become a reality in California, the councils of government would be the logical choice. But since it is unlikely that such authority will be given to the councils, and since the second proposal would require less extreme changes, the study recommends single-purpose air basinwide agencies.[33]

The report recommends strengthening existing basin coordinating councils, rather than creating a new single-purpose agency, in order to capitalize on their experience and to avoid creating a new layer of government. New legislation will be required to expand the powers of the basin coordinating councils. Laws relating to local planning and to environmental impact reports would have to include requirements that emission limits be respected and that plans be submitted to the basin coordinating council. Local agency-formation commissions would have to consider the air quality effects of proposals for annexation, incorporation, and the formation or expansion of special districts. Air pollution control districts would be required to amend their permit procedures to be consistent with the emissions allocations.[34]

At the time of this writing, it seems likely that some form of emission allocation will be implemented in the State of California. The consultant's report has been accepted by ARB and a formal proposal is to be made to the legislature in 1974. ARB, however, is already moving to implement aspects of the program and is building up a land use planning capability within the agency. The proposed complex source regulations demonstrate one use of emission allocation.

COMPLEX SOURCE REGULATIONS

ARB has proposed a two-level program for reviewing and regulating indirect sources in response to the regulations promulgated by EPA. The first level, what is called the "Basic Program," is aimed at the localized impact of sources, which would be evaluated by local air pollution control districts on an individual source-by-source basis. The districts would be required to deny an authorization to construct if they found that the source would prevent the attainment or maintenance of any national ambient air quality standard. This Basic Program relies on the expansion of the districts' permit systems to provide for the review and regulations of new indirect sources and would be applicable all over the state. It is therefore similar to complex source regulations proposed in other states.

As noted earlier, as a result of the California Environmental Quality Act of 1970 and the 1973 Amendments to the Act, EIRs are required for all projects, both public and private, that would have a "significant" impact on the environment. The Air Resources Board has suggested that the EIRs could serve as possible sources of information for monitoring indirect sources to determine if a construction permit from an air pollution control district is required. If necessary, the districts would request additional information from the project proponents, and local and state planning agencies would provide data on traffic generation.

In addition to the Basic Program, a "Supplemental Program" was proposed for the parts of the state with serious air pollution problems—the San Diego, South Coast, San Joaquin Valley, San Francisco Bay Area, and Sacramento Valley Air Basins. This supplemental program would be integrated into the emission allocation program and thereby provide a regional framework for the review of individual indirect sources. Developers of major projects that would qualify as indirect sources would have to apply to the air pollution control districts for authority to construct or modify the indirect source. The district would not issue authority if the projected emissions would cause the allocated limits of the affected subdivisions to be exceeded. This requirement would be in addition to the review process required by the Basic Program.

A proposed new indirect source would be subject to indirect source review if it met any one of the following criteria: (1) the associated motor vehicle miles traveled (VMT) would be greater than 30 million miles per year; (2) it would have a VMT greater than 100,000 miles during any twenty-four hour period; or (3) it would have more than 1,500 new parking spaces available to users of the project.

Indirect sources include, but are not limited to:

1. Highways and roads
2. Parking lots and garages
3. Shopping centers and other retail facilities
4. Recreational centers and amusement parks
5. Sports stadiums
6. Airports
7. Commercial or industrial developments
8. Metropolitan redevelopment projects
9. Governmental buildings
10. Hospitals and other medical facilities
11. Educational institutions
12. Hotels and motels
13. Office buildings
14. Restaurants
15. Theaters

AIR QUALITY MANAGEMENT IN THE
SAN FRANCISCO BAY AREA

Since World War II, the San Francisco Bay Area has experienced tremendous urban growth, which has been accompanied by steadily increasing air pollution levels. Realizing that the continuance of this trend would engulf the basin in air pollution, and noting the failure of direct regulation of source emissions to be 100 percent effective, the Bay Area Air Pollution Control District has paid increasing attention to the question of regional growth controls, and has concluded that land use controls are necessary to complement emission regulations in an effective air quality management system. In July 1972 the District adopted a permit system requiring a permit of any person intending to construct a new source or to modify an existing source. The permit system, discussed in Chapter 4, is the means by which the District plans to control new sources emitting air pollutants, and for all practical purposes this system gives the District an indirect control over land use.

Topography and Meteorology

The San Francisco Bay Area, containing well over four million inhabitants, is a large, shallow basin surrounded by hills. Thus its topography alone gives it a great potential for trapping air pollutants. Concentrations are determined by the interaction of circulations around the great high and low pressure areas—the continental and maritime air masses. The continental air mass centered over the Great Basin to the east is cold and dry in winter and warm and dry in summer. The Pacific air mass is more moist, denser, less given to temperature extremes.[35]

The amount of air available to dilute pollutants depends primarily on the character of the inversion layer and the amount of wind flow. Inversion layers, which are characterized by a blanket of air overlying cool air immediately below, are naturally formed on the mid-latitude west coasts of continents by "subsidence," which compresses and heats air, or by the cooling of the lower layers at night by radiation. In the Bay Area, temperature inversions occur about two out of every three days of the year. Temperature inversions can prevent vertical dispersion since colder air cannot rise through the warmer air and pollutants are trapped in the colder air closer to the ground. When the inversion layer is lower than the hills surrounding the Bay Area, it becomes a lid, sealing the low-lying, pollutant-bearing air into the Bay Area Basin.[36]

The other factor influencing the buildup of pollutants is wind speed. Together, these two factors determine the ventilation factor, which in the San Francisco Bay Area Basin is normally adequate to disperse most pollutants. However, during the "smog season," the warm, sunny months between May and October, more photochemical oxidants are formed. Strong inversions and stagnant air conditions are also regularly experienced during the summer and early fall. Poor ventilation leads to buildup of smog and other pollutants.[37]

The meteorological, geographic, and other characteristics of California have established the need for controls more stringent than federal controls. California is the only state allowed to conduct its own program on automobiles and to establish and enforce its own standards. The state program is administered by ARB.[38]

Under the Clean Air Act Amendments of 1970, as noted earlier, states were required to submit a plan providing for the implementation, maintenance, and enforcement of federal ambient air quality standards within the state. California law requires the Bay Area Air Pollution Control District to supply that portion of the plan dealing with the control of stationary sources in the San Francisco Bay Area Basin.

The Administrative Framework of the Bay Area Air Pollution Control District

The Bay Area Air Pollution Control District was created by the California Legislature in 1955. Its jurisdiction is limited to stationary sources of air pollution within the Bay Area and to rail and sea transportation. All gasoline or diesel powered motor vehicles are controlled by the state, and aircraft are controlled by the federal government.[39]

The District encompasses all of seven counties—Alameda, Contra Costa, Marin, San Francisco, San Mateo, Santa Clara, and Napa—and portions of two others—southwestern Solano and southern Sonoma. It is governed by an 18-member Board of Directors. Each county is represented by two members, one selected by each County Board of Supervisors from among their number, and the other a mayor or city councilman selected by the City Selection Committee. The Board has the power to develop and enforce regulations for the control of air pollution within the District.

To advise the Board and to assist it in developing regulations, there is a 20-member Advisory Council appointed by the Board. Members of the Advisory Council represent special interest groups and must include three representatives from public health agencies, four representatives from environmental protection groups, and single representatives from the areas of agriculture, architecture, labor, industry, mass public transportation, education, community planning, general contractors, engineers, regional park districts, park and recreation commissions, and universities.

The District has an independent Hearing Board to consider and, when necessary, to grant variances from regulations, since it is impossible to adopt regulations that will accomplish equitable control in all cases. The Hearing Board has the power to make special provisions in unusual cases. It is also the District's judicial body. The law requires that most enforcement cases be heard first by the Hearing Board. The Hearing Board makes findings of fact and can issue orders for abatement, which are then enforced under the injunctive power of the Supreme Court. The Hearing Board was made independent of the Board of Directors to separate the legislative and judicial powers.

The following regulations have been passed by the Bay Area Air Pollution District:[40]

1. Open burning is either prohibited outright or limited according to meteorological conditions under Regulation 1. As originally adopted in 1957, Regulation 1 was enforceable through civil injunction. When it was demonstrated to the legislature that this was impractical in some cases, misdemeanor power was given to the District in 1965.

2. Regulation 2 instituted direct controls on particulate matter, sulfur dioxide, sulfuric acid from industrial and commercial sources, and particulate matter and organic gases from incinerators. On November 3, 1971, the Board adopted a regulation governing the emission of lead particles from stationary sources.

3. Direct controls on the emission of certain kinds of organic gases are exercised through Regulation 3. The measure describes the gases to be controlled as reactive—that is, relatively quick in reacting with nitrogen dioxide in the atmosphere to form oxidant. Regulation 3 affects the formulation, storage, shipment, and use of such materials as solvents, paint, gasoline, and ink. Other requirements of Regulation 3 are designed to compel the use of submerged fill pipes, vapor recovery systems, and floating roof tanks for the transfer and storage of large quantities of reactive materials, so that evaporation loss to the atmosphere is minimized.

4. Regulation 4 directly controls some of the organic compounds from used automobiles. It was originally passed to require residents of Contra Costa County to install crankcase ventilation devices on cars upon transfer of ownership or upon reregistration of a car from outside the state. The other counties in the District were already required to do this by state law. Regulation 4 was expanded to include Napa County and the residents of Solano and Sonoma Counties that are within the District. The crankcase ventilation device recirculates gases into the combustion chamber of the automobile engine so that the emission of unburned hydrocarbons is reduced.

Field inspectors are responsible for checking whether or not sources are complying with these regulations. Inspection is part of the Enforcement Division. The enforcement effort of the Bay Area Air Pollution Control District is based on performance standards. The District establishes emission limits for contaminants, and sources may use whatever means necessary to come into compliance with these limits. Although the District engineers may review company plans, the staff cannot specify any particular process or equipment to bring the company into compliance. However, the District can make recommendations which are considered by the Hearing Board along with alternatives presented by the company.[41]

The first step in enforcement of the District's regulations is to advise the offending party of the nature of its violation. Most of the time the District receives a satisfactory explanation and either immediate compliance results or the company presents acceptable plans for compliance. The District requires the attendance of company officials at an office conference when an unsatisfactory reply to a violation notice is received or if no reply is forthcoming within ten days. If the company is unwilling or unable to present any alternatives to continuing violations, abatement actions or penalties may result.[42]

The Permit System

In 1971, the Board, in formulating the long-term goals of air pollution control in the District, included a new concept: "The incorporation of air quality standards in the development of a regional land use plan which includes decisions concerning the location and size of subdivisions, industrial and commercial expansion, transportation systems, high rise developments, new power plants, as well as other relevant planning decisions."[43] This marked the beginning of a new approach to air pollution control in the Bay area.

In 1972, amendments to the District's Regulation 2 established a permit system, effective July 1, 1972, for the review of construction of new facilities, the modification of facilities, and the change of ownership or location of facilities that may either cause or alter the emission of air contaminants.[44]

Permits are issued both to construct and operate. The following information is required:

1. Emission Point Summary Form. Form should list all emission points for the equipment in this application.
2. Plot Plan of Facility. To scale, must show location of all emission points and the nearest street intersections.

3. Topographical Map. Exact location of facilities should be shown on a U.S. Coast and Geodetic Survey seven-and-one-half-minute quadrant map.
4. Process Flow Diagram. Show process equipment and pounds per hour of materials flow if continuous, or batch schedule and pounds of all material charged to batch.
5. Description of Operation and Facilities. Name all ingredients used, and list particle sizes of all bulk solids involved. Describe control procedures and equipment in sufficient detail to show degree of expected air contaminant control.[45]

The Permit Services Group was created to handle inquiries and initial application processing. The Group receives and logs all permit applications and then sends them to proper quarters for evaluation. After making sure that all pertinent information has accompanied the application, the Group places the appropriate data in computer memory banks. The application will then be sent to an engineering specialty group for evaluation and, if necessary, to the Research and Planning Section for their evaluation.[46]

The Permit System is based on three criteria: (1) As designed, will this operation meet District emission standards? (2) Will its operation cause any air quality standards to be exceeded anywhere in the District? (3) Will the operation result in a significant quantity of emissions in an area where the air quality standards are already exceeded? If the answer to any of these questions is yes, then a permit to construct must be denied.

The implications of the permit criteria are significant. Anyone wishing to build in an area where air quality is near or at unacceptable levels will have to develop methods of operation that will safeguard air quality, or else he must go elsewhere. Section 1311 of the Permit Regulations, which governs improvements of source emissions by replacing equipment, will perform a similar service. Under its provisions, plants that wish to expand or refurbish their operations must achieve a reduction in emissions at the source in question.[47]

The permit regulation (Section 1315) also requires a permit for construction and operation of the following sources:

1. All stationary sources causing emissions in excess of 100 tons per year of any pollutant for which there is a National or State of California air quality standard.

2. Without regard to the amount of emission, stationary sources listed in the Appendix C of the Federal

Register, Saturday, August 14, 1971, Volume 36, Number
158, Part 11, Page 15497.[48]

There are over 100 sources on this list. Exemptions are listed in
Section 1316 and include such sources as homes, apartments, and
office buildings.[49] The applicant is responsible for compliance with
these regulations.

During the first four years, after adoption of the permit system,
none of the operations listed in Section 1316 would be required to
obtain permits for construction or operation. After four years, the
exemptions would expire, enabling the District to review the impact
of emissions from these exemptions in the light of air quality levels.[50]

Sections 1308 and 1309 of the permit regulations deal with the
denial of construction authorization by the District if emissions from
the facility or the use of the facility would cause or had already caused
air quality standards to be exceeded. A four-year period was originally
proposed before Sections 1308 and 1309 were to become effective
because of the need for the District to develop an acceptable air pollution model relating emissions to meteorological factors. This would
enable the District to determine the impact of specific source emissions on air quality. This requirement was deemed necessary to the
enforcement of Sections 1308 and 1309. However, the Board of Directors made Sections 1308 and 1309 effective immediately when EPA
threatened to disapprove that part of the Implementation Plan and
promulgate their own instead.[51]

The authority of the Board of Directors to require permits prior
to construction is based on the following statutes: The Clean Air Act
Amendments of 1970, discussed in Chapter 2, provide in Section 110
that states shall submit plans for implementation, maintenance, and
enforcement of national ambient air quality standards in each air
quality control region, or portion thereof, within the state. Section
110(a)(2)(B) states that the plan should include "emission limitations,
schedules, and timetables for compliance with such limitations, and
other such measures as may be necessary to insure attainment and
maintenance of such primary or secondary standards, including but
not limited to land use and transportation controls."

Section 110(a)(2)(D) states that the plan should provide for "a
procedure . . . for review (prior to construction or modification) of
the location of new sources to which a standard of performance will
apply." Such procedure must provide (1) adequate authority to prevent
or modify any new source to which a standard of performance will
apply at any location within the state where the state determines that
otherwise federal standards will not be attained or maintained, and
(2) that prior to the construction or modification of any such source
of pollution, the owner or operator thereof shall submit to the state

such information as may be necessary to permit the state to determine whether the construction or modification will in fact prevent the attainment or continuance of such standards.[52]

The Bay Area Air Pollution Control Law, the California Health and Safety Code Sections 24345 through 24374, gives the Board power to adopt and enforce orders, rules, and regulations.[53] Section 24362 provides that the Board may by resolution declare it necessary that the District adopt rules and regulations to control the release of air contaminants in order to reduce or alleviate air pollution within the District. Section 34362.1 provides that at any time after such a resolution has been adopted, the Board may make and enforce all necessary orders, rules, and regulations to accomplish the purpose of the Bay Area Air Pollution Control Law. Section 24362.3 provides that:

> Whenever the board finds that the air in the district is so polluted as to cause discomfort or property damage at intervals to a substantial number of inhabitants of the district, the board may make and enforce such general orders, rules and regulations as will reduce the amount of air contaminants released within the district, but no order, rule or regulation of the board shall specify the design of equipment, type of construction, or particular method to be used in reducing the release of contaminants.

Section 24362.4 provides that the Control Officer of the Board "may require from any person subject to regulations of the board, such information and analysis as will disclose the nature, extent, quantity or degree of air contaminants which are or may be discharged by such source." Under this section the Board has the means of obtaining information prior to construction about the contaminants that may be discharged after the source is constructed and put into operation.

The permit system may be used in connection with performance standards to control sources of air contamination prior to construction. The permit system would not merely involve permits to construct and operate, which would only specify allowable emissions from a source regardless of the air quality effects of clustering. It would also involve a permit to locate, since it is concerned with the impact of a new source on surrounding air quality.

The Effectiveness of the Permit System

On October 27, 1972, the Bay Area Air Pollution Control District announced that it had denied authority to construct 18 gas stations. Under Section 1309 of the Permit Division, the Air Pollution Control Officer must deny permits to build facilities that emit air pollutants in areas where air quality standards are exceeded. The air quality standard for oxidant is currently exceeded over most of the Bay Area. Oxidant is formed when hydrocarbons and oxides of nitrogen combine in the atmosphere under the influence of sunlight. Reactive hydrocarbons evaporate into the atmosphere from filling stations when gasoline is pumped into cars and when storage tanks are filled. The District's refusal to grant permits to build service stations marks the first time in the Bay Area that growth controls have been imposed to prevent the deterioration of local air quality.[54]

On January 3, 1973, the Board lifted the ban on the construction of new gasoline stations. Oil companies, gas station developers, and labor unions had protested the ban vehemently, claiming that it created undue economic hardships without reducing smog.[55] However, construction permits will be issued only to new stations equipped to recover at least 90 percent of the fumes emitted when underground storage tanks are filled. Also, the stations were required to install, by January 1, 1974, equipment to control 90 percent of the vapors emitted when vehicle tanks are filled with gasoline. The ban on gasoline station construction lasted only ten weeks. It was originally adopted without any specific land use planning goals in mind, and was only intended to reduce the emissions of one pollutant into the atmosphere. The conditions imposed on the granting of the permit eventually served the same purpose.

Evaluation

Given the physical nature of the San Francisco Bay Area and its present rapid growth rate, one can perceive the obvious need for some form of land use control that influences urban growth, which in turn influences the maintenance of air quality standards. As originally designed, Sections 1308 and 1309 of the Permit Regulations were not to take effect until four years after they were adopted, in order to allow time for the development of mathematical dispersion models. These models will allow the District to isolate the impact of specific sources on the air quality of the region, thereby providing a verification and legal support for the enforcement of the permit regulations. However, since the Board decided to make the regulations apply in 1972 rather than in 1976, they are not operating as effectively as they eventually will when more effective dispersion modeling techniques are operational.

Significantly more attention will have to be addressed to air quality monitoring as an aid in the development and verification of dispersion models.[56] Additional monitoring is also necessary because without more adequate observational coverage of the District, air quality data will only be valid for locations adjacent to existing monitoring stations. This is a speculative point, however, since mobile monitors can be utilized as the occasion demands. Still, the processing of a large number of permits would place a severe burden on the District if mobile monitoring were relied upon.

Like many other California agencies with functional responsibilities, the Bay Area Air Pollution Control District has become involved in land use controls in a very ad hoc, incremental fashion. Without conscious design, the District will increasingly be making land use decisions that some would argue should be the responsibility of a land use planning agency. The District feels it has a mandate to achieve and maintain the ambient air quality standards applicable in California, and that it will institute whatever controls—including land use controls—are necessary to achieve this objective. Although the staff realizes that some of its policies might eventually run counter to other urban development goals often advocated by planners, it views itself as the only agency presently capable of implementing stringent and possibly politically unpopular decisions restricting the growth of land use types that emit air pollution. Although these types of land use restricted will be limited for the near future to industrial and commercial point sources, and special cases like gasoline stations, the indirect effects on the location and amount of urban growth will clearly be significant

The regional agencies in the Bay Area with which the District keeps closely in touch are the Association of Bay Area Governments, a council of governments operation of the type discussed in Chapter 4, and the Metropolitan Transportation Commission (MTC), a unique regional transportation planning agency set up by the State of California. Because of a strengthening concern for urban planning in the Bay Area, these two agencies have a greater impact than metropolitan agencies in other parts of the country. The District has agreed to assist the MTC and ABAG in an evaluation of the air pollution emissions associated with ABAG's regional plan and the MTC's transportation plan. The District also maintains contact with local planning agencies, principally in connection with its advisory role in reviewing environmental impact reports. The District's two land use planners also maintain informal relationships with planning agencies.

CONCLUSION

We have examined the California Air Resources Board and the Bay Area Air Pollution Control District in this chapter because they

289

have gone farther than any other air pollution control agencies in considering land use planning in their decisions.[57] As is evident, both agencies are in a very preliminary stage with regard to this process. During 1975 their procedures will be considerably refined. It will not be surprising to see other states follow California's lead during the second half of the 1970s.

NOTES

1. For an earlier review of experience in California, see G. Hagevik, Decision-Making in Air Pollution Control (1970).

2. Air and Water News, October 26, 1972. The Air Resources Board was created by the Mulford-Carrell Air Resources Act in 1967. The Act consolidated the duties of the old Motor Vehicle Pollution Control Board, the State Vehicular Pollution Laboratory, and the Bureau of Air Sanitation of the Department of Public Health. Under a reorganization effective in 1972, the ARB members were reduced in number from 14 to 5, and the Technical Advisory Committee was abolished. ARB members are appointed by the governor with the consent of the Senate.

3. Staff Memo, November, 7 1971, p. 181.

4. Id.

5. Id.

6. Id.

7. Staff Memo, January 10, 1972, p, 29.

8. Id.

9. No date, p. 117.

10. January 30, 1972, pp. 81-82.

11. The Office of Planning and Research was somewhat embarrassed in 1971 and produced a "plan" for the state ahead of the state agency. See: Alfred Heller, ed., The California Tomorrow Plan (1972).

12. Public Resources Code, Sec. 21000.

13. Public Resources Code, Sec. 21151, as amended.

14. Friends of Mammoth v. Board of Supervisors of Mono County, 8 Cal. 3d. 1 (1972).

15. Office of the Secretary of Resources, "Guidelines for Implementation of the California Environmental Quality Act of 1970" (1973).

16. See: Donald Hagman, "Ecology v. Building: A Knockout in the Fifth," Planning 40-1 (March-April 1973); Gerald Mylroie, California Environmental Law: A Guide (1973).

17. One view of land use planning in California that cannot be called complimentary is that of the Ralph Nader Study Group, in Robert Fellmeth, Politics of Land (1973).

18. Staff memo entitled "SB 981 Program Discussion," January 23, 1973. In other states the general plan might be called the master or comprehensive plan. Few states, however, have such detailed specifications on the content of the general plan as does California.

19. Id.

20. Id.

21. Livingston and Blayney, Concepts of an Air Pollution Control Element (March 28, 1973), at 4 (mimeo).

22. Id.

23. Livingston and Blayney, Report on Guidelines for Relating Air Pollution Control to Land Use and Transportation Planning in the State of California 1 (1973).

24. Id. at 23.

25. Id. at 26-7.

26. Id. at 28-9.

27. Id.

28. Id. at 2-3, 30-4.

29. Id. at 35.

30. Id. at 36.

31. Id. at 55-6.

32. Id. at 56.

33. Id. at 57.

34. Id. at 56.

35. Bay Area Air Pollution Control District, Air Pollution and the San Francisco Bay Area 8 (1972), hereinafter cited as BAAPCD.

36. BAAPCD, 9. The reactive pollutants are the major problem.

37. BAAPCD, 10.

38. BAAPCD, 18.

39. BAAPCD, 19-20.

40 Bay Area Air Pollution Control District, Summary of District Regulations (1972).

41. BAAPCD, 24-26.

42. Id.

43. Bay Area Air Pollution Control District, "The Permit System: A New Direction in Air Pollution Control," 15 Air Currents 1 (June 1972).

44. Bay Area Air Pollution Control District, Permit Information 108 (1972).

45. Bay Area Air Pollution Control District, General Instructions for Permit Applications 107 (1972).

46. Bay Area Air Pollution Control District, supra note 9.

47. Bay Area Air Pollution Control District, supra note 9.

48. Bay Area Air Pollution Control Law, Reg. 2, Div. 13 Sec. 1315.

49. Id. Sec. 1316.

50. Robert Hoyer, letter of general information (May 1, 1972).

51. Personal communication with Ralph Mead (December 4, 1972).

52. Clean Air Act Amendments of 1970, P.L. 91-604 Sec. 110 (a)(4).

53. Bay Area Air Pollution Control Law, Health and Safety Codes Sec. 24345-24374.

54. Personal communication with the Bay Area Air Pollution Control District.

55. "New Gas Station Ban is Lifted," Marin County Independent Journal, Jan. 4, 1973.

56. Richard Thuiller, "Air Monitoring and Its Application to Land Use Planning" (prepared for the 13th Conference on Methods in Air Pollution and Industrial Hygiene Studies, Berkeley, Calif. 1972).

57. A further discussion of the emission allocation procedures suggested in the Livingston and Blayney report is found in George Hagevik et al., Maintaining Air Quality through Land Use Planning (1974).

10

THE CONTROVERSY
OVER NONDEGRADATION

This study would not be complete without at least a brief examination of the issues involved in the debate over "nondegradation." Nondegradation as applied to air quality management is a policy providing that in areas of the country where the air is of higher quality than the federal secondary standards, the air quality should not be allowed to deteriorate significantly. The policy would probably mainly affect rural areas without concentrations of heavy industry or population.

On June 11, 1973, the United States Supreme Court upheld a lower court decision in favor of four environmental groups who brought suit against the federal Environmental Protection Agency (EPA) concerning the question of nondegradation.[1] The following is a discussion of the suit brought by the environmental groups against the Administrator of EPA, the arguments for and against such a policy developed before the Court, the implications of the decision, and the possible approaches advanced by EPA to implement the Court decision. At the time of this writing EPA has not promulgated final nondegradation regulations; thus the following material must be considered an incomplete statement of federal policy. Nevertheless, the central issues are raised.

On May 24, 1972, four environmental groups—the Sierra Club, the Metropolitan Washington Coalition for Clean Air, New Mexico Citizens for Clean Air and Water, and the Clean Air Council of San Diego County—brought suit against William D. Ruckelshaus, Administrator of EPA, over the issue whether the Administrator must disapprove those portions of state implementation plans that fail to effectively prevent the significant deterioration of existing air quality in any portion of the state.[2]

On May 30, 1972, a preliminary injunction was issued by the United States District Court restraining EPA from approving any state implementation plan unless it did not permit significant deterioration of existing air quality in any portion of any state where the existing air quality is better than the secondary standards. The Administrator of EPA was ordered to complete a review of all state plans in four months and to promulgate and publish within six months regulations concerning state plans that permit significant deterioration in any portion of any state.[3]

On June 2, 1972, Judge Pratt of the United States District Court issued a memorandum stating that the court found the plaintiffs (Sierra Club et al.) had standing under the citizen suit provision of the Clean Air Act and that Section 101(b) of the Act, which states that the Act is designed "to protect and enhance the quality of the Nation's air resources,"[4] "would appear to declare Congress' intent to improve the quality of the Nation's air and prevent deterioration of that air quality, no matter how presently pure that quality in some sections of the country happens to be."[5] The court considered the legislative history of the Air Quality Act of 1967 and the Clean Air Act of 1970, as well as the administrative interpretations of those statutes. On the basis of this analysis, the court declared:

> it is our judgement that the Clean Air Act of 1970 is based in important part on a policy of non-degradation of existing clean air and that 40 C.F.R. 51.12(b), in permitting the states to submit plans which allow pollution levels of clean air to rise to the secondary standard level of pollution is contrary to the legislative policy of the Act and is therefore invalid.[6]

On June 5, 1972, the EPA filed an appeal for the reversal of this decision. On November 2, 1972, the United States Court of Appeals affirmed the lower court decision,[7] and on November 23, EPA disclosed that it was seeking Supreme Court appeal of the District Court decision.[8] The arguments of the two opposing parties are summarized below.

ARGUMENT OF THE SIERRA CLUB

The Sierra Club et al. argued[9] that the Clean Air Act, first adopted by Congress in 1963, states as the first purpose of the statute:

> . . . to protect and enhance the quality of the nation's air resources so as to promote the public health and welfare and the productive capacity of its population.[10]

Thus the Act was designed to ensure that air would not be further harmed by a lowering of its quality and that it would also be improved. The national primary and secondary ambient air quality standards adopted by the Administrator of EPA provide that:

> The promulgation of national primary and secondary air quality standards shall not be considered in any manner to allow significant deterioration of existing air quality in any portion of any state.[11]

This regulation provides that air quality which is better than secondary standards cannot be permitted to deteriorate significantly. However, on August 14, 1971, the Administrator of EPA adopted Requirements for Preparation, Adoption and Submittal of Implementation Plans, which states:

> In any region where measured or estimated ambient levels of a pollutant are below levels specified by an applicable secondary standard, the state implementation plan shall set forth a control strategy which shall be adequate to prevent such ambient pollution levels from exceeding such secondary standard.[12]

Thus it was made clear that the Administrator of EPA would approve state implementation plans that permit the significant deterioration of air quality so long as pollution levels do not exceed the secondary standard. The Sierra Club argued that this regulation is in direct conflict with the provisions of the Clean Air Act and contested the validity of the regulation.

Most of the state implementation plans filed with EPA did not have provisions prohibiting significant deterioration,[13] and approval of these plans would most likely result in the significant deterioration of air quality in areas where the air quality is better than secondary standards.

The Sierra Club maintained that there can be levels below secondary standards which may produce health hazards. The National Air Pollution Control Administration (NAPCA) Guidelines for the Development of Air Quality Standards and Implementation Plans stated:

> . . . the [air quality] criteria are not an indication of how much air pollution man and his environment can tolerate without biological risk . . . air quality criteria cannot be interpreted as threshold values; indeed for many types of air pollutants, there may not be a threshold of risk to health and the environment.[14]

The Sierra Club maintained that the legislative history of the Clean Air Act is fully consistent with its language. The interpretation of the Act and its predecessor, the Air Quality Act of 1967, was also consistent with the language of the Act until the Administrator promulgated the regulation allowing the approval of state implementation programs that permit significant deterioration.

The Clean Air Act was first adopted by Congress in 1963. The Act provided:

> The purposes of this Act are . . . to protect the nation's air resources so as to promote the public health and welfare and the productive capacity of its population.[15]

The 1963 Act was not specifically designed to improve air quality. In the Air Quality Act of 1967, Congress strengthened the Act and added the phrase "and enhance the quality of." Thus, the Sierra Club argued, the Act was intended to improve, not just maintain, air quality. The Senate Report underlying the Air Quality Act of 1967 seems to make clear that the Act was designed to improve air quality throughout the country, including areas with relatively clean air:

> The prime purpose of the proposed legislation is to strengthen the Clean Air Act, to expedite a national program of air quality improvement, and to enhance the quality of the atmosphere.[16]

The National Air Pollution Control Administration was charged with the responsibility of carrying out the Air Quality Act of 1967. The Sierra Club asserted that the administrative interpretation of the Act by NAPCA was not to allow any significant deterioration of air quality in any part of the country. In 1969, NAPCA promulgated the Guidelines for the Development of Air Quality Standards and Implementation Plans, which stated:

> An explicit purpose of the Act is to "protect and enhance the quality of the Nation's air resources." Air quality standards, which, even if fully implemented, would result in significant deterioration of air quality in any substantial portion of an air quality region clearly would conflict with this expressed purpose of the law.[17]

The Clean Air Act of 1970 retained the language "to protect and enhance air quality." The Senate Report that preceded the Clean Air Act of 1970 stated that no significant deterioration of air quality would be permitted under the Act:

In areas where current air pollution levels are already equal to, or better than, the air quality goals, the Secretary should not approve any implementation plan which does not provide, to the maximum extent practicable, for the continued maintenance of such ambient air quality. Once such national goals are established, deterioration of air quality should not be permitted except under circumstances where there is no available alternative. Given the various alternative means of preventing and controlling air pollution—including the use of the best available control technology, industrial processes, and operating practices—and care in the selection of sites for new sources, land use planning and traffic controls—deterioration need not occur.[18]

The Sierra Club suggested that the administrative interpretation of the Clean Air Act by EPA was inconsistent with this position. On April 30, 1971, the Administrator of EPA promulgated national primary and secondary ambient air quality standards, which provided that the "standards shall not be considered in any manner to allow significant deterioration of existing air quality in any portion of any state."[19] But on August 14, 1971, the Requirements for Preparation, Adoption and Submittal of Implementation Plans provided that in areas where air quality was below the secondary standard, "the control strategy shall include procedures for preventing such ambient levels from exceeding such secondary standards."[20] Thus, the air quality could be degraded to the secondary standard.

ARGUMENT OF THE ENVIRONMENTAL PROTECTION AGENCY

EPA argued[21] that 40 C.F.A. Section 51.12(b), ruled invalid by the District Court, reflects the Administrator's doubts as to his authority to impose such a policy upon the states in their implementation plans. EPA maintained that the words of the operative section of the Clean Air Act and the relevant legislative history support the Administrator's interpretation that he lacks authority to reject a state plan that meets the specific requirements of Section 110.

According to EPA, the Clean Air Act does not authorize the Administrator to reject a state implementation plan because it fails to prevent deterioration of air quality in any area where it is better than the secondary standards. Section 110 requires the Administrator to "approve such plan, or any portion thereof, if he determines that it was adopted after reasonable notice and hearing" and that it fulfills the eight specific criteria set forth in Section 110:

(A) (i) in the case of a plan implementing a national primary ambient air quality standard, it provides for the attainment of such primary standard as expeditiously as practicable but (subject to subsection (e)) in no case later than three years from date of approval of such plan (or any revision thereof to take account of a revised primary standard); and (ii) in the case of a plan implementing a national secondary ambient air quality standard, it specifies a reasonable time at which such secondary standards will be attained.

(B) it includes emission limitations, schedules, and timetables for compliance with such limitations, and such other measures as may be necessary to insure attainment and maintenance of such primary or secondary standard, including, but not limited to, land use and transportation controls.

(C) it includes a provision for establishment and operation of appropriate devices, methods, systems and procedures necessary to (i) monitor, compile, and analyze data on ambient air quality and (ii) upon request, make such data available to the administrator.

(D) it includes a procedure, meeting the requirements of paragraph (4) for review (prior to construction or modification) of the location of new sources to which a standard of performance will apply.

(E) it contains adequate provisions for intergovernmental cooperation, including measures necessary to insure that emissions of air pollutants from sources located in any air quality control region will not interfere with the attainment and maintenance of such primary or secondary standard in any portion of such region outside of such State or in any other air quality control region.

(F) it provides (i) necessary assurances that the State will have adequate personnel, funding and authority to carry out such implementation plan, (ii) requirements for installation of equipment by owners or operators of stationary sources to monitor emissions from such sources, (iii) for periodic reports on the nature and amount of such emissions; (iv) that such reports shall be correlated by the State agency with any emission limitations or standards established pursuant to this Act, which reports shall be available at reasonable times for public inspection; and (v) for authority comparable to that in Section 303, and adequate contingency plans to implement such authority.

(G) it provides, to the extent necessary and practicable for periodic inspection and testing of motor vehicles to enforce compliance with applicable emission standards; and

(H) it provides for revision, after public hearings, of such plan (i) from time to time as may be necessary to take account of revisions of such national primary or secondary ambient air quality standard or the availability of improved or more expeditious methods of achieving such primary or secondary standard; or (ii) whenever the administrator finds on the basis of information available to him that the plan is substantially inadequate to achieve the national ambient air quality primary or secondary standard which it implements.[22]

If a plan meets these requirements, which do not mention preventing deterioration of air quality in areas with clean air, the Administrator must approve the plan. EPA thus concluded that nowhere does the Act give him the authority to reject a plan for any other reason.[23]

EPA argued that the aim of the Clean Air Act was to protect the public health and welfare by establishing the national primary and secondary standards. The secondary standards are based on the best technical knowledge of the concentration levels below which there are no known or anticipated adverse effects of air pollutants. Section 116 of the Act provides that any state may adopt stricter standards than those required by the national secondary standards. Section 116 was designed to leave this type of determination to the states, and therefore the Administrator's interpretation of Section 110 is correct. EPA contends that in an Act drawn with such care and detail, if Congress has intended that nondeterioration be included, it would have specifically provided so in Section 110.[24]

EPA said the legislative history of the Act supported the Administrator's interpretation. The Clean Air Act of 1967 provided that each state would have to establish ambient air quality standards for the regions within its jurisdiction and would have to submit implementation plans to the Secretary of Health, Education, and Welfare (HEW) describing how the ambient air quality standards would be enforced.[25] In the 1970 Clean Air Act the Administrator of EPA is required to establish national ambient air quality standards. States need not set any ambient air quality standards themselves, although they can set stricter ones. The Clean Air Act of 1970 is more comprehensive than the 1967 Act or the 1970 Senate bill that was the basis for a large portion of the 1970 Act. In the 1970 Act, federal standards were required to protect public health and welfare, whereas the 1967 Act did not provide for any federal standards and the 1970 Senate bill provided for only federal primary standards, EPA noted.[26]

Section 110 of the Senate bill provided that the Administrator should set national ambient air quality goals as well as national ambient air quality standards. The bill did not require the attainment of air quality goals within a specified time period. The bill was amended so that the reference to air quality goals, with their lack of any time-table, was replaced by the specific secondary standards, which were to be implemented within a reasonable time. The secondary standards must protect the public from any "known or anticipated adverse effects" resulting from air pollution. The language used by Congress does not deal with nondegradation or nondeterioration, EPA concluded. The agency maintained that the language within the Senate Report, relied upon by the District Court, is irrelevant to the Act as passed, since the language refers to the Senate bill dealing with the goals, and this portion of the bill was never enacted into law. Even in the Senate bill there was no mention of nondeterioration or nondegradation. Deterioration of air quality is prohibited by the implementation of standards except where the existing air quality is better than the secondary standards.[27]

EPA believed that Section 111 of the Act indicated that Congress intended the new source performance standards rather than the approval of implementation plans under Section 110 to be the means of attacking the deterioration problem. Section 111 established performance standards for new stationary sources or modifications of existing sources. The standards are based on the best available technology, taking cost into account. States can have stricter standards and are in a better position to attack the problem since they can weigh their own needs. EPA cited the Senate Report, which covers the states' responsibility for construction of new sources:[28]

In addition to direct emission controls, other potential parts of an implementation plan include land use and air and surface transportation controls. These should insure that any existing or future stationary source of air pollution will be located, designed, constructed, equipped and operated, and that any moving source will be located and operated so as not to interfere with the implementation, maintenance, and enforcement of any applicable air quality standard or goal.

The Committee acknowledges that this would require each region to make difficult judgements about the siting of facilities which may emit pollution agents, including decisions to prohibit the location of new sources, which, although in compliance with Section 113, would contribute to a violation of a regional air quality standard. These factors would necessitate long-term decisions about the character of the growth and development of such region. In air quality control regions where present air quality is below standard, rigorous restrictions must be placed on existing sources to provide a margin for future growth, or only pollution-free growth development will be possible.

EPA also argued that it is logical to attack the problem of deterioration at the construction stage because the problem does not exist until new sources are introduced into areas where air quality is better than the secondary standards.

EPA also presented problems concerning the interpretation of the term "significant deterioration" and the feasibility and extreme cost of implementing the plaintiff's interpretation of the term. The question of how much deterioration is significant was raised, since EPA asserted that national secondary ambient air quality standards are established at levels below which there are no known anticipated effects on public health or welfare. If deterioration is to be measured in terms of ambient air levels, expansion of monitoring systems would be required, and this would detract funds from areas that have serious air pollution problems. A policy of no significant degradation would also have economic and social costs. It could stifle economic growth and the attainment of other national economic goals, prevent the construction of housing, stores, and industrial plants in clean air areas where they are needed, and also deprive heavily polluted areas of clean fuel.[29]

IMPLICATIONS OF THE DECISION

The decision by the United States Supreme Court in favor of the Sierra Club was an extremely important, if controversial, milestone in air quality management. The decision prohibited EPA from allowing significant deterioration of air quality. This meant that air pollution problems could not be solved at the expense of cleaner areas of the country by dispersing heavy sources of pollution. This will have the effect of forcing industry to direct more attention to the control of pollution problems at the source. In the absence of this decision, industries would arguably have had the incentive to locate in rural areas until all parts of the country were degraded to the secondary standard. Pure air areas such as the Grand Canyon and vast areas of Montana and Wyoming were being threatened by the growth of coal-burning power plants. It is asserted that without the nondegradation decision, the air in areas that now have 100-mile visibility could be legally loaded with new pollutants that could cut visibility to 12 miles.[30] Nondegradation emphasizes the importance of considering air quality in future land use planning. Growth will theoretically not be allowed to occur haphazardly without regard for air quality, but must be planned so as not to significantly deteriorate air quality. The decision obviously will foster long-range planning, which combating deterioration at the construction of new sources stage, as argued by EPA, would not.

The decision provides some degree of uniform regulation of air quality for the entire country. Leaving the determination of stricter standards up to the states would not lead to uniform enforcement, since the state that enforced stricter air quality would be at a disadvantage in the competition for new industry. This is probably the reason why twenty states joined the Sierra Club as friends of the court.

The Supreme Court decision will not go uncontested, however; the National Coal Association and others have called on Congress to rewrite the Clean Air Act in order to modify the decision.[31]

One important issue left unresolved by the courts was the definition of the term "significant deterioration." The Supreme Court affirmed the lower court ruling in a 4-4 decision with Justice Lewis F. Powell not participating. In accordance with traditional procedures, since the tie vote does not set legal precedent, no opinion was written and the Justices' votes were not disclosed.[32] Because of the nature of the decision, the Court's interpretation of this important terminology is unknown.

APPROACHES TO IMPLEMENTING NONDEGRADATION

EPA was left with the task of formulating a strategy for implementing nondegradation and defining "significant deterioration," since it was not defined by the courts. On July 13, 1973, EPA proposed four possible methods of defining and preventing deterioration, each considerably different from the others. One or a combination of the alternatives was to be selected for implementation.[33] Each of the four proposals would require that the best control technology available be applied to certain categories of new sources of sulfur dioxide, particulate matter, carbon monoxide, hydrocarbons, and nitrogen oxides. Thus, EPA states, the nondegradation requirement would apply directly or, in the case of photochemical oxidants, indirectly to all pollutants covered by national ambient air quality standards. But this requirement would only apply to 16 categories of sources, and significant deterioration would only be prevented for two pollutants, sulfur dioxide and particulates. (The state of the art technology would also be required for any other stationary source emitting more than 4,000 tons a year of any pollutant covered by national ambient air quality standards. The 16 categories include:

fossil fuel-fired steam electric plants of more than 1 billion BTU per hour heat input, coal cleaning plants, kraft pulp mill recovery furnaces; Portland cement plants, primary aluminum ore reduction plants; primary copper smelters; municipal incinerators capable of charging more than 250 tons a day, sulfuric acid plants, petroleum refineries, lime plants, phosphate rock processing plants, byproduct coke oven batteries, sulfur recovery plants, and carbon black plants.) It was assumed that EPA's requirements of a 90 percent reduction in automobile emissions and of the application of the best available technology would prevent the occurrence of a degradation problem for the other pollutants.

The first alternative would be to establish a maximum allowable increase in ambient air concentrations on a nationwide scale. For instance, particulate matter might be allowed to increase over 1972 levels by 10 micrograms per cubic meter on an annual average and by 30 micrograms on a 24-hour average. Sulfur dioxide could rise by 15 micrograms on an annual average, 100 on a 24-hour average, and 300 on a 3-hour average. (The primary sulfuric acid national air quality standard is 80 micrograms per cubic meter, annual arithmetic mean; the secondary is 60. The 24-hour maximum not to be exceeded more than once a year is 365 and 260 respectively. The 3-hour maximum is only for the secondary standard and is 1,300. For particulate matter, the annual geometric means are 75 and 60, the 24-hour maximum is 260 and 150.)

The second alternative would require a ceiling on increases in total emissions, with sulfur dioxide emissions limited to a 20 percent increase over 1972 levels or to 10 tons per year per square mile, whichever is greater. Particulates would be limited to a 20 percent increase, or 3 tons per year per square mile, whichever is greater.

The third possibility would require the states to determine on a case-by-case basis whether any new source would cause significant deterioration. The fourth possibility would be to allow states to classify areas into two zones with different levels of allowable degradation. Zone II areas would use ambient air quality levels established under the first alternative. Zone I areas would not be allowed to increase emissions of particulates by more than 5 micrograms per cubic meter on an annual average or by more than 15 for a 24-hour average; sulfur dioxide would not be allowed to increase by more than 2 micrograms per cubic meter on an annual average, 5 on a 24-hour average, or 25 on a 3-hour average. In Zone II areas, certain exceptions could be made to allow air pollution levels to rise to the secondary standards in order to allow certain tradeoffs, such as utilizing the unusual availability of natural resources, or to lend support to a comprehensive development plan.

IMPLICATIONS OF THE PROPOSALS

The suit of the Sierra Club v. William D. Ruckelshaus, Administrator of the Environmental Protection Agency, has determined that the nondegradation interpretation of the Clean Air Act was intended by Congress. In response, EPA prepared four alternative courses of action. Depending on one's position, each proposal has some merit or deficiency, but there is some agreement on the impact of the proposals. For example, the first alternative would probably result in a wide dispersion of new sources over a region with clean air and tend to force much of the new settlement and development into the same areas where most of the population now lives. The second alternative would create a situation in which the development of small residential and commercial sources could be restricted if the available increment were used up by a few large emitters. With the third possibility (case-by-case decisions), there would be no control over the degree of deterioration up to the secondary standards. This alternative is particularly unpopular with environmental groups. The fourth alternative would result in banning the construction of even one small power plant or medium-scale urban development in Zone I areas and would be applied in very clean areas like national parks and wilderness areas.

At the time of this writing, EPA has not selected any of the alternatives to promulgate as regulations. It is the authors' feeling that some combination of alternatives three and four will be selected, since some degree of local choice would be allowed but limits would be established that would require comprehensive long-range planning by the states. One can be sure, however, that the complex issues raised by a nondegradation policy will be the subject of extensive litigation. In any case, it is clear that such a policy places a constraint upon the use of land and constitutes an interpretation of the Clean Air Act that commands the consideration of air quality in the land use planning process at all levels of government in the United States. In the future, much more attention will also have to be addressed to monitoring—monitoring air quality levels throughout the various states and monitoring changes in land use. It is inevitable that greater knowledge of the interaction between land use and air quality will be required.

NOTES

1. W. Weaver, "Court Tells States They Cannot Permit Air Quality to Drop," New York Times, June 11, 1973.

2. Brief for Appellees, Sierra Club v. Ruckelshaus, U.S. Court of Appeals for the District of Columbia Circuit (1972).

3. Id. at 11-13.

4. Clean Air Act, 42 U.S.C. 1857 (b)(1) (1970).

5. Sierra Club v. Ruckelshaus, supra note 2, at 12.

6. Sierra Club v. Ruckelshaus, supra note 2, at 12.

7. "Appeals Court Upholds Non-degradation of Air Quality Ruling" Weekly World Environmental Newsletter, Nov. 6, 1972, at 441.

8. "EPA Asks Justice Department to Appeal Nondegradation Ruling to High Court," Air/Water Pollution Report, Nov. 27, 1972, at 474.

9. Sierra Club v. Ruckelshaus, supra note 2.

10. Clean Air Act, 42 U.S.C. 1857 (b)(1) (1970).

11. 36 Fed. Reg. 22384, 50.2(c)(1971).

12. 36 Fed. Reg. 15489, 420.12(b)(1970).

13. Sierra Club v. Ruckelshaus, supra note 2, at 5.

14. NAPCA, Guidelines for the Development of Air Quality Standards and Implementation Plans Sec. 2.10 (1969). (NAPCA, a part of HEW, is integrated into EPA.)

15. Clean Air Act, 42 U.S.C. 1857 (b)(1) (1970).

16. S. Rep. No. 403, 90th Cong., 1st sess. 2 (1970).

17. NAPCA, supra note 14, at Sec. 1.51.

18. S. Rep. No. 1196, 91st Cong., 2d sess. 2(1970).

19. 36 Fed. Reg. 22384, 50.2(c)(1971).

20. 36 Fed. Reg. 15489, 420.12(b) (1971).

21. Brief for Appellant, Sierra Club v. Ruckelshaus, U.S. Court of Appeals for the District of Columbia Circuit (1972).

22. Clean Air Act, 42 U.S.C. 1857, 110 (A-H) (1970).

23. Sierra Club v. Ruckelshaus, supra note 21, at 13.

24. Sierra Club v. Ruckelshaus, supra note 21, at 14-15.

25. Air Quality Act of 1967, P.L. 90-148, 108.

26. Sierra Club v. Ruckelshaus, supra note 21, at 17.

27. Sierra Club v. Ruckelshaus, supra note 21, at 20-2.

28. S. Rep. No. 91-1196, 91st Cong., 2d Session 12-13 (1970).

29. Sierra Club v. Ruckelshaus, supra note 21, at 31-2.

30. G. Hill, "Supreme Court and Air Pollution," New York Times, Jan. 3, 1972.

31. Weaver, supra note 1.

32. Weaver, supra note 1.

33. 38 Fed. Reg. 18986 (1973).

11

A PERSPECTIVE ON
LAND USE CONTROLS

CONSTITUTIONAL ISSUES

Looking back over this volume, can we say with any optimism that land use controls will be effective tools to assist in the achievement and maintenance of air quality standards? More specifically, can we say that the courts will allow land use controls to be used as an effective tool? As in any other area of public regulation of economic activity, land use controls that implement air pollution goals must meet certain basic constitutional requirements aimed at protecting property interests from unsupportable regulation. It should be noted, however, that land use controls aimed at achieving air pollution objectives come to the courts with comparatively strong legal backing. First, the United States Supreme Court, and to a lesser extent the state supreme courts, have accorded regulatory controls in the economic area a strong presumption of constitutionality. Second, this presumption is reinforced when health or safety objectives are the purpose of the regulation.

This comment, however, does deserve a caveat. In recent years the courts have become sensitive to the possible exclusionary impact of local land use controls as they affect housing opportunities, especially minority housing opportunities. So far the constitutionality of exclusionary controls is not yet clear. Some courts have accepted environmental protection objectives to justify land use controls that exclude housing, and others have not. As the trend of the law is not yet clear, we will assume in this discussion that in the ordinary case the traditional presumptions of constitutionality will apply.

Due Process of Law

By due process of law we mean to include what lawyers call
"substantive" due process of law. When courts review legislation to
determine whether it is in accord with substantive due process of
law, they review to determine whether the content of the legislation
is consistent with constitutionally permissible purposes. In the early
part of this century, the United States Supreme Court would often hold
legislation unconstitutional if the Court did not approve of the purpose
of the legislation. For example, laws prescribing minimum hours of
work were held unconstitutional. This tendency has now reversed.
Ordinarily, if the legislation serves objectives that are reasonably
debatable, the courts will affirm the legislation. And in the areas of
health and pollution, courts will ordinarily accord a strong presumption
of constitutionality to the purposes to be served by the legislation.

The second part of the substantive due process of law requirement relates to the means chosen to achieve the purposes that have
been approved. This part of the due process requirement is slightly
more difficult. A law may serve a constitutionally acceptable purpose,
but the means chosen to carry it out may be unconstitutional. For
example, the control of air pollution is a constitutionally acceptable
purpose in land use regulation, but if the legislature attempts to
achieve this purpose by restricting the size of all industrial plants to
1500 square feet or less, the law will probably be held unconstitutional.
The court might find that the method of control—restricting the size
of the industrial plants—is not related to the objective. Or the court
might find that other suitable alternatives for regulations are possible.
Or it might approve the concept of restricting plant size but find that
the legislation in question has gone too far, and has overrestricted.

Equal Protection of Law

No law can apply equally to all of the objects it regulates; some
classification is necessary. The purpose of the constitutional protection that lawyers call the equal protection of the law is to ensure
that classifications among different objects of regulation will be
fairly drawn. If they are not fairly drawn, they will be held unconstitutional. For example, the constitution specifically prohibits a classification based on race.

In the economic field, the courts have been sympathetic to classifications selected by the legislative body. But, once again, the
United States Supreme Court tends to be more lenient than the state
courts. The test applied here is roughly similar to the test applied
in the due process area. That is, the criteria chosen for making the

classification must be reasonably related to the purpose of the legislation, and must be reasonably applied to the subject matter that is being classified.

For example, let us assume a land use control system that decides to classify various areas of a region for purposes of reducing air pollution. A basis must be chosen for distinguishing one area of the region from another. Since the aim of the control is the reduction of air pollution, it would be reasonable under this system to control land uses in the region on the basis of the amount of air pollution they generate. It is then necessary to apply this criteria to different areas. One approach is to provide by regulation that no additional pollution generating uses may be permitted in areas that have passed a defined pollution level, but that these uses may be permitted in other areas where this level has not been reached. Again, this would be a reasonable application of the pollution criteria under which land use is regulated.

Delegation of Power

A final problem affecting governmental regulation in the area of land use control concerns the delegation of power by the legislative to administrative bodies in order to apply and enforce the regulations that are enacted. At the federal level the courts are fairly lenient about the nature and content of the standards that are adopted to implement delegations of power. At the state level, the courts are more cautious. When health and safety factors are used as the basis of the delegation, the delegation standards present few problems. More problems arise with the use of more generalized standards related not to health and safety but to other factors that affect land use and development. It has proved difficult to develop appropriate standards for more generalized land use regulation. For example, zoning ordinances that authorize administrative decisions based only on "general welfare" and similar criteria have been held unconstitutional by some state courts. More specific and less qualitative standards will have to be worked out to avoid constitutional objections to legislative delegations of power in some jurisdictions.

Effective Use of Controls

It seems likely that land use controls to achieve air quality objectives, if properly administered, will meet little objection from the courts. Indeed, it seems that legal issues should be considered a relatively minor matter among the spectrum of problems that must be faced in relating air quality management to land use planning. Two recent surveys of planning agencies suggest that the prime problems are more technical and psychological in nature.

VIEWS OF PLANNING AGENCIES

A recent survey of interagency relationships among state and local air pollution control agencies and comprehensive planning agencies in the United States revealed that there is at present little communication between such agencies.[1] There was evidence that the planning agencies went to air pollution control agencies for advice and counsel, but little evidence of the converse. Somewhat paradoxically, the planning agencies felt they had a role in air pollution control but were unable to clearly define it. The standard response seems to have been that the agencies are interested in air pollution control but that other work has already established itself as having a higher priority. As might be expected, the chief limitations the agencies see have to do with staff and information.

This emphasis on staff trained in air quality work and the desire for more technical information is viewed as an expression of a general uneasiness about moving into a new area of work. Air quality, in particular, seems to create insecurities concerning methodology.[2]

A somewhat similar survey, completed in 1972, concluded that the extent to which air quality is currently considered in the planning process is largely related to the resources available to the planning agency in terms of staff size, skills, scope of planning projects, and funds for in-house or consultant studies. This survey found that in most cases where air pollution has been considered, federal funds have been involved to some extent, and most of the studies have been undertaken by universities or consultants. It was also noted that planners varied widely in their attitudes towards the relative importance of air pollution as a factor in land use planning. Most were sympathetic with the concern about air pollution; but many felt that it was a largely overplayed issue relative to other planning concerns.[3] As a general rule, it was found that planning agencies within regions where air pollution is not currently a problem attached little importance to air quality as a planning criteria, even though it potentially could become a significant problem because of expanding population and urban growth. The survey concluded that planning agencies devote no more than the minimal essential effort to considering air pollution; it noted that "perhaps the greatest constraint to the consideration of air pollution is the fact that planning agencies do not have staff with appropriate background and skills in air pollution, do not have access to the required analytic tools nor the data base required to project air quality resulting from proposed future land use plans, and generally do not have the resources required to develop these capabilities."[4]

No similar surveys have been made of air pollution control agencies. The examples reported in this volume are about the extent of information available. This information is not at all representative because we have consciously picked those agencies which have been engaged in innovative activity. It has been our experience, however, that somewhat similar problems exist in air pollution control agencies. It is only a slight exaggeration to state that urban planners know little about air pollution control and that air pollution control personnel know little about land use planning. Clearly there is a need for an educational effort of considerable proportions aimed at the staff level of both air pollution and land use agencies if land use controls are to effectively aid in the maintenance of air quality standards. In addition, adequate resources will have to be set aside within both types of agencies if there is to be anything more than lip service to air pollution control.

EDUCATIONAL EFFORTS

These recommendations suggest a strong educational role for the Environmental Protection Agency and state agencies with land use and air pollution responsibilities. This role should be effective on two levels: (1) a general educational effort by EPA on the role of land use planning in environmental management and an associated effort by the states; (2) technical assistance in the form of manuals and guidelines prepared both by EPA and the states.

EPA does offer short courses on the relations between land use and air quality, and these courses perform a useful function, but since they are only offered in EPA's ten regional offices, much of the potential audience is missed. As the states become more involved in land use planning, it is incumbent upon them to take on a greater educational role, possibly with the assistance of EPA. In the longer run, the provision of technical assistance must be given more attention. State and local agencies will not be able to develop and implement land use programs that meet air quality objectives unless they are given assistance. One can conclude this on the basis of the two surveys mentioned above. Large and experienced agencies like the California Air Resources Board can develop effective programs with federal financial assistance, but the mere provision of funds will not be adequate for the more typical agency. The preparation of guidelines and manuals, including a standardized compilation of land-use-based air pollution emission factors, will need to be made available to the states. The states in turn will need to adapt these documents to their own specific needs.

POLITICAL BARRIERS TO IMPLEMENTATION

Land use controls that relate to air quality management may become as unpopular as transportation controls unless adequate attention
is given to informing the public of the need for and effectiveness of
such controls. During the next decade, when control over land use will
shift perceptibly from the local to the state level, the issue of citizen
participation in environmental management will need increased attention
because of the almost inaccessible nature of many agencies in state
capitals. Land use controls that might mandate changes in one's way of
life cannot be announced in the newspaper by a government bureaucrat.
Public involvement, which has been notably lacking in the development
of the transportation control strategies, will be of critical importance
if such regulations are to become effective.

It seems likely that for the foreseeable future land use controls
will be implemented at the option of the states rather than mandated
across the board. This would seem to be desirable, since the controls
would not be viewed as being externally imposed, as were the transportation controls. But there is no question in the minds of the authors
that the major barrier to effective implementation of land use controls
for air quality management purposes is a political one. A major recommendation, therefore, must be that land use controls should not be
viewed by air pollution agency personnel solely as technical procedures
that will yield a clearly specified level of pollution abatement. Land
use planning has an impact over the long run as the result of a whole series
of major and minor incremental decisions, only some of which are
related to air pollution control. In all of these decisions, however,
there is a political element. For better or worse, air pollution control
agency staffs who become involved in land use decisions must realize
that they are no longer dealing with a strictly scientific issue where
there is a clear cause-and-effect relationship.

THE DEFICIENCIES OF SINGLE
SECTOR PLANNING

It is becoming apparent that land use control programs with air
quality objectives are coming into conflict with other single-purpose
and more comprehensive planning efforts. More attention will have
to be given in the future to the coordination of functional environmental
programs and the coordination of environmental programs with other
economic and social decisions that impact upon land use. Although
there is a considerable tradition of special-purpose planning associated
with public works agencies in the United States, such planning associated
with regulatory programs has a much more mixed history. This is

because the regulatory programs often have to be implemented by agencies other than those promulgating the regulations. An excellent case in point is the example of the transportation control strategies, which have involved state highway departments and other similar agencies. Coordination between agencies, a major concern of the urban planner, must receive considerable attention.

* * *

Will the backlash associated with the transportation control strategies also occur in the area of land use controls? At this time, it is difficult to say, but it seems unlikely to happen if controls are understood by the general public and if governmental agencies of various types build up the capability to develop efficient and equitable programs that are aimed at long-term results. Short term ad hoc efforts seemed doomed to failure. Let us look optimistically to the future, realizing that the issues to be faced are exceedingly complex, but that the will to face them exists in American society.

NOTES

1. American Society of Planning Officials, Air Quality Control And Comprehensive Planning (1973).
2. Id. at 6.
3. A survey prepared under contract by Environmental Research and Technology for the Environmental Protection Agency during 1972.
4. Id. at 4.

VERMONT'S LAND USE AND DEVELOPMENT LAW

Permit Issuance Conditions and Criteria

Section 6086. Issuance of permit; conditions and criteria

(a) Before granting a permit, the board or district commission shall find that the subdivision or development:

(1) Will not result in undue water or air pollution. In making this determination it shall at least consider: the elevation of land above sea level; and in relation to the flood plains, the nature of soils and subsoils and their ability to adequately support waste disposal; the slope of the land and its effect on effluents; the availability of streams for disposal of effluents; and the applicable health and water resources department regulations.

(A) Headwaters. A permit will be granted whenever it is demonstrated by the applicant that, in addition to all other applicable criteria, the development or subdivision will meet any applicable health and water resources department regulation regarding reduction of the quality of the ground or surface waters flowing through or upon lands which are not devoted to intensive developments, and which lands are:

(i) headwaters of watersheds characterized by steep slopes and shallow soils; or
(ii) drainage areas of 20 square miles or less; or
(iii) above 1,500 feet elevation; or
(iv) watersheds of public water supplies designated by the Vermont department of health; or
(v) areas supplying significant amounts of recharge waters to aquifers

(B) Waste disposal. A permit will be granted whenever it is demonstrated by the applicant that, in addition to all other applicable criteria, the development or subdivision will meet any applicable health and water resources department

313

regulations regarding the disposal of wastes, and will not involve the injection of waste materials or any harmful or toxic substances into ground water or wells.

(C) Water conservation. A permit will be granted whenever it is demonstrated by the applicant that, in addition to all other applicable criteria, the design has considered water conservation, incorporates multiple use or recycling where technically and economically practical, utilizes the best available technology for such applications and provides for continued efficient operation of these systems.

(D) Floodways. A permit will be granted whenever it is demonstrated by the applicant that, in addition to all other applicable criteria:

> (i) the development or subdivision of lands within a floodway will not restrict or divert the flow of flood waters, and endanger the health, safety and welfare of the public or of riparian owners during flooding; and
>
> (ii) the development or subdivision of lands within a floodway fringe will not significantly increase the peak discharge of the river or stream within or down stream for the area of development and endanger the health, safety, or welfare of the public or riparian owners during flooding.

(E) Streams. A permit will be granted whenever it is demonstrated by the applicant that, in addition to all other applicable criteria, the development or subdivision of lands on or adjacent to the banks of a stream will, whenever feasible, maintain the natural condition of the stream, and will not endanger the health, safety, and welfare of the public or of adjoining landowners.

(F) Shorelines. A permit will be granted whenever it is demonstrated by the applicant that, in addition to all other criteria, the development or subdivision of shorelines must of necessity be located on a shoreline in order to fulfill the purpose of the development or subdivision, and the development or subdivision will, insofar as possible and reasonable in light of its purpose:

> (i) retain the shoreline and the waters in their natural condition,
>
> (ii) allow continued access to the waters and the recreational opportunities provided by the waters,

314

(iii) retain or provide vegetation which will screen the development or subdivision from the waters, and

(iv) stabilize the bank from erosion, as necessary, with vegetation cover.

(2) Does have sufficient water available for the reasonably foreseeable needs of the subdivision or development.

(3) Will not cause an unreasonable burden on an existing water supply, if one is to be utilized.

(4) Will not cause unreasonable soil erosion or reduction in the capacity of the land to hold water so that a dangerous or unhealthy condition may result.

(5) Will not cause unreasonable highway congestion or unsafe conditions with respect to use of the highways existing or proposed.

(6) Will not cause an unreasonable burden on the ability of a municipality to provide educational services.

(7) Will not place an unreasonable burden on the ability of the local governments to provide municipal or governmental services.

(8) Will not have an undue adverse effect on the scenic or natural beauty of the area, aesthetics, historic sites or rare and irreplaceable natural areas.

(A) Necessary wildlife habitat and endangered species. A permit will not be granted if it is demonstrated by any party opposing the applicant that a development or subdivision will destroy or significantly imperil necessary wildlife habitat or any endangered species, and

(i) the economic, social, cultural, recreational, or other benefit to the public from the development or subdivision will not outweigh the economic, environmental, or recreational loss to the public from the destruction or imperilment of the habitat or species, or

(ii) all feasible and reasonable means of preventing or lessening the destruction, diminution, or imperilment of the habitat or species have not been or will not continue to be applied, or

(iii) a reasonably acceptable alternative site is owned or controlled by the applicant which would allow the development or subdivision to fulfill its intended purpose.

(9) Is in conformance with a duly adopted capability and development plan, and land use plan when adopted. However, the legislative findings of sections 6(a)(1) through 6(a)(19) of this

act shall not be used as criteria in the consideration of applications by a district commission or the environmental board.

(A) Impact of growth. In considering an application, the district commission or the board shall take into consideration the growth in population experienced by the town and region in question and whether or not the proposed development would significantly affect their existing and potential financial capacity to reasonably accommodate both the total growth and the rate of growth otherwise expected for the town and region and the total growth and rate of growth which would result from the development if approved. After considering anticipated costs for education, highway access and maintenance, sewage disposal, water supply, police and fire services and other factors relating to the public health, safety and welfare, the district commission or the board shall impose conditions which prevent undue burden upon the town and region in accommodating growth caused by the proposed development or subdivision. Notwithstanding section 6088 of the act the burden of proof that proposed development will significantly affect existing or potential financial capacity of the town and region to accommodate such growth is upon any party opposing an application, excepting however, where the town has a duly adopted capital improvement program the burden shall be on the applicant.

(B) Primary agricultural soils. A permit will be granted for the development or subdivision of primary agricultural soils only when it is demonstrated by the applicant that, in addition to all other applicable criteria, either, the subdivision or development will not significantly reduce the agricultural potential of the primary agricultural soils; or,

> (i) the applicant can realize a reasonable return on the fair market value of his land only by devoting the primary agricultural soils to uses which will significantly reduce their agricultural potential; and
>
> (ii) there are no nonagricultural or secondary agricultural soils owned or controlled by the applicant which are reasonably suited to the purpose; and
>
> (iii) the subdivision or development has been planned to minimize the reduction of agricultural potential by providing for reasonable population densities, reasonable rates of growth, and the use of cluster planning and new community planning designed to economize on the cost of roads, utilities and land usage; and

(iv) the development or subdivision will not significantly interfere with or jeopardize the continuation of
agriculture or forestry on adjoining lands or reduce their
agricultural or forestry potential.

(C) Forest and secondary agricultural soils. A permit
will be granted for the development or subdivision of forest
or secondary agricultural soils only when it is demonstrated
by the applicant that, in addition to all other applicable criteria,
either, the subdivision or development will not significantly
reduce the potential of those soils for commercial forestry,
including but not limited to specialized forest uses such as
maple production or Christmas tree production, of those or
adjacent primary agricultural soils for commercial agriculture; or

(i) the applicant can realize a reasonable return
on the fair market value of his land only by devoting the
forest or secondary agricultural soils to uses which will
significantly reduce their forestry or agricultural potential; and
(ii) there are no non-forest or secondary agricultural soils owned or controlled by the applicant which
are reasonably suited to the purpose; and
(iii) the subdivision or development has been planned
to minimize the reduction of forestry and agricultural
potential by providing for reasonable population densities,
reasonable rates of growth, and the use of cluster planning
and new community planning designed to economize on
the cost of roads, utilities and land usage.

(D) Earth resources. A permit will be granted whenever it is demonstrated by the applicant, in addition to all
other applicable criteria, that the development or subdivision
of lands with high potential for extraction of mineral or earth
resources, will not prevent or significantly interfere with
the subsequent extraction or processing of the mineral or
earth resources.
(E) Extraction of earth resources. A permit will be
granted for the extraction or processing of mineral and earth
resources:

(i) when it is demonstrated by the applicant that,
in addition to all other applicable criteria, the extraction
or processing operation and the disposal of waste will

not have an unduly harmful impact upon the environment or surrounding land uses and development; and

(ii) upon approval by the district commission or the board of a site rehabilitation plan which insures that upon completion of the extracting or processing operation the site will be left by the applicant in a condition suited for an approved alternative use or development. A permit will not be granted for the recovery or extraction of mineral or earth resources from beneath natural water bodies or impoundments within the state, except that gravel, silt and sediment may be removed pursuant to the regulations of the water resources board.

(F) Energy conservation. A permit will be granted when it has been demonstrated by the applicant that, in addition to all other applicable criteria, the planning and design of the subdivision or development reflect the principles of energy conservation and incorporate the best available technology for efficient use or recovery of energy.

(G) Private utility services. A permit will be granted for a development or subdivision which relies on privately owned utility services or facilities, including central sewage or water facilities and roads, whenever it is demonstrated by the applicant that, in addition to all other applicable criteria, the privately owned utility services or facilities are in conformity with a capital program or plan of the municipality involved, or adequate surety is provided to the municipality and conditioned to protect the municipality in the event that the municipality is required to assume the responsibility for the services or facilities.

(H) Costs of scattered development. The district commission or board will grant a permit for a development or subdivision which is not physically contiguous to an existing settlement whenever it is demonstrated that, in addition to all other applicable criteria, the additional costs of public services and facilities caused directly or indirectly by the proposed development or subdivision do not outweigh the tax revenue and other public benefits of the development or subdivision such as increased employment opportunities or the provision of needed and balanced housing accessible to existing or planned employment centers.

(J) Public utility services. A permit will be granted for a development or subdivision whenever it is demonstrated that, in addition to all other applicable criteria, necessary supportive governmental and public utility facilities and services are available or will be available when the development is completed under a duly adopted capital program or plan, an excessive or uneconomic demand will not be placed on such facilities and services, and the provision of such facilities and services has been planned on the basis of a projection of reasonable population increase and economic growth.

(K) Development affecting public investments. A permit will be granted for the development or subdivision of lands adjacent to governmental and public utility facilities, services, and lands, including, but not limited to, highways, airports, waste disposal facilities, office and maintenance buildings, fire and police stations, universities, schools, hospitals, prisons, jails, electric generating and transmission facilities, oil and gas pipe lines, parks, hiking trails and forest and game lands, when it is demonstrated that, in addition to all other applicable criteria, the development or subdivision will not unnecessarily or unreasonably endanger the public or quasi-public investment in the facility, service, or lands, or materially jeopardize or interfere with the function, efficiency, or safety of, or the public's use or enjoyment of or access to the facility, service, or lands.

(L) Rural growth areas. A permit will be granted for the development or subdivision of rural growth areas when it is demonstrated by the applicant that in addition to all other applicable criteria provision will be made in accordance with section 6086(a)(9)(A) "impact of growth", (G) "private utility service", (H) "costs of scattered development" and (J) "public utility services" for reasonable population densities, reasonable rates of growth, and the use of cluster planning and new community planning designed to economize on the cost of roads, utilities and land usage.

(10) Is in conformance with any duly adopted local or regional plan or capital program under chapter 91 of Title 24.

MAINE LAND USE GUIDANCE DISTRICTS
AND GUIDANCE STANDARDS

1. Classification and districting of lands. The commission, based on sound land use planning and development guidance, shall determine the boundaries of areas within the unorganized portions of the State that fall into land use guidance districts and designate each area in one of the following major district classifications: Protection, management, development and holding.

The commission shall set standards for determining the boundaries of each major type of district:

A. Protection districts shall include, but not be limited to, areas where development would jeopardize significant natural, recreational and historic resources, including flood plains, precipitous slopes, wildlife habitat and other areas critical to the ecology of the region or State.

B. Management districts shall include, but not be limited to, those lands which are currently being utilized for commercial forest product or agricultural uses and for which plans for additional development are not presently formulated nor additional development anticipated.

C. Holding districts shall include, but not be limited to, reserve areas adjoining development districts, for growth needed when the development district is saturated, and those lands not presently in development districts but for which development plans have been submitted pursuant to section 685-B, subsection 2 or where additional development is otherwise formulated or anticipated.

D. Development districts shall include, but not be limited to, those lands now discernible as relatively homogeneous patterns of intensive residential, recreational, commercial, industrial use or commercial removal of minerals or natural resources.

In addition to delineating the major district classifications listed herein, the commission may delineate such subclassifications as may be deemed necessary and desirable to further carry out the intent of this chapter.

3. District land use guidance standards. The commission, based on the principles of sound land use planning and development guidance, shall prepare land use guidance standards prescribing the standards for and restraints upon the use of air, lands and waters in the various districts.

In addition to the purposes set forth in section 681 of this chapter, the district land use guidance standards shall:

A. Encourage the most desirable and appropriate use of air, land and water resources;

B. Protect public health by reduction of noise, air pollution, water pollution and other environmental intrusions;

C. Protect and preserve significant natural, scenic, and historic features where appropriate and beneficial;

D. Advise and assist the State Highway Commission and other concerned agencies in transportation planning and operation and require landowners to develop effective and nonintrusive land, air and water traffic movement, routes, parking and loading provisions including requirements with respect to frontage on, or access to, public roads, water, safety, and other aspects;

E. Encourage minimal adverse impact of one use upon the use of surrounding areas by setting standards of performance describing desirable and acceptable levels of operation in connection with any use and its relation to surrounding areas, including provisions for the eventual amelioration of existing adverse impact;

F. Relate the availability and capability of the natural resources base, including soils, topography, or sufficient healthful water supplies to land use.

In addition to preparing the general district land use guidance standards, listed in this chapter, the commission may prepare such special guidance standards as may be deemed necessary and desirable to further carry out the intent of this chapter.

Me. Rev. Stat. Ann. Tit. 12, Sec. 685-A (Supp. 1972)

BOOKS

Anderson, F. NEPA in the Courts: A Legal Analysis of the National Environmental Policy Act. Washington, D.C.: Resources for the Future, 1973.

Blunden, W. The Land Use/Transport System. New York: Pergamon Press, 1971.

Boyce, D.; Day, N.; and McDonald, C. Metropolitan Plan Making. Philadelphia: Regional Science Research Institute, 1970.

Brown, J., et al. Empirical Models of Urban Land Use: Suggestions on Research Objectives and Organization. New York: National Bureau of Economic Research, 1972.

California Institute of Technology Environmental Quality Laboratory. Smog—A Report to the People, 1972. Los Angeles: Anderson, Ritchie and Simon, 1972.

Chadwick, G. A Systems View of Planning. New York: Pergamon Press, 1971.

Chapin, F., Jr. Urban Land Use Planning, 2d. ed. Urbana: University of Illinois, 1965.

Creighton, R. Urban Transportation Planning. Urbana: University of Illinois, 1970.

Fellmeth, R. Politics of Land. New York: Grossman Publishers, 1973.

Hagevik, G. Decision Making in Air Pollution Control. New York: Praeger Publishers, 1970.

Hagevik, G., ed. The Relationship of Land Use and Transportation Planning to Air Quality Management. New Brunswick, N.J.: Rutgers University, Urban Studies Center, 1972.

Harris, B. "Quantitative Models of Urban Development: Their Role in Metropolitan Policy Making," Issues in Urban Economics, H. Perloff and L. Wingo, eds. Baltimore: Johns Hopkins, 1968.

Haskell, E., and Price, V. State Environmental Management: Case Studies of Nine States. New York: Praeger Publishers, 1973.

Krveckeberg, D., and Silvers, A. Urban Planning Analysis: Methods and Models. New York: John Wiley and Sons, forthcoming.

Livingston and Blayney. A Report on Guidelines for Relating Air Pollution Control To Land Use and Transportation Planning in the State of California. San Francisco: Livingston and Blayney, 1973 (Mimeo).

Lynch, K. Site Planning, 2d ed. Cambridge, Mass.: Massachusetts Institute of Technology, 1971.

Mandelker, D. The Zoning Dilemma. Indianapolis, Ind.: Bobbs-Merrill, 1971.

McLoughlin, J. Urban and Regional Planning: A Systems Approach. New York: Praeger Publishers, 1969.

Pasquill, F. Atmospheric Diffusion. Princeton, N.J.: Van Nostrand, 1962.

Reilly, W., ed. The Use of Land: A Citizen's Policy Guide to Urban Growth. New York: Thomas Y. Crowell, 1973.

Stern, A., ed. Air Pollution, vols. 1, 2, 3, 2d. ed. New York: Academic Press, 1968.

Sutton, O. Micrometeorology. New York: McGraw-Hill, 1953.

ARTICLES

"Aftermammoth: Friends of Mammoth and the California Environmental Quality Act." Ecology Law Quarterly 3 (1973): 349.

Alonso, W. "Predicting Best with Imperfect Data." Journal of the American Institute of Planners 34, no. 4 (July 1968): 248.

"Appeals Court Upholds Non-degradation of Air Quality Ruling."
Weekly World Environmental Newsletter, November 6, 1972.

Berg, C. "Energy Conservation Through Effective Utilization."
Science, July 13, 1973, p. 128.

Bernatsky, A. "The Importance of Protective Plantings Against Air
Pollutants." Translated by Belov and Associates. Air Pollution
Proceedings, First European Conference on the Influence of
Air Pollution on Plants and Animals, 1968, p., 383.

Bibbero, R. "Systems Approach Toward Nationwide Air Pollution
Control, Mathematical Models." Spectrum 8, no. 12 (Institute
of Electrical and Electronics Engineers, December 1971): 47.

Borman, F., et al. "Fallout on the Vegetation of New England During
the 1957 Atom Bomb Test Series." Ecology 39 (1958): 376.

Breivogel, A. "Air Pollution Potential Advisory Service for Industrial
Zoning Cases." Journal of the Air Pollution Control Association
11 (1961): 334.

Brussat, W. "A-95: Evaluating the Process of Review." In Planning
1971. Chicago: American Society of Planning Officials, 1971,
p. 58.

Chapin, S., Jr. "Taking Stock of Techniques for Shaping Urban Growth."
Journal of the American Institute of Planners 29, no. 23 (May
1963): 76.

"Clean Air Act Amendments of 1970: A Congressional Cosmetic."
Georgetown Law Journal 61 (1972): 153.

"The Clean Air Act and the Concept of Non-degradation: Sierra Club
v. Ruckelshaus." Ecology Law Quarterly 2 (1972): 801.

"The Constitutionality of Local Anti-Pollution Ordinances," Fordham
Journal of Urban Law (1972): 208.

Council on Environmental Quality. "Environmental Impact Statements."
102 Monitor 1, no. 10 (November 1971): 4.

"Courts Say NEPA is a Law for All People." Federal Report 6, no.
3 (March 1972): 210.

Embleton, T., and Thiessen, G. "Propagation of Train Noise and Adjacent Land Use." Journal of the Acoustical Society of America 33 (1961): 1676.

Fan, L., and Horie, Y. "Review of Atmospheric Dispersion and Urban Pollution Models." CRC Critical Reviews in Environmental Control, vol. 1 (October 1971): 431.

Fonoroff, A. "Controlling Traffic Through Zoning." Syracuse Law Review 21 (1970): 857.

Gilette, R. "National Environmental Policy Act: How Well Is It Working?" Science, April 14, 1972, p. 146.

Gillespie, D. "Industrial Zoning and Beyond: Compatibility Through Performance Standards." Journal of Urban Law 46 (1964): 723.

Goldner, W. "The Lowry Model Heritage." Journal of the American Institute of Planners 37, no. 2 (March 1971): 100.

Goldstein, P., and Ford, R. "The Management of Air Quality: Legal Structures and Official Behavior." Buffalo Law Review 21 (1971): 1.

Greenberg, M. "A Test of Alternative Models for Projecting County Industrial Employment at the 2, 3, 4-Digit Standard Industrial Code Levels." Regional and Urban Economics, vol. 4 (February 1972), 397.

Hagman, D. "Ecology v. Builder: A Knockout in the Fifth." Planning 39 (March-April 1973): 40.

Hanks, E., and Hanks, J. "An Environmental Bill of Rights: The Citizen Suit and the National Environmental Policy Act of 1969." Environment Law Review, 1971, edited by H. Floyd Sherrod.

Hanna, S. "A Simple Method of Calculating Dispersion from Urban Area Sources." Journal of the Air Pollution Control Association 21, no. 12 (December 1971): 774.

Hanson, G., and Thorne, L. "A Partial Pollution Solution: Plant Trees." Lasca Leaves 19 (June 1970): 35.

Heeter, D. "Toward a More Effective Land Use Guidance System: A Summary and Analysis of Five Major Reports." Planning

Advisory Service, no. 250 (American Society of Planning Officials, 1969).

Hirst, E., and Moyers, J. "Efficiency of Energy Use in the United States," Science, March 30, 1973, p. 1299.

"The Impact of the Highway on the Urban Environment," Catholic University Law Review 20 (1970): 1.

Kahn, E. "Air Flow Around Buildings." Architectural Forum 107 (September 1957): 166.

Keeney, G. "Enforcement of Philadelphia's 1969 Air Management Code: The First Three Years." Villanova Law Review 18 (1972): 173.

Kurtzweg, G. "Urban Planning and Air Pollution Control: A Review of Selected Recent Research." Journal of the American Institute of Planners 39, no. 2 (March 1973): 82.

Lee, D., Jr. "Requiem for Large-Scale Models." Journal of the American Institute of Planners 39, no. 3 (May 1973): 163.

Lincoln, G. "Energy Conservation," Science, April 13, 1973, p. 155.

"Litigating the Freeway Revolt: Keith v. Volpe," Ecology Law Quarterly 2 (1972): 761.

Lunche, R. "Administration of a Permit System." Journal of the Air Pollution Control Association 19, no. 1 (January 1969): 9.

Macbeth, A., and Sly, P. "Federal-Aid Highways: Public Participation in the Administrative Stages." Natural Resources Defense Council Newsletter 1, no. 3 (1971): 1.

McGiven, W. "Putting a Speed Limit on Growth." Planning 38, no. 10 (November 1972): 262.

McLean, M. "Zoning Buffers: Solution or Panacea?" Planning Advisory Service, no. 133 (American Society of Planning Officials, 1960).

Magulof, M. "Regional Planning, Clearance, and Evaluation: A Look at the A-95 Process." Journal of the American Institute of Planners 37, no. 6 (November 1971): 418.

Markus, T. "Climatology and Architecture." Architectural Review 128 (December 1960): 452.

Martin, D. "An Urban Diffusion Model for Estimating Long-Term Average Values of Air Quality." Journal of the Air Pollution Control Association 21, no. 1 (January, 1971): 16.

Mandelker, D. "Control of Competition as a Proper Purpose in Zoning." Zoning Digest 14 (1962): 33.

Mosher, B. "Proximity Regulation of the Modern Service Station." Syracuse Law Review 17 (1965): 1.

"NEPA Challenges the Nation's Plans and Priorities." The Conservation Foundation Letter, May 1972, p. 5.

NOAA Environmental Research Laboratories. "Air Pollution in the Locality of Buildings." In World Health Organization Bulletin vol. 40, edited by H. Georgii, 1969, p. 624.

Page, A., et al. "Lead Quantities in Plants, Soil and Air Near Some Major Highways in Southern California." Hilgardia 41, no. 1 (July 1971): 1.

"Recent California Planning Statutes and Mountain Area Subdivisions: The Need for Regional Land Use Control." Ecology Law Quarterly 3 (1973): 107.

Russell, R. "An Introductory Review: Interception and Retention of Airborne Materials on Plants." Health Physics 11 (1965): 1305.

Rydell, P. and Schwarz, G. "Air Pollution and Urban Form: A Review of Current Literature." Journal of the American Institute of Planners 34, no. 2 (March 1968): 115.

Salzenstein, M. "Industrial Performance Standards." Planning Advisory Service, Report No. 272, 1971.

Schulze, E. "Performance Standards in Zoning." Journal of the Air Pollution Control Association 10 (1960): 156.

Smith, V. "The Intergovernmental Cooperation Act of 1968: Opportunity for State Government." Planning 1971. Chicago: American Society of Planning Officials, 1971, p. 63.

Smith, W. "Trees in the City." Journal of the American Institute of Planners 36, no. 6 (November 1970): 429.

"Sports Complex in Hackensack Meadowlands." New Jersey Reports 62 (1973): 248; Atlantic Reporter 300, Second Series (1973): 337.

Strong, A. "The Impact of Pre-emption on Environmental Regulation," Land-Use Controls Annual, (1972), 15.

"Substantive Review Under the National Environmental Policy Act: Environmental Defense Fund v. Corps of Engineers." Ecology Law Quarterly 3 (1973): 173.

Trumbull, T. "Federal Control of Stationary Source Air Pollution." Ecology Law Quarterly 2 (1972): 283.

Waggoner, P. "Role of Plants in Improving the Environment." Journal of Environmental Quality 1, no. 2 (1972): 123.

Walter, J. "The Law of the Land: Development Legislation in Maine and Vermont." Maine Law Review 23 (1971): 315.

Weaver, W. "Court Tells States They Cannot Permit Air Quality to Drop." New York Times, 11 June 1973.

Weiner, F., and Keast, D. "Experimental Study of the Propagation of Sound Over Ground." Journal of the Acoustical Society of America 31 (1959): 724.

Wohlers, H. C., et al. "A Rapid Emission Survey Procedure for Industrial Air Pollutants." Journal of the Air Pollution Control Association 19, no. 5 (May 1969): 309.

GOVERNMENT PUBLICATIONS

Benson, F., et al. Indoor-Outdoor Air Pollution Relationships: A Literature Review. Research Triangle Park, N.C.: Air Pollution Technical Information Center, Environmental Protection Agency, (Pub. No. AP-112), 1972.

Bosselman, F., and Callies, D. The Quiet Revolution in Land Use Control. Washington, D.C.: U.S. Government Printing Office, 1971.

Cook, D., and Van Haverbeke, D. Trees and Shrubs for Noise Abatement. U.S. Department of Agriculture (Research Bulletin No. 246), Washington, D.C.: U.S. Government Printing Office, 1971.

Croke, E.; Croke, K.; Kennedy, A.; and Hoover, L. The Relationship Between Land Use and Environmental Protection. Springfield, Va.: National Technical Information Service (Pub. No. PB 209 642), 1972.

Federer, C. "Effects of Trees in Modifying the Urban Microclimate." In Trees and Forests in an Urbanizing Environment. Amherst, Mass.: Holdsworth Natural Resources Center, University of Massachusetts, 1971, pp. 23-27.

General Electric Company. Final Report on Study of Air Pollution Aspects of Various Roadway Configurations. Springfield, Va.: National Technical Information Service (Pub. No. PB 211 235), 1971.

Kennedy, A., et al. Air Pollution—Land Use Planning Project, Phase I Final Report. Springfield, Va.: National Technical Information Service (Pub. No. ANL/ES-7), 1971.

Larson, R. A Mathematical Model for Relating Air Quality Measurements to Air Quality Standards. Research Triangle Park, N.C.: Air Pollution Technical Information Center, Environmental Protection Agency (Pub. No. AP-89), 1971.

McCormick, R. Air Pollution in the Locality of Buildings. Springfield, Va.: National Technical Information Service, 1971.

Marshall, J. The Efficacy of Vermont's Act 250. Montpelier, Vt.: Vermont Natural Resources Council, Environmental Planning Information Center, 1971.

Office of Air Programs, U.S. Environmental Protection Agency, Compilation of Air Pollutant Emission Factors. Springfield, Va.: National Technical Information Service (Pub. No. PB 209 559), 1972.

Ozolins, G., and Smith, R. A Rapid Survey Technique for Estimating Community Air Pollution Emissions. Washington, D.C.: U.S. Government Printing Office, Public Health Service (Pub. No. 999-AP-29), 1966.

Rich, S. "Effects of Trees and Forests in Reducing Air Pollution."
In Trees and Forests in an Urbanizing Environment. Amherst,
Mass.: Holdsworth Natural Resources Center, University of
Massachusetts, 1971.

Rote, D., Guedenas, J., and Conley, L. Studies of the Argonne Integrated-Puff Model. Argonne, Ill.: Center for Environmental
Studies, Argonne National Laboratory (Pub. No. ANL/ES-9),
1971.

Stein, A. Guide to Engineering Processing. Research Triangle Park,
N.C.: Air Pollution Technical Information Center, Environmental Protection Agency (Pub. No. APTD-1164), 1972.

Stern, A., ed. Proceedings of Symposium on Multiple-Source Urban
Diffusion Models. Research Triangle Park, N.C : Air Pollution
Technical Information Center, Environmental Protection Agency
(Pub. No. AP-86), 1970.

Turner, B. Workbook of Atmospheric Dispersion Estimates. Research
Triangle Park, N.C.: Air Pollution Technical Information Center,
Environmental Protection Agency, (Pub. No. AP-26) 1970;
Washington, D.C.: U.S. Government Printing Office (GPO 5503-
0015), 1973.

U.S. Senate. Air Pollution-1970. Hearings before a subcommittee
on Air and Water Pollution of the Senate Committee on Public
Works, 91st Congress, 2d. Session, 1970.

U.S. Senate. Implementation of the Clean Air Act Amendments of
1970. Hearings before a subcommittee on Air and Water Pollution
of the Senate Committee on Public Works, 92d Congress, 2d.
Session, 1972.

Voorhees, A., and Associates. A Guide for Reducing Air Pollution
Through Urban Planning. Springfield, Va.: National Technical
Information Service (Pub. No. PB 207 510), 1971.

Yocum, J., et al. A Study of Indoor-Outdoor Air Pollutant Relationships. Springfield, Va.: National Technical Information Service
(Pub. No. PB 195338), 1970.

UNPUBLISHED MATERIAL

Andrews, R. Environmental Policy and Administrative Change: "The National Environmental Policy Act of 1969, 1970-71." Ph.D. dissertation, University of North Carolina, 1972.

Cermack, E. and Chaudhry, F. "Urban and Architectural Planning for Air Pollution Control." Prepared for presentation at the 65th Annual Meeting of the Air Pollution Control Association, June 1972.

Cohen, A.; Hoover, L.; and Norce, J. "The Impact of Economic Growth on Air Quality in the St. Louis Region." Paper presented at the Meeting of the American Institute of Chemical Engineers, May 1972.

Cohen, A. "The Use of Three Growth Models to Evaluate the Future Effectiveness of Air Pollution Control Regulations." Paper presented at the Annual Meeting of the Air Pollution Control Association, June, 1972.

Cross, F. Community Air Pollution Protection Using Buffer Zones. Unpublished manuscript, n.d.

Environmental Research and Technology. Hackensack Meadowlands Air Pollution Study. Boston, Mass.: Environmental Research and Technology, 1972.

Hagevik, G. "The Relationship Between Land Use and Air Pollution in Middlesex County, New Jersey." Studio report, Rutgers University, Department of Urban Planning and Policy Development, 1973.

Kurtzweg, J., and Weig, D. "Determining Air Pollution Emissions from Transportation Systems." Paper presented at the meetings of the Association for Computing Machinery, October, 1969.

McCurdy, T. "Vehicular Emissions and the Location of Highways in Urban Areas." Master's thesis, Pennsylvania State University, Regional Planning Program, 1969.

Ott, W., and Eliassen, R. "An Urban Survey Technique for Measuring the Spatial Variation of Carbon Monoxide Concentrations in Cities." Paper presented at the Annual Meetings of the Air Pollution Control Association, June, 1972.

Reethof, G. "Effect of Plantings on Radiation of Highway Noise." Paper presented at the Annual Meeting of the Air Pollution Control Association, 1972.

Singer, I. "An Objective Method for Site Evaluation." Paper presented at the Annual Meeting of the Air Pollution Control Association, 1959.

Thuiller, R. "Air Monitoring and Its Application to Land Use Planning." Prepared for the 13th Conference on Methods in Air Pollution and Industrial Hygiene Studies, Berkeley, California, 1972.

Thuiller, R. "A Regional Air Pollution Modeling System for Practical Applications of Land Use Planning Studies 1." Unpublished paper, May 17, 1973.

Willis, H., and Mahoney, B. Planning for Air Quality. Paper presented at the Annual Meeting of the American Institute of Planners, November, 1972.

GEORGE HAGEVIK is Chief of the Environmental Resources Division of the Association of Bay Area Governments in Berkeley, California. He has served as consultant to the U.S. Environmental Protection Agency and the Library of Congress.

Dr. Hagevik has published three other books on air quality management, including Decision-Making in Air Pollution Control (Praeger, 1970). He has also written a number of articles on environmental quality management.

Dr. Hagevik earned his Ph.D. in City and Regional Planning at the University of North Carolina, Chapel Hill. He was formerly Assistant Professor of Urban Planning and Research Associate at the Center for Urban Policy Research at Rutgers University.

DANIEL MANDELKER is Professor of Law at the Washington University School of Law. He has served as consultant to numerous governmental agencies on environmental, land use, housing, and urban renewal policies.

Dr. Mandelker has published numerous books on urban and environmental issues, including The Zoning Dilemma and Managing Our Urban Environment, and many articles on urban problems.

Dr. Mandelker earned his LL.B. at the University of Wisconsin and his J.S.D. at Yale University and has been involved in urban planning studies in England, Korea, the Philippines, Australia, and, most recently, Hawaii.

RICHARD BRAIL is Assistant Professor of Urban Planning at Rutgers University. He has served as a consultant to the U.S. Environmental Protection Agency and local governmental agencies.

Dr. Brail has published a number of articles on air pollution, land use, and transportation and is completing a book on transportation and land use.

Dr. Brail earned his Ph.D. in City and Regional Planning at the University of North Carolina, Chapel Hill. He was formerly Assistant Professor at the Urban Studies Center, University of Chicago.

ENFORCING AIR POLLUTION CONTROLS: Case
Study of New York City
> Esther Roditti Schachter

EXCLUSIONARY ZONING: Land Use Regulation
and Housing in the 1970s
> Richard F. Babcock and Fred P.
> Bosselman

IMPACT OF FEDERAL LEGISLATION AND
PROGRAMS ON PRIVATE LAND IN URBAN AND
METROPOLITAN DEVELOPMENT
> Joseph L. Stevens

THE POLITICS OF LAND USE: Planning, Zoning,
and the Private Developer
> R. Robert Linowes and Don T.
> Allensworth

STATE ENVIRONMENTAL MANAGEMENT: Case
Studies of Nine States
> Elizabeth H. Haskell and Victoria
> S. Price

Date Due